MATHEMATICS
FOR ALL

I'm very well acquainted too with matters mathematical,
I understand equations, both the simple and quadratical.

W. S. GILBERT

First published 1954
Reprinted 1957
Reprinted 1958
Reprinted 1960 (*Jan.*)
Reprinted 1960 (*Mar.*)

MATHEMATICS FOR ALL

A Popular Approach to Mathematics in Everyday Life

EDITORIAL ADVISER: R. WESLEY, B.Sc.

CONTRIBUTORS:

G. C. T. BOWEN, B.Sc.

A. G. G. RICHARDS, B.Sc.

I. R. VESSELO, M.Ed., B.Sc.

R. W. WEBSTER, M.A. (Cantab.)

R. WESLEY, B.Sc.

ODHAMS PRESS LIMITED

LONG ACRE, LONDON

Contents

A Few Words of Explanation

TO CLEAR the consciences of the contributors and to be fair to the readers, some explanation of the book and its title is necessary. If you look at the reference bookshelves of any public library you will see that there are very few which do not contain volumes in which mathematical processes are employed. It follows that the people who use such books are expected to understand mathematical language; and, secondly, that the extension of mathematical knowledge and skill should in turn produce extensions in many other kinds of knowledge or skill.

Most people were put through the hoops of calculation at school. Many were taught the tricks of algebra and the knack of working out "riders." And there are text-books galore, some of them excellent, for those who never had the chance.

The writers of this book did not intend it to be yet another text-book of mathematics. They recognize that there are thousands of people in every walk of life who look back on their mathematics lessons with regret, either because they never really understood the point of them all, or because the pleasure of them ceased when they left school, or because much of what they once learned, now forgotten, would be useful to them if only it could be recalled.

Therefore, the book consists of two parts. The first, which is brief, describes the nature of mathematics and picks up the threads of previous knowledge. The second, which serves the main purpose of the writers, explores the application of mathematics to a variety of topics representing subjects of scientific or practical interest.

The topics chosen range over the same mathematical ground in different ways, thereby developing a more thorough appreciation of that ground. The reader may choose as his starting point the chapter that deals with the most attractive or familiar topic. Afterwards he will be better prepared to tackle others more remote from his own experience.

Contrary to the convention of the text-book there are no set exercises. Examples are frequently left for the reader to complete. We think he will find it more interesting and more rewarding to think things out for himself.

More than three centuries ago Francis Bacon said "Many parts of nature can neither be invented with sufficient subtilty, nor demonstrated with sufficient perspicuity, nor accommodated with sufficient dexterity without the aid and intervening of mathematics; of which sort are *perspective*, *music*, *astronomy*, *cosmography*, *architecture*, *enginery* and divers others. I may make only this prediction," he says, "that there cannot fail to be more kinds of (mathematics) as nature grows further disclosed."

The writers of this book accept that opinion. They have also been guided by the wisdom of Professor Hardy, who wrote: "Mathematics is itself a useless subject for study; the mathematician presses on with his pursuit of abstract truths without any better reason than that he likes doing it and has the necessary ability. The conclusions of the mathematician may or may not be very useful; indeed many of them are indispensable to the material civilization of the age. A book on mathematics for the layman should indicate how extensively and variously mathematical ideas can be applied in other fields of human thought and activity."

R. WESLEY

÷×÷×÷×÷×÷×÷×÷×÷×÷×÷×÷×÷×÷×÷×÷×÷×÷×
×   ÷
÷   ×
×   *For Your Recreation*   ÷
÷   ×
×   Sprinkled about the book in panels such as this one are teasers ÷
÷   and problems of many kinds, some simple and some not so simple. ×
×   They are there to amuse and entertain. The answers may some-   ÷
÷   times surprise you, but in any case you will be able to check your ×
×   own solutions by those given at the end of the book.   ÷
÷   ×
×÷×÷×÷×÷×÷×÷×÷×÷×÷×÷×÷×÷×÷×÷×÷×÷×÷×÷

1

What Mathematics Is

WHEN you woke up this morning your first conscious thoughts were probably about the time. What day was it? Had you to get up betimes? Were you early or late? A little reflection would give you the answer to the first question. There may have been a watch or clock in the room to help you with the third. Or the amount of daylight might have told you something about the time; or the kinds of noise you could hear in or near the house. How quickly you got moving depended no doubt on what time it was, what day it was, and what kind of programme you had before you.

If you had to be out of the house by 7.45 a.m. you did not give a thought to the meaning of "7.45 a.m." You simply concentrated on getting through the routine of things to be done before leaving home. You may have put on the wireless just to make sure that the BBC announcer's clock was not in conflict with your watch. If you are a methodical person you probably organized things so as to have a few minutes to spare for reading the morning paper.

HOW MANY DAYS IN A YEAR?

Mathematics, the bane of so many young lives, had already staked its claim in your affairs for the day. Take zero hour for example. What is 7.45 a.m.? And who is responsible for seeing that it is? "Ah, Greenwich Mean Time," you will be saying. "We all set our clocks by the pips from Greenwich, and it is the people at the Royal Observatory who have to make sure that the pips are heard at the right time." Quite right. Frank Tilsley's delightful fantasy *A Week of Sundays* reminds us how completely we tend to rely on the experts in these matters. Before the days of radio and telegraph, when life moved on at a more leisurely pace, when people worked by the piece rather than by the clock, when travel was not governed strictly by time-tables, no one but the navigators worried about the accurate measurement of time.

Time, nevertheless, has caused quite a few headaches in the past. Centuries ago, in Babylonian times, people fitted together the rhythm of the seasons and the rhythm of day and night to form a calendar in which one year was composed of 360 days. It seems that the Egyptians became weary of the trouble this kind of calendar created; it must have been irritating for the spring to come on later and later each year, causing the farmers to worry about their seed-time and harvest. To correct this creeping tendency they invented five feast-days to be added to the calendar each year. But even so, 365 days were not quite enough to put the year in a right relation to the day. We still wrestle with the problem and there are few people who can claim to know much more of our formula than the bit about leap-years.

The measurement of time is by no means simple; it is a science in its own right, and one in which mathematics plays a very prominent part. Truly the idea of a day seems simple enough; namely, the time

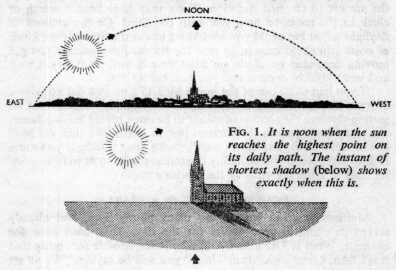

FIG. 1. *It is noon when the sun reaches the highest point on its daily path. The instant of shortest shadow (below) shows exactly when this is.*

between one noon and the next (Fig. 1). By means of a shadow-stick you can identify noon—if the sun is shining. As a little mathematical exercise you might now close this book and describe with the aid of a sketch exactly how you would do it. If you get into difficulty why not carry out the experiment and worry out the solution practically?

We shall assume that you have now done the experiment. You had to trace the tip of the shadow during the period which contains noon and find the instant of shortest throw (that is, when the sun was highest). Several problems arose. One was to select the point on the shadow-track which was nearest the stick (Fig. 2). The text-books will tell you to describe a circle with its centre at the base of the stick

FIG. 2. *We know that the noon shadow is some-where between A and B (left), but where exactly? A circle with its centre at the stick (right) gives A¹ and B¹, and a line from the stick to a position midway between these points is the noon-line—but how is it drawn?*

to cut off the middle part of your curve (the shadow-track). This presupposes that the stick is exactly vertical (are you sure that it was?). Then you have to bisect the arc of your curve cut off by the circle; and how did you do that? The point of bisection represents noon on the day of your experiment—a time that has passed irrevoc-

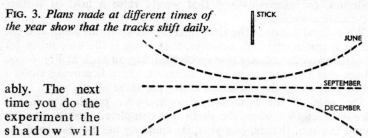

FIG. 3. *Plans made at different times of the year show that the tracks shift daily.*

ably. The next time you do the experiment the shadow will move on a slightly different track (Fig. 3), and unless it crosses some previously marked spot you will still be unable to say "It is noon—*now.*" By this time you have become quite deeply involved in the mathematics of the situation; the stick must be exactly vertical and the ground must be exactly horizontal and flat (Fig. 4). Even so, your identification of noon will be very coarse. To make it finer you would

FIG. 4. *What happens if the stick is not vertical and the ground is uneven?*

need a longer stick with a very fine point (Fig. 5). So far your work will have been entirely geometrical. To measure the interval between one noon and the next would require some kind of reliable timepiece—a

FIG. 5. *The movement of the tip of the minute hand is more perceptible on (b) than on (a), because more space is traversed in the same time. So it is with the shadow of the long stick and the short stick in the shadow experiment.*

pendulum, for example—and that would raise a host of further mathematical problems.

We defined a day as the time interval between one noon and the next. It is frequently said, however, that a day is the time taken for the earth to make exactly one revolution. If you look at Fig. 6 you will see that this cannot be so, because the earth is moving along a curved path—and the curvature is not the same all the way.

The root of the how-many-days-in-a-year puzzle lies in the awkward fact that when the earth has completed exactly one lap around the sun, that is, one year, its spinning has not returned the same line on its surface to the position nearest the sun (Fig. 7).

There are many more mathematical problems for the time measurer. For example, everyone knows that when it is noon in one place it is not noon anywhere else to the east or west. So these days of rapid travel and almost instantaneous communication by telephone and wireless call for some ingenuity in relating together the clocks in different parts of the world. Even in a small country like Britain, where we agree that all the clocks shall be synchronized, "lighting-up time" varies from place to place. The chronologist must consider

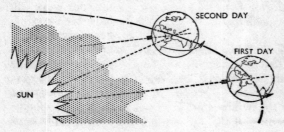

FIG. 6. *Because it moves on a curved path (here exaggerated), Earth spins more than one complete turn between consecutive noons.*

10

whether the earth moves and spins at constant speeds, and whether it is lapping the sun on exactly the same orbit (track) year after year.

The problems to which we have referred have occupied the minds of thoughtful people for centuries past. They have approached them first by careful and sustained observation and secondly by trying to understand and interpret what they have observed. Their observations of the sun, the moon, the planets and the stars have required a great amount of skilful counting, measuring and calculating, and also the invention of systems of geometry and algebra. It is in this side of their work that mathematics is brought into play as an instrument of thought, a kind of language.

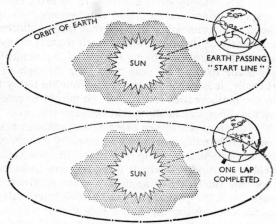

FIG. 7. *In the first drawing Earth is beginning one lap of its movement round the sun. In the second it has completed the lap but is seen to have spun a little beyond its original position. There are, then, more than 365 days in a year.*

Fortunately for the man in the street, there was absolutely no need for him to understand the first thing about chronology (time-measuring) or horology (the designing of instruments that tell the time) in order to be out of the house by 7.45 a.m. The mathematics of time-measuring may fascinate some people but it leaves most people stone cold. For the moment, therefore, we will leave the experts to their labours, comforted by the knowledge that they appear to do their work very competently.

USING MATHS *VERSUS* LEARNING MATHS

Let us assume that you set off from home this morning for the day's work. You may have walked. It is more likely that you travelled on a cycle, or a motor-cycle, or in a car, or on a bus or a train. In the payment of fares or the purchase of petrol you had a bit of arithmetic to do. And in the course of the day you probably had a great many

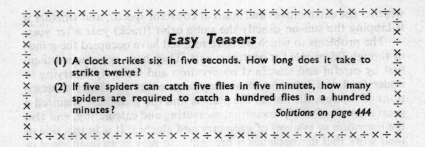

Easy Teasers

(1) A clock strikes six in five seconds. How long does it take to strike twelve?

(2) If five spiders can catch five flies in five minutes, how many spiders are required to catch a hundred flies in a hundred minutes?

Solutions on page 444

more bits. Money sums confront us so often that children are made to spend hours and hours of their young lives learning how to do them. It is interesting to note that most children thoroughly enjoy their early arithmetic lessons, albeit a great many lose their enthusiasm as the soul-destroying rigours of mechanical arithmetic lessons are made to drag on year after year throughout their school lives. Happily, it is becoming more fashionable today for school children to *use* mathematics rather than be taught to calculate—and there is all the difference in the world between the two.

You may remember being given specious reasons for having to learn arithmetic, algebra and geometry at school, or for having to learn particularly futile processes or proofs. For instance, you probably wondered why it was necessary to learn how to prove that any two sides of a triangle are together greater than the third—a perfectly self-evident fact. Or that two intersecting chords of a circle divide one another in such a way that the rectangle formed by the two portions of one chord is equal in area to the rectangle formed by the two portions of the other. The truth is that it was not necessary—unless you were destined to become a mathematician or a scientist. Millions of people live happily and efficiently without even knowing what the chords of a circle are.

It is perhaps rather surprising to read in the first chapter of a mathematics book that a great deal of time is wasted on the subject. Mathematics, let us hasten to note, does not stand alone in this respect. The same thing might be said of a foreign or classical language, of music, of history, or of science, all of which impinge on our lives in greater or lesser degree. For the student of any one of these subjects there are disciplines of thought to be accepted and cultivated. So it is with mathematics for the would-be mathematician. In one respect mathematics is probably unique: one may study the subject for a lifetime, make mathematical discoveries galore, and yet not display the least interest in the usefulness of one's efforts. There

12

are sure to be plenty of practical people waiting for the mathematical crumbs. Although they are not interested in the recipes by which the cake was made they do require a digestive system which will assimilate it; or, to abandon the metaphor, they require a working knowledge of the language of mathematics.

In this book we shall think about mathematics chiefly from the standpoint of the practical man. We shall assume, however, that the reader is not averse from a little intellectual exercise for its own sake and, therefore, although there will be no large slabs of "exercises" at the ends of the chapters, questions will be put to the reader from time to time. Sometimes the "answer" will be given immediately afterwards. Sometimes the question will be left entirely to the reader and he will have to judge for himself whether his answer is satisfactory. Some of the questions will be "practical" in the sense that their answers are useful. Others will be set with the intention of developing an idea or applying a general mathematical truth to a particular situation. It will be well as a rule to find the answer before proceeding.

THE LANGUAGE OF MATHS

Number is one of the roots of mathematics; indeed, it may be regarded as the tap-root. Let us clear up some of the common misconceptions about number. For example, it is frequently asserted that "two and two make four" is a law of nature. Is it? Put two cats and two mice together and what do you get? Add two pounds of sugar to two pounds (or pints) of water and what do you get? Add two pints of water to two pints of water in a quart jug and what do you get?

When the mathematician writes

$$2 + 2 = 4$$

(which in the language of words may be translated "two with two is the same as four") he is not concerned with cats, mice, pints, quarts, water, sugar and so on; he is not concerned with things of any kind but with "twoness" and "fourness." The symbols denote a concept (or idea); they are part of the language of abstract thought.

Arithmetic starts with the notion of counting and employs a language of symbols (1, 2, 3, 4, etc.) and signs ($=$, $+$, $-$, etc.), the signs enabling the symbols to be related to one another. To appreciate this to perfection you might invent new symbols and signs. You might, for instance, use the symbols

$$\textit{w ı ı ʁ ʃ ɔ ɒ ʌ}$$

to count up to eight and limit yourself to them only. You could use the sign / for addition, the sign ? for subtraction, and the sign & for equality. Then ʌ ! ɔ & ʃ and ı ? ʁ & ʌ.

FIG. 8. *Which is the better value—two boxes of fifty* (ab), *or fifty loose pairs* (ba)?

If you feel so inclined you can have plenty of fun doing simple sums with those symbols and signs. You may care to consider how you will denote nine, eleven and fourteen. Perhaps the temptation to use the familiar symbol for nought will be too strong to resist.

As we all had to go through this stage when we were η or $\imath$ years old it is perhaps unnecessary to dwell on it once again, especially as we do not wish to spend a few more years on "the four rules of number." The point of all this is that certain conventions and rules have to be agreed at the outset of mathematics. They are not laws of nature at all, but rules of play. After agreeing about the symbols we must agree about the meaning of the sign language.

$$7 + 5 = 5 + 7,$$
$$3 + 4 = 4 + 3, \text{ and so on,}$$

are statements based on the following general statement

$$a + b = b + a \qquad (1)$$

Similarly, $a + (b + c) = (a + b) + c \qquad (2)$

Clerks make regular use of these rules by adding in two or more different ways to make sure that the answer is correct. Adding machines are made to observe the same rule, so that it does not

FIG. 9. *Which is the better value—two of the large sheets,* a(bc), *or three of the small sheets,* c(ab)? *If you are satisfied that they are the same, then* a(bc) = c(ab).

14

matter what order is followed in feeding them with the sum.

Again, $2 \times 8 = 8 \times 2$

and $2 \times (6 \times 3) = (2 \times 6) \times 3$

are forms of the rules

$$ab = ba \tag{3}$$

and $a(bc) = (ab)c$ (4)

The fifth fundamental rule in arithmetic is

$$a(b + c) = ab + ac. \tag{5}$$

If these five rules seem self-evident it is because we are accustomed to accepting them, first by using visible counters of some kind and later by distilling the concept from the concrete things we have been using. The really clever thing is that the language enables us to express the ideas simply and clearly on paper. If you have

FIG. 10. *Six lampholders at 1s. 7½d. each* (ab) *and six lamps at 2s. 4½d. each* (ac) *together cost the same as six of the 4s. assemblies:* a(b+ c).

not previously used such symbols as *a*, *b* and *c* to represent numbers it will repay you to test the rules by using particular numbers (such as 4, 7, and 9) until you feel confident that you understand them. Figs. 8, 9 and 10 should help in this respect.

THE PRACTICAL BASIS OF GEOMETRY

We shall return to number a little later on in this chapter. Meanwhile, the motor-car will provide us with plenty of material for geometry—much more than we care to draw on at present. Beyond the fact that it still has four wheels and a body the modern car hardly resembles its predecessor of 1910. The change that has come

15

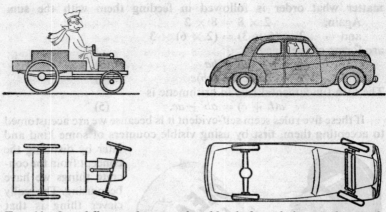

FIG. 11. *One difference between the old vehicle and the new lies in the steering, and this is where practical geometry comes in.*

over its appearance has been a gradual process resulting from technical advances which, in turn, have required the application of mathematics. Think of the steering. The horseless carriage used the same steering device as the horse-drawn carriage (Fig. 11). It was very simple and quite satisfactory for steel tyres travelling at low speeds on bumpy roads. In the modern car the front axle is fixed and each wheel is turned on a kind of hinge. This is part of a scheme of steering which is better suited to higher speeds of travel in which very fine changes of direction are required. (Even so, it is not impossible for a car to turn over because the front wheels have changed direction too violently.) Unless both wheels try to pull the car in the same manner, one tyre, or both, will be subjected to a dragging at the side, which will soon wear away the rubber. Fig. 12

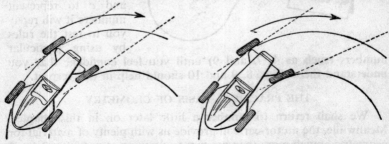

FIG. 12. *If both wheels are turned through the same angle one of them (the inner wheel in the left-hand drawing) has a bad time! Both wheels of the car in the right-hand drawing are trying to turn the car by the same amount.*

16

illustrates the need for the inner wheel to be turned through a greater angle than the outer. See if you can find out how the steering on a car provides for this (or see if you can invent a method for yourself). In the first place, this is a geometrical problem concerning circles and their tangents. In the second place, you will need to know something about triangles and quadrilaterals. Chapter 2 includes an introduction to the essentials of geometry.

All who have played with a pair of compasses know a little geometry, even if they have not thought much about it. First of all they know what a circle is, although they might find it difficult to describe it accurately in words. By making patterns like those in Fig. 13 they use the knowledge that the radius can be fitted exactly

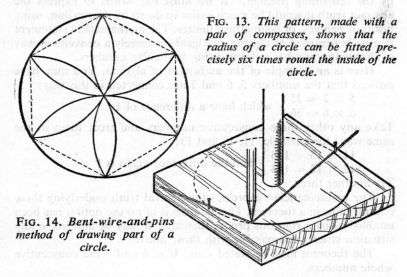

FIG. 13. *This pattern, made with a pair of compasses, shows that the radius of a circle can be fitted precisely six times round the inside of the circle.*

FIG. 14. *Bent-wire-and-pins method of drawing part of a circle.*

six times around the inside of the circle. This crude way of putting it would be very distasteful to the mathematician, and rightly so, because its meaning could be misunderstood. He would prefer to say that the length of the side of the regular hexagon inscribed in a circle is equal to its radius.

Suppose you wish to draw a circle in a place where some obstruction covers the centre, for example, on a floor around a buttress or column. How would you do it? One method is to use a piece of rigid wire suitably bent and a pair of well-placed pins or nails. You will then have to make use of the fact that all the angles in the same segment of a circle are equal. Centuries ago someone proved beyond doubt that that was so. Fig. 14 illustrates the method. The mathematician makes the discovery and ties it up neatly to the satisfaction of all other mathematicians in a "theorem." Good practical men use the theorem in their daily work whilst the mathematician presses on towards new theorems.

WHAT ALGEBRA IS ABOUT

Rule 4 on page 15 was $a(bc) = (ab)c$, and it was noted that this was a very concise and compact way of avoiding such a clumsy statement in words as "If you multiply the product of two numbers by a third you will get the same result as you would obtain by multiplying the product of the third number and one of the others by the remaining number." If we must use words to express the abstract truth it would be much easier to do so by illustration, using beads or pebbles, or geometrical figures. The mathematical statement is usually regarded as algebraic. Algebra is merely a convenient way of discussing number without using particular numbers.

Here is an example of the usefulness of algebra. You may have noticed that the numbers 5, 6 and 7 are connected in this way:

$$\left.\begin{array}{l} 5 \times 7 = 35 \\ 6 \times 6 = 36 \end{array}\right\} \text{ which have a difference of 1}$$

Take any other three consecutive numbers and treat them in the same way; for example, 11, 12 and 13:

$$\left.\begin{array}{l} 11 \times 13 = 143 \\ 12 \times 12 = 144 \end{array}\right\} \text{ and the difference again is 1}$$

Try another three.

The mathematician expresses the general truth underlying these relationships in a theorem. The theorem is of no use until it has been established by a rigorous proof; thereafter it may be applied to any situation strictly comparable with those above.

The theorem may be stated thus: If a, b and c are consecutive whole numbers,

$$b^2 - ac = 1$$

If the theorem is sound—and we have not tried to prove that it is—it may be applied to such a trio as 1954, 1955 and 1956. It is quite a dramatic truth and lends itself to some dramatic uses. To take a very simple example, 199 times 201 may be done mentally by squaring 200 and taking away 1 (39,999).

Another theorem concerning three consecutive numbers a, b and c is stated thus:

$$b = \tfrac{1}{2}(a + c)$$

It may be such an obvious truth that no proof is considered necessary. The apostle Paul said, "Prove all things; hold fast that

18

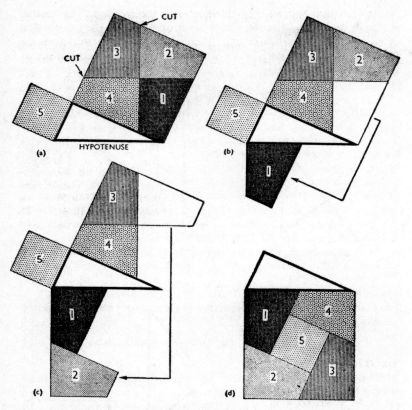

FIG. 15. *This practical method of proving the theorem of Pythagoras is called Perigal's Dissection. The cutting lines in* (a) *are parallel and at right-angles to the hypotenuse, intersecting at the centre of the square. After cutting out the five shaded pieces refit them on the hypotenuse to form a new square. Sliding only—no rotation—is allowed.*

which is good." The theorem may be proved as follows:

Let b be any positive integer; then $(b - 1)$ and $(b + 1)$ are the integers which immediately precede and follow it (corresponding with a and c above), and

$$(b - 1) + (b + 1) = b - 1 + b + 1$$
$$= 2b$$

Therefore $b = \frac{1}{2}\{(b - 1) + (b + 1)\},$

which is what we set out to prove. The brackets are used like baskets

19

simply to hold things together. In a later chapter their use will be considered more fully.

The last theorem was perhaps not very exciting. Let us think about another which is probably the best known theorem of all. Pythagoras, the Greek mathematician, is usually given the credit for being the first to postulate it, although it was probably known to others long before him.

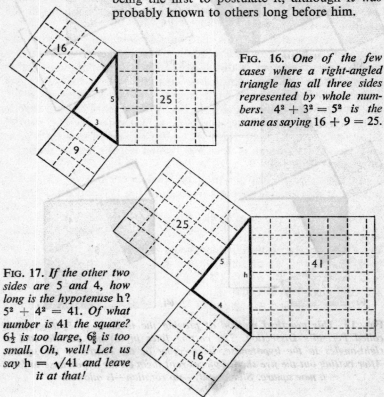

FIG. 16. *One of the few cases where a right-angled triangle has all three sides represented by whole numbers.* $4^2 + 3^2 = 5^2$ *is the same as saying* $16 + 9 = 25$.

FIG. 17. *If the other two sides are 5 and 4, how long is the hypotenuse* h? $5^2 + 4^2 = 41$. *Of what number is* 41 *the square?* $6\frac{1}{2}$ *is too large,* $6\frac{2}{5}$ *is too small. Oh, well! Let us say* h $= \sqrt{41}$ *and leave it at that!*

If squares are drawn on each of the sides of a right-angled triangle, the area of the largest (the one on the longest side, called the *hypotenuse*) is equal to the sum of the areas of the other two. There are several ways of proving the theorem but we do not propose to deal with any of them here. Instead, we suggest that you test it practically by drawing one or two right-angled triangles, constructing the squares on the sides, and in each case piecing the smaller squares together to fill the bigger one. Fig. 15 suggests a way of doing it.

20

This theorem can be expressed with the help of algebra as follows:
$$h^2 = a^2 + b^2$$
where h, a and b are the lengths of the hypotenuse and the remaining sides of a right-angled triangle, in that order.

As you will find out in reading this book, an enormous weight of mathematics rests on this theorem, and, strange as it may seem, in much of it neither the squares nor even the right-angled triangle itself appear on the scene; instead they lurk like phantoms in the invisible background.

You must notice that this theorem has something of arithmetic and algebra about it, as well as geometry. It is by no means rare for them to stand together in this way. Another interesting matter that emerges from the consideration of the theorem is that there are comparatively few right-angled triangles all three sides of which can be represented by whole numbers. You probably found that to be so when you made your drawings. If you make the two shorter sides 3 and 4 units long, the hypotenuse should be exactly 5 units long, because 3^2 (which is 9) and 4^2 (which is 16) together make 25, which is 5^2 (Fig. 16).

Likewise, 5, 12 and 13 may be used because $5^2 + 12^2 = 13^2$. But if the shorter sides are 4 and 5, as in Fig. 17 opposite, what is the hypotenuse?
$$4^2 + 5^2 = 16 + 25$$
$$= 41$$
But 41 is not the square of any whole number. The most that can be said about it at present is that it is the square of a number between 6 ($6^2 = 36$) and 7 ($7^2 = 49$). The hypotenuse is therefore greater than 6 but less than 7.

The right-angled triangle with shorter sides 2 and 6, by a similar argument, has a hypotenuse greater than 6 and less than 7. Which of the two hypotenuses is the greater?

Clearly we must find a way of writing these two results which is more precise than "between 6 and 7." We may express them as $\sqrt{41}$ and $\sqrt{40}$ respectively, and read our symbolisms as "the square root of 41" and "the square root of 40" (usually abbreviated to "root 41" and "root 40"). You may be wondering if this is a dead end; whether, for example, $\sqrt{41}$ is $6\frac{1}{2}$ or $6\frac{2}{5}$ or some such fraction. Why not pursue the idea? After rejecting these (because the square of $6\frac{1}{2}$ is $42\frac{1}{4}$ and the square of $6\frac{2}{5}$ is $40\frac{24}{25}$—a near miss!) try one or two more guesses. You will soon begin to doubt whether that elusive answer can be written in fractional form. It must be admitted that it cannot!

So here is a remarkable discovery. There are numbers arising in quite sober and real circumstances which defy expression in the ordinary way. Needless to say, the mathematicians have revelled in the study of these numbers. Later on we shall return to them.

HOW LONG IS AN INCH?

We have talked glibly about right-angled triangles with sides 3, 4 and 5 units long. And what we have said has been perfectly sound because we have seen those triangles perfectly in our minds; we have not really needed a drawing. Immediately we try to draw them we find ourselves up against another disconcerting difficulty: it is not possible to draw them accurately.

What is one inch? One sheep, one chair and one book are all very well; so, too, is the idea of one inch. When we try to draw a line one inch long we have to ask if the ruler is accurate. And what about the thickness of the pencil point? And what about the reliability of one's eyesight?

No wonder Euclid, the Greek geometer, talked about a point having "position but no magnitude." All his theorems were about idealized points and lines; his geometrical figures were such as exist in heaven only. We mortals have not the perfect skill to draw them. With the best possible measuring and drawing instruments we can only approach perfection; we can never quite achieve it.

It is therefore quite erroneous to say that the theorem of Pythagoras is self-evident because we can test it as often as we like by drawing. We cannot. Even the 3-4-5 combination cannot be tested by drawing. Pythagoras (or Euclid) reasoned the thing out with the aid of a rough sketch; no measurements whatsoever.

For the practical man this may be disappointing. If he wishes to build a house he will make many measurements. In buying his materials he may be able to dispose of some transactions by counting —bricks by the thousand, tiles by the score, nuts and bolts by the gross—but for others he will need the rule, the weighing machine and the liquid measure, and he will almost always measure time. If he wishes to make instruments, machines and appliances he may need to make very fine measurements.

FRACTIONS—VULGAR AND OTHERWISE

It is evident that the simple number system of integers (1, 2, 3, 4, etc.) is inadequate for the practical man. He needs halves, sixteenths, thousandths, and so on. Such numbers are called vulgar fractions. Useful as they are for coarse measurement, they are cumbersome and clumsy for fine measurement. Imagine how inconvenient it would be to have to describe a measurement as $\frac{278}{359}$ in the same breath

22

as $\frac{136}{221}$. And how difficult it would be to make measuring rods for vulgar fractions of such denominators! No wonder the decimal fraction is more popular. 1·287 can be said quickly, written quickly, and compared significantly with any other decimal fraction; 1·831 is seen at once to be bigger—about half as big again.

The expressions 1·287 and 1·831 stand in exactly the same relationship as 1,287 and 1,831. The dot, like the comma, is a *marker*: it tells where the whole-number part ends and the fractional part begins.

One of the beauties of the decimal is that it can be used conveniently to state a measurement with perfect truth. For example, you may say that a line is 3·0 inches long (to the first decimal place) or, if you have sufficient confidence, 3·00 inches long (to the second decimal place). The latter means that you are not more than 5 thousandths of an inch out either way. You are advised to make yourself familiar with the ordinary arithmetical calculations; that is, the four rules of decimals.

FIGURES AND FALLACIES

This opening chapter began by a reference to the measurement of time. Since then reference has been made to some of the rules and theorems of arithmetic, algebra and geometry. It has been suggested that it is for the mathematician to press on with his abstract studies and for the practical men to employ his discoveries on our behalf. We are fairly safe in the hands of the mathematicians and the technologists, for if a man is designing a refrigerator or a washing machine or a helicopter he will make many rigorous tests of his prototype before marketing it.

There are others who employ mathematics. We should be on our guard against the subtlety of some and the carelessness of

The Dishonest Waiter

Three men having dinner together decided to share the cost. The waiter produced a bill for £3, so each contributed £1. In presenting the money to the cashier the waiter found that the correct total should have been £2 10s. The cashier returned 10s. to the waiter, who pocketed 4s. and returned 2s. to each of the diners. Thus each had paid 18s. and the total payment was £2 14s. But the waiter had only 4s.; what happened to the other 2s.?

Solution on page 444

others. The propagandist, the advertiser and the politician seem to be making more use of graphs, statistics and formulae. They get away with some surprising statements and inferences.

"The N.U.R.," says the newspaper columnist, "contends that 11 per cent of all railwaymen get the 92-shilling minimum and 55 per cent less than £5. But British Railways claim that the average earnings of all their employees are more than £5 a week. They say earnings average £5 12s. 6d. per week."

The inference is that someone is lying. Suppose that there are 100 railwaymen (or any other number): on the B.R. statement their total weekly pay is £562 10s. Is it not possible for 55 of them to account for less than £275? The writer's trouble is "averagitis," no doubt—a very common disease. Or, of course, he may have been unable to discriminate between "all" and "each of."

"Eightpence won't buy a shillingsworth of goods," says another. "But for every shillingsworth of cotton, rubber, tea, or food that we get from abroad we had only eightpennyworth of exports to offer last year. The rest we are getting on tick. Now you see why we must export one-third more this year and still more after that. We must pay our way or get less and fare worse."

If only he had been able to cope more successfully with his vulgar fractions!

And how many taxpayers have been taken in by this mathematical slant on the costs of public education?

"A thousand footballs at £1 each cost £1,000.

A thousand pencils at a penny each cost £4 3s. 4d.

A thousand exercise books at 3d. each cost £12 10s."

If we are gullible enough we can infer from this that the nation is spending approximately 160 times as much on organized games as on writing and arithmetic. Where is the fallacy?

For one reason or another, then, the writers of this book commend to their readers the succeeding chapters. In the next two this preliminary excursion will be followed by a review of the elementary mathematics required for the topics which provide the material for Chapters 4 to 12.

2

The Language of Mathematics

(a) Arithmetic: Doing it by Numbers

THE purpose of this section of the book is to recall to mind some of the basic arithmetical processes for those who may be lacking recent practice. If you are already familiar with fractions, decimals, percentages and the formulae of mensuration you should skip rapidly over the rest of the chapter or omit it altogether.

Let us consider first the ordinary rules of addition, subtraction, multiplication and division with fractions and decimals, for these form the very foundations for later work.

SPADEWORK WITH FRACTIONS

In ordinary practical measurement, apart from scientific and microscopic measurement, very few fractions are used and these are generally found on an ordinary ruler. There you will usually find halves, quarters, eighths, sixteenths, tenths and twelfths of an inch, and in addition you can use the ruler to measure thirds, fifths and sixths. These, together with thirty-seconds and sixty-fourths, and, for very accurate precision work in engineering, thousandths, are all the common fractions.

A fraction is always a part of something; the number on top is called the numerator and the one at the bottom the denominator. It is the denominator which denotes the name of the fraction, and the numerator which indicates how many parts of that kind of portion are to be taken. For example, the fraction $\frac{5}{8}$ denotes that the unit is to be divided into eight equal parts and that five of these parts have to be taken.

If you look at a ruler you will readily see the truth of the following statements:

$$\frac{6}{12} = \frac{1}{2} \left(\text{that is, } \frac{6 \div 6}{12 \div 6} \right) \qquad \frac{1}{2} = \frac{5}{10} \left(\text{that is, } \frac{1 \times 5}{2 \times 5} \right)$$

$$\frac{4}{16} = \frac{1}{4} \left(\text{that is, } \frac{4 \div 4}{16 \div 4} \right) \qquad \frac{2}{3} = \frac{8}{12} \left(\text{that is, } \frac{2 \times 4}{3 \times 4} \right)$$

$$\frac{6}{8} = \frac{3}{4} \left(\text{that is, } \frac{6 \div 2}{8 \div 2} \right) \qquad \frac{3}{5} = \frac{6}{10} \left(\text{that is, } \frac{3 \times 2}{5 \times 2} \right)$$

25

Any fraction, then, may be multiplied or divided both in the numerator and denominator by the same number without changing its value. This simple rule is the secret of all the arithmetic of fractions.

Fractions can be added to or subtracted from each other just as whole numbers are, provided all the fractions are of the same kind. There is no difficulty in adding $\frac{7}{8}$ and $\frac{5}{8}$, or of subtracting $\frac{3}{10}$ from $\frac{7}{10}$, since in each case we are dealing with the same sort of fractions. The answers are $\frac{12}{8}$ (or $1\frac{1}{2}$) and $\frac{4}{10}$ (or $\frac{2}{5}$) respectively. There is no more to it than this: first convert all fractions to the same denominator and then add and subtract their numerators. It may then be necessary to simplify the result. A few examples will serve to remind you if you have forgotten the technique.

What is the value of $\frac{5}{8} + \frac{7}{12} - \frac{5}{6}$?

Converting all the fractions to twenty-fourths (a number into which all the denominators will divide) we have

$$\frac{15}{24} + \frac{14}{24} - \frac{20}{24} = \frac{9}{24} = \frac{3}{8}$$

The answer $\frac{3}{8}$ is the fraction reduced to its lowest terms.

When adding or subtracting mixed numbers (fractions and whole numbers together) first deal with the whole numbers and then treat the fractions separately. For example, $5\frac{1}{2} + 2\frac{1}{8} - 4\frac{11}{16}$ is equivalent to

$$3 + \frac{1}{2} + \frac{1}{8} - \frac{11}{16} = 3 + \frac{8 + 2 - 11}{16} = 3 + \frac{10 - 11}{16}$$

We cannot subtract 11 from 10 so we use a whole number 1 as $\frac{16}{16}$ and put it with the $\frac{10}{16}$.

The answer now becomes $2\dfrac{26 - 11}{16} = 2\dfrac{15}{16}$

For multiplication the rule is to multiply the numerators together to obtain the new numerator, and to multiply the denominators together to get the new denominator. In division, invert the fraction by which you are dividing and then multiply. The final result may be reduced to its lowest terms by dividing numerator and denominator by the same number ("cancelling"). Such division, if it is possible, is usually done before the final processes of multiplication; this cuts down the work involved. For example:

$$\frac{3}{8} \times \frac{7}{10} = \frac{21}{80} \qquad \text{but} \qquad \frac{\overset{1}{\cancel{5}}}{8} \times \frac{7}{\underset{2}{\cancel{10}}} = \frac{7}{16}$$

In the second example top and bottom have each been divided by 5 before the final multiplication to avoid the fraction $\frac{35}{80}$, which is not in its simplest form.

Let us divide $\dfrac{11}{12}$ by $\dfrac{2}{3}$:

$$\dfrac{11}{12} \div \dfrac{2}{3} = \dfrac{11}{\overset{}{\underset{4}{12}}} \times \dfrac{\overset{1}{3}}{2} = \dfrac{11}{8} = 1\dfrac{3}{8}$$

If you are surprised by the answer $1\frac{3}{8}$ you must remember that you are really asking how many times $\frac{2}{3}$ is contained in $\frac{11}{12}$. Since $\frac{11}{12}$ is the larger amount, the result, not very surprisingly, is more than 1.

In dealing with mixed numbers all that is necessary is to express the mixed number as an "improper" fraction and proceed as for an ordinary fraction. For example:

$$1\dfrac{1}{8} \times \dfrac{2}{3} = \dfrac{\overset{3}{9}}{\underset{4}{8}} \times \dfrac{\overset{1}{2}}{\underset{1}{3}} = \dfrac{3}{4}$$

and

$$4\dfrac{3}{8} \div \dfrac{5}{16} = \dfrac{\overset{7}{35}}{\underset{1}{8}} \times \dfrac{\overset{2}{16}}{\underset{1}{5}} = 14$$

It is sometimes necessary to express one quantity as a fraction of another. One and sixpence, for instance, expressed as a fraction of one pound is $\dfrac{3}{40}$, since we can write it as $\dfrac{1\frac{1}{2}}{20}$ after expressing both amounts in terms of the same unit (shilling).

So far we have been concerned only with ordinary or "vulgar" fractions and it is time to move on to refresh our memory about decimal fractions.

THE SIMPLICITY OF DECIMALS

The decimal system is a logical extension of our ordinary number notation. When we write the number 333 we understand that it means $300 + 30 + 3$. Each figure 3 is ten times the value of the previous one, reading from right to left, and is one-tenth of the previous one, reading from left to right. Quite logically we might proceed to regard 333/33 as standing for $300 + 30 + 3 + \dfrac{3}{10} + \dfrac{3}{100}$ if we decide that the stroke / should separate the whole numbers from the fractional parts. In actual practice a dot, or "point," is used for this purpose and the number is written 333·33. Decimals, then, are fractions in which the denominators are understood to be 10, 100, 1,000, and so on, according to the position of the figure after the decimal point. How are they used?

27

Adding and subtracting decimals are done in exactly the same way as for whole numbers. Care must be taken, however, that the decimal points are all written under one another: this is quite logical, since it ensures that figures of similar place value fall in the same column. It works as follows:

Add 11·68 + 5·076 + 21·5

$$
\begin{array}{r}
11\cdot68 \\
5\cdot076 \\
21\cdot5 \\
\hline
38\cdot256 \\
\end{array}
$$

From 28·2 subtract 15·85

$$
\begin{array}{r}
28\cdot20 \\
15\cdot85 \\
\hline
12\cdot35 \\
\end{array}
$$

Notice that 28·2 and 28·20 are the same. But we could not omit the intermediate 0 in 5·076 without altering the value.

Where there is no whole-number part, in order to avoid error a nought is often written before the decimal point. Thus ·375 is often written 0·375.

One of the many advantages of decimals is the ease with which they can be multiplied or divided by 10, 100, 1,000, and so on. Consider, for example, what happens when 1·6 is multiplied by 10. The unit figure 1 becomes a 10 and the ·6 or $\frac{6}{10}$ becomes 6 units, since $\frac{6}{10} \times 10 = 6$ by the ordinary multiplication of fractions. In the same way $2\cdot85 \times 10 = 28\cdot5$ and $1\cdot055 \times 100 = 105\cdot5$. Conversely, 1·6 divided by 10 becomes 0·16, $28\cdot5 \div 10 = 2\cdot85$, and $21\cdot65 \div 1{,}000 = 0\cdot02165$.

If you are already proficient in the multiplication and division of ordinary whole numbers, the multiplication and division of decimals should present no difficulty at all; the only new process is the fixing of the decimal point.

To multiply 4·12 by 2·06, first multiply disregarding the points:

$$
\begin{array}{r}
412 \\
206 \\
\hline
824 \\
2472 \\
\hline
84872 \\
\end{array}
$$

Count the total number of figures after the decimal points in both of the quantities to be multiplied (in this case four). In the product (answer to a multiplication) count this total number of figures from the right and insert the decimal point. The answer then is 8·4872.

You will see that the answer is of the right size because $4 \times 2 = 8$.

Now for an example of division. To divide 13·75 by 2·5, first convert the divisor (2·5) into a whole number by multiplying it by 10.

28

To compensate for this, multiply the dividend also by 10; 13·75 then becomes 137·5. Now proceed as in ordinary division, inserting the decimal point in the answer as soon as you meet it in the course of division.

$$
\begin{array}{r}
5\cdot5 \\
25)\overline{137\cdot5} \\
125 \\
\hline
125 \\
125
\end{array}
$$

The division in this case is exact and the answer is 5·5. To see what happens when there is a remainder, let us divide 11·364 by 2·35.

Make the divisor into 235 and to compensate for this move the decimal point two places in the dividend, so that it becomes 1136·4.

$$
\begin{array}{r}
4\cdot8 \\
235)\overline{1136\cdot4} \\
940 \\
\hline
1964 \\
1880 \\
\hline
84
\end{array}
\qquad
\begin{array}{r}
4\cdot835 \\
235)\overline{1136\cdot400} \\
940 \\
\hline
1964 \\
1880 \\
\hline
840 \\
705 \\
\hline
1350 \\
1175 \\
\hline
175
\end{array}
$$

The answer 4·8 is not exact because there is a remainder; it can be carried on by writing as many noughts as required on the end of the dividend. If the answer is required correct to two decimal places the division should be continued to three places of decimals and the answer expressed correct to two places.

The answer correct to two decimal places is 4·84. The process of division is just the same even if the dividend, after the decimal point has been moved, contains no whole numbers and consists of a decimal part only. For example, divide ·048 by 1·2. Moving the decimal points as before, the division becomes:

$$
\begin{array}{r}
0\cdot04 \\
12)\overline{0\cdot48}
\end{array}
$$

Two other matters connected with decimals need to be mentioned briefly: the conversion of a decimal to a vulgar fraction and vice versa. Simple examples will illustrate the process.

1·065 expressed as a vulgar fraction is $1\frac{65}{1000}$ and this can be simplified to $1\frac{13}{200}$. See if you agree with the following:

$$
1\cdot05 = 1\frac{1}{20}, \qquad 3\cdot64 = 3\frac{16}{25}, \qquad 0\cdot045 = \frac{9}{200}
$$

The reverse process is equally simple. Suppose it is desired to express $\frac{3}{4}$ as a decimal. The fraction $\frac{3}{4}$ means 3 divided by 4 and if we carry out the division the required decimal fraction results:

$$\frac{4)3 \cdot 00}{0 \cdot 75}$$

All fractions can be converted into decimals in this way though not all will work out as easily or as exactly as this. Some of the commoner fractions with their decimal equivalents are given below: confirm these results for yourself. It is as well to memorize those in common use.

$$\frac{1}{4} = 0 \cdot 25 \qquad \frac{1}{10} = 0 \cdot 1$$
$$\frac{1}{2} = 0 \cdot 5 \qquad \frac{1}{5} = 0 \cdot 2$$
$$\frac{1}{8} = 0 \cdot 125 \qquad \frac{1}{20} = 0 \cdot 05$$
$$\frac{7}{8} = 0 \cdot 875 \qquad \frac{1}{3} = 0 \cdot 333 \ldots$$

Conversion of $\frac{1}{3}$ to a decimal leads as you see to an endless succession of 3's; this is known as a recurring decimal and in order to avoid endless repetition is written 0·3. Try to discover for yourself other examples of recurring decimals and devise a rule for writing them as vulgar fractions.

PERCENTAGES IN A NUTSHELL

Percentage is a particular form of fraction in which the denominator is always one hundred (cent). The main thing to understand is that 100% is 1 and that you may therefore multiply by 100% without changing the value. All that is necessary to express any fraction or decimal as a percentage is to multiply it by 100% as in the examples below:

$$\frac{1}{2} = \frac{1}{2} \times 100\% = 50\%$$
$$\frac{1}{5} = \frac{1}{5} \times 100\% = 20\%$$
$$\frac{1}{3} = \frac{1}{3} \times 100\% = 33\frac{1}{3}\%$$

It is useful to know the percentage equivalents of the common fractions, and when percentages are in constant use it is obviously useful to have a ready reckoner. Fig. 1 shows the beginnings of such a table; you can easily expand it for yourself if you wish to do so and feel it is worth while.

THE METRIC WAY OF DOING THINGS

The great advantage of this system of measuring is that it is built up by tens and so lends itself to decimalization. Thus the metre (one forty-millionth part of the earth's circumference) is divided into decimetres, centimetres and millimetres (tenths, hundredths and thousandths of a metre). Units of mass, capacity, area, and even

FRACTION	$\frac{1}{10}$	$\frac{1}{5}$	$\frac{1}{4}$	$\frac{1}{2}$	$\frac{3}{4}$	$\frac{1}{8}$	$\frac{1}{3}$	$\frac{2}{3}$
DECIMAL	0·1	0·2	0·25	0·5	0·75	0·125	0·$\dot{3}$	0·$\dot{6}$
PERCENTAGE	10	20	25	50	75	$12\frac{1}{2}$	$33\frac{1}{3}$	$66\frac{2}{3}$

FIG. 1. *Some common fractions and their decimal and percentage equivalents.*

money, follow a similar pattern. This metric system has been adopted throughout the world for scientific purposes and in many countries for everyday usage.

The metre is equivalent to 39·37 in.—3·37 in. longer than one yard. The centimetre, which is a hundredth of a metre, is ·3937 in. or approximately ·4 in. If you examine an ordinary ruler you will notice that 4 in. = 10 cm. approximately, or 1 in. = 2·5 cm.

On the Continent it is usual to express distances between towns and villages in kilometres, just as we use miles. One kilometre is equal to 1,000 metres.

$$1 \text{ kilometre} = 1,000 \times 39\cdot37 \text{ in.}$$
$$= \frac{1,000 \times 39\cdot37}{36} \text{ yd.}$$
$$= 1,094 \text{ yd. approx.}$$

A kilometre is therefore a smaller unit than the mile. It is only 6 yards short of 5 furlongs, or $\frac{5}{8}$ mile.

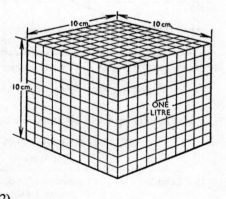

FIG. 2. *One litre is the volume of a cube whose sides are each of 10 centimetres (or 1 decimetre).*

Petrol, milk, wines and other liquids are bought on the Continent in litres. A litre is the volume of a cube with each edge measuring 1 decimetre, or 10 cm. (Fig. 2).

Hence a litre = 1 cubic decimetre = 1,000 cubic cm. (written c.c. for short). How does the litre compare with the pint? Let us start from the fact that 1 metre = 39·37 in. Then 1 decimetre = 3·937 in. = 0·328 ft., and 1 litre, which is a cubic decimetre,

$$= 0·328 × 0·328 × 0·328 \text{ cu. ft.} = 0·0353 \text{ cu. ft.}$$

In the British measures it is known that 1 cu. ft. = 6¼ gallons = 50 pints. Therefore 1 litre = 50 × 0·0353 pints = 1·76 pints.

For ordinary purposes the approximate conversion relation can be taken as 1 litre = 1¾ pints.

If the weight of 1 c.c. of pure water is taken to be 1 gram, then the litre, which is 1,000 c.c., will weigh 1,000 grams. This unit of weight is called the kilogram—it is the weight of a standard lump of platinum preserved in Paris. How does this unit of weight compare with the pound? You will find that 1 kilogram = 2·2 lb.

A very useful and easy way of converting metric units into British units, and vice versa, is to construct simple ready reckoners in graphical form. One of these, for conversions from kilograms to to pounds, is shown below (Fig. 3). You should construct for yourself similar graphs to show the relationship between metres and yards and between litres and pints. From the graph: 8 lb. = 3·6 kilograms.

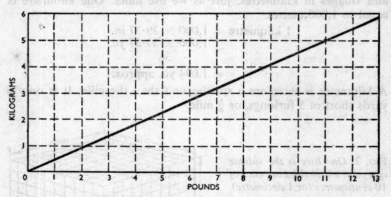

FIG. 3. *This graph enables you to convert kilograms to pounds, or vice versa.*

The results we have obtained are summarized in the table below:

BRITISH-METRIC CONVERSION TABLE

	Approximate	*More Exact*
Lengths ..	1 metre = 1 1/11 yd.	1 metre = 39·37 in.
	2·5 cm. = 1 in.	2·54 cm. = 1 in.
	1 kilo = 5 furlongs	1 kilo = 1,094 yd.
Capacity ..	1 litre = 1¾ pints	1 litre = 1·76 pints
Weight ..	1 kilo = 2⅕ lb.	1 kilo = 2·205 lb.

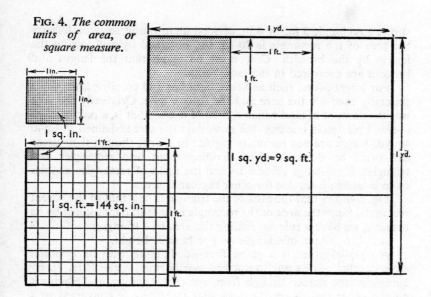

FIG. 4. *The common units of area, or square measure.*

1 in.

1 in.

1 sq. in.

1 ft.

1 sq. ft.=144 sq. in.

1 ft.

1 yd.

1 ft.

1 ft.

1 sq. yd.=9 sq. ft.

1 yd.

CALCULATION OF AREAS

While measuring lengths is normally done with ruler, tape measure or surveyor's chain, there is no simple instrument in general use for measuring area. For area we think of a square inch—that is, a square of which each side is one inch—or a square foot, or a square yard, and so on. Fig. 4 shows the common units of area, from which you can readily deduce the table of square measure:

$$144 \text{ sq. in.} = 1 \text{ sq. ft.}$$
$$9 \text{ sq. ft.} = 1 \text{ sq. yd., etc.}$$

To find the value of an area involves reckoning the number of unit squares within its boundaries, though you will realize this is not usually done by actual counting. Instead we make use of the simple rules for finding the area of a rectangle. Fig. 5

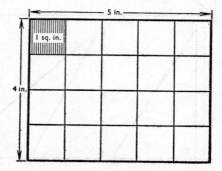

5 in.

1 sq. in.

4 in.

FIG. 5. *It can be seen that the area of the rectangle is 5 in. × 4 in., or 20 unit squares.*

shows a rectangle 5 in. by 4 in. divided up into unit squares. Clearly the area of the rectangle is 20 sq. in., obtained by multiplying the length by the breadth. Care must be taken that the length and breadth are measured in the same units.

For larger areas, such as fields, counties and countries, the units generally used are the acre and the square mile. Originally the acre was the amount of land which a yoke of oxen—that is, a pair of oxen—could plough in one day, but nowadays the acre is defined as 4,840 sq. yd. Fields are not normally regular in shape, though their areas can often be determined by dividing them into rectangles and triangles. Knowledge of how to find the areas of rectangles enables us to establish formulae for other regular figures.

Fig. 6 shows that the area of the triangle is half that of the parent rectangle. Since the area of the rectangle is its length multiplied by its breadth, we have a rule for finding the area of a triangle:

Area of triangle = $\frac{1}{2}$ × base × height.

A parallelogram is a plane four-sided figure with its opposite sides parallel but its angles not necessarily right-angles (Fig. 7). By cutting off the shaded triangle from one end as shown, and placing it on the other end, it can be seen that the figure is converted to a

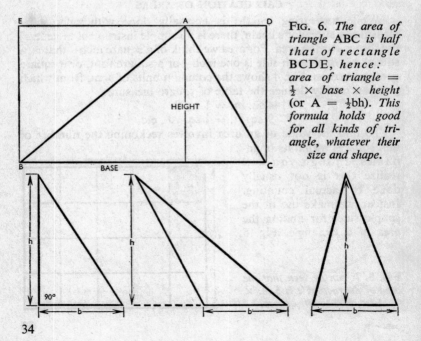

FIG. 6. *The area of triangle* ABC *is half that of rectangle* BCDE, *hence:* area of triangle = $\frac{1}{2}$ × base × height (or A = $\frac{1}{2}$bh). *This formula holds good for all kinds of triangle, whatever their size and shape.*

34

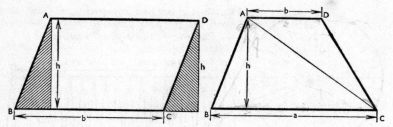

FIG. 7. *By making the parallelogram rectangular we can see that its area is* **bh.** *The trapezium becomes two triangles; its area is therefore* ½ (a + b)h.

rectangle. Its area is therefore length × breadth, where breadth is the perpendicular distance between one pair of parallel sides.

A trapezium is a plane four-sided figure with one pair of parallel sides (Fig. 7). Divide this figure into two by drawing a diagonal and you will see how to find its area. Most surfaces can be broken up into a mosaic of triangles and hence their areas calculated.

FACTS ABOUT CIRCLES

Centuries ago it was discovered that when the circumference of a circle is divided by the diameter the answer is always the same. The result of this division is so important and occurs so frequently that it is given a special symbol π (*pi*).

Draw a square of any size and inscribe a circle in it so that the circle touches each of the sides of the square (Fig. 8). It is clear that

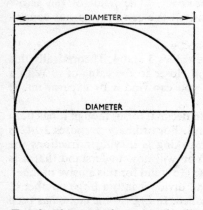

FIG. 8. *The circumference is clearly less than four times the diameter.*

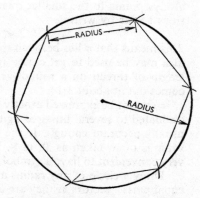

FIG. 9. *Here we see that it is rather more than six times the radius.*

35

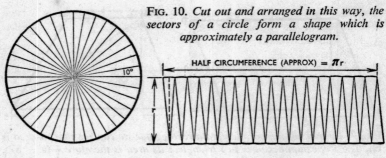

FIG. 10. *Cut out and arranged in this way, the sectors of a circle form a shape which is approximately a parallelogram.*

HALF CIRCUMFERENCE (APPROX) = πr

the circumference of the circle is less than the perimeter of the square. But the distance round the square is four times the diameter and so the circumference must be less than this. Another way of saying this is that $\dfrac{\text{circumference}}{\text{diameter}}$ is less than 4. Now draw a regular hexagon (six-sided figure) inside the circle. To do this keep the compasses open to the radius of the circle and step round the circumference with them; you get just six steps. Join the marks obtained to form the regular hexagon, each side of which will be equal to the radius of the circle (Fig. 9). The circumference of the circle is obviously greater than the perimeter of the hexagon; that is, six times the radius, or three times the diameter. Hence the ratio $\dfrac{\text{circumference}}{\text{diameter}}$ is certainly greater than 3.

Mathematicians have symbols for "greater than" and "less than"; these are $>$ and $<$ respectively. (The point of the arrow always points to the smaller quantity.) We can sum up our conclusions so far by writing

$$3 < \pi < 4$$

This means that π lies between the values 3 and 4. Theoretically this idea may be used to get closer and closer to the value of π. With a length of thread on a round jar you can find π by experiment. It comes out at about 3·14.

π cannot be expressed exactly in decimal form, though it has been evaluated to several hundred figures. For ordinary purposes 3·142 is usually accurate enough. If the working is in vulgar fractions the value is often taken as $3\frac{1}{7}$, or $\frac{22}{7}$. You will now understand that it is very convenient to have a symbol (π) to stand for this elusive number.

Draw a circle of any radius and divide it into a large number of equal parts—sectors as they are called. In Fig. 10 the circle has been divided into thirty-six equal parts. Cut the circle up into these thirty-six parts and rearrange the sectors side by side as shown; you will see that the resulting figure is approximately a parallelogram whose area is half the circumference times the radius.

Now circumference of circle = π × 2 × radius.

∴ Area of circle   = π × radius × radius, or πr^2 (where r stands for the radius). If you know this "formula" and the length of the radius, the rest is simple arithmetic.

SURFACE AREAS OF SOLIDS

Once familiarity is established with the areas of the commoner plane figures—rectangle, triangle, parallelogram, trapezium and circle—it is a comparatively easy matter to deal with the surface areas of the regular solids. The remainder of this section can be regarded as mensuration by formulae. In Fig. 11 you will find diagrams and a statement of the formulae for some of the well-known solids. Try and build these up for yourself from the simple formulae that we have already established.

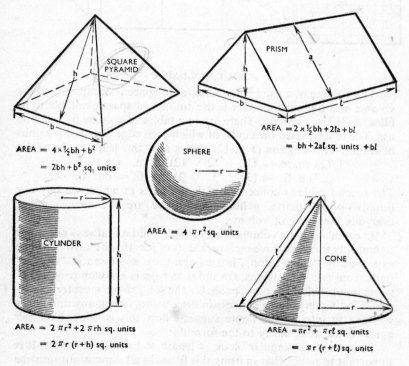

SQUARE PYRAMID

AREA = $4 \times \frac{1}{2}bh + b^2$

      = $2bh + b^2$ sq. units

PRISM

AREA = $2 \times \frac{1}{2}bh + 2la + bl$

      = $bh + 2al$ sq. units + bl

SPHERE

AREA = $4 \pi r^2$ sq. units

CYLINDER

AREA = $2 \pi r^2 + 2 \pi rh$ sq. units

      = $2 \pi r (r+h)$ sq. units

CONE

AREA = $\pi r^2 + \pi rl$ sq. units

      = $\pi r (r+l)$ sq. units

FIG. 11. *Useful formulae for finding the surface areas of regular solids.*

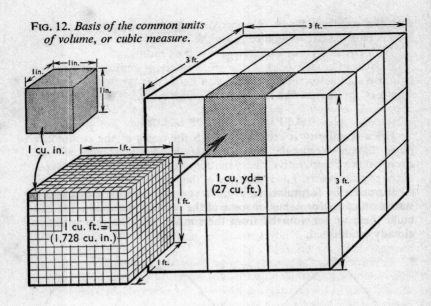

FIG. 12. *Basis of the common units of volume, or cubic measure.*

1 in.
1 in.
1 in.

1 cu. in.

1 cu. ft.=
(1,728 cu. in.)

1 ft.
1 ft.
1 ft.

1 cu. yd.=
(27 cu. ft.)

3 ft.
3 ft.
3 ft.

ABOUT VOLUMES

The volume of a solid is the amount of space it occupies, and the volume of a hollow container is the amount of space available to be filled, called its capacity. There are two tables of volume in common use. The first is based on a cube of which each edge is one of the units of length. The diagram (Fig. 12) shows how this leads to the table:

$$1{,}728 \text{ cu. in.} = (12 \times 12 \times 12) \text{ cu. in.} = 1 \text{ cu. ft.}$$
$$27 \text{ cu. ft.} = (3 \times 3 \times 3) \text{ cu. ft.} = \text{cu. yd.}$$

The second table is concerned with the units in which we buy our liquids—pints, quarts, gallons—and these are the most familiar everyday measures of volume.

In calculating the volume of any simple solid it is always necessary to multiply together three measurements of length; the answer will be expressed in "cubic" units, just as areas are expressed in "square" units from two dimensions. On the next page is a sketch (Fig. 13) of a rectangular block or tank, probably the solid shape most frequently met. Finding its volume consists in discovering how many unit cubes will just fit into it; the figure suggests how this is done. You will agree that it leads easily to the formula:

Volume of rectangular block = length × breadth × height. It is important to notice that in using this formula all dimensions must be in the same units or converted to the same units before substitution.

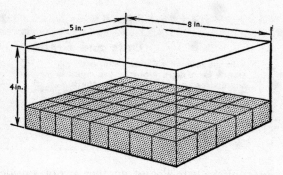

FIG. 13. *Building up the volume of a rectangular block. The bottom layer contains 8 × 5 = 40 cubes. There will be four such layers, so the total number of cubes will be 4 × 40 = 160. The volume is therefore 8 × 5 × 4 = 160 cu. in.*

Knowledge of the volumes of the simpler solids is frequently useful; fortunately it is not necessary to work from first principles each time and try to fill them with unit cubes. We shall rely as before on simple formulae. Figures and formulae for the solids you are most likely to meet are given in Fig. 14.

If you examine the formulae for volumes carefully you may note two interesting facts. The first is that for all solids of uniform cross-section such as the rectangular block, prism and cylinder, the volume can be written as:

Volume = area of cross-section × length.

The second fact is that for solids such as the pyramid and cone, which

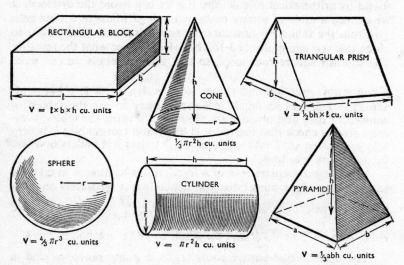

FIG. 14. *Useful formulae for calculating the volumes of regular solids.*

Dots and Digits

In the following division sum each dot stands for a digit. None of the digits in the divisor occurs elsewhere in the sum. There is no remainder. What is the answer? *Solution on page 444*

135) . . . . (. .
      . . .
      ———
      . . .
      . . .
      ———

taper uniformly to a point, another way of considering the volume is:

$$\text{Volume} = \tfrac{1}{3} \text{ area of base} \times \text{height}.$$

Confirm these facts for yourself; this will prove very useful in dealing with the volumes of other solids not mentioned here.

SQUARE AND CUBE ROOTS BRIEFLY EXPLAINED

It is the simplest matter to find the area of a square when the length of the side is known; it is a more puzzling proposition when the problem requires calculation in the opposite direction. What is the length of the side of a square when the area is 10? Of what number is 10 the square? We might guess that the answer is not much greater than 3. The answer, known as the square root of 10, can be found by arithmetical calculation, but we can avoid the drudgery if we consult a table of square roots or use logarithms or a slide rule.

From the tables we find that the square root of 10 is 3·162; to check this you can multiply 3·162 by 3·162 and see what the result is. The sign for square root is $\sqrt{}$, so that using symbols we can write

$$\sqrt{10} = 3 \cdot 162.$$

Using root notation we have $\sqrt{16} = 4$, $\sqrt{81} = 9$, $\sqrt{144} = 12$, $\sqrt{6 \cdot 25} = 2 \cdot 5$, and so on. It is not necessary to use the tables, of course, for easy and obvious square roots. In using the tables, however, always check that the result is likely and reasonable; it is very easy to confuse $\sqrt{17}$ with $\sqrt{170}$ or $\sqrt{1 \cdot 7}$ unless it is understood that the result lies near to 4.

In finding the square root of a fraction it is legitimate to take the square roots of the numerator and denominator separately and it is sometimes helpful to do this. For example, $\sqrt{\dfrac{27}{4}}$ can be calculated either as $\sqrt{6 \cdot 75}$ or $\dfrac{\sqrt{27}}{2}$, and the result by either method is 2·598.

The need to find square roots arises in many problems and in the use of formulae containing quantities under square root signs.

40

We must also mention briefly cube roots. What is the length of the side of a cube of which the volume is 20 cu. in? The volume of a cube is found by multiplying length by breadth by height, and these are all equal. The edge when "cubed" in this case must give 20. The length of edge is called the cube root of 20 and is written:

$$\text{Length of edge} = \sqrt[3]{20} \text{ in.}$$

The answer lies between 2 and 3 and with the help of logarithms or cube root tables is found to be 2·714.

With this brief explanation of how to deal with square and cube roots when they crop up, we may regard our review of the basic arithmetical facts, formulae and processes as sufficient for a fuller understanding of later parts of this book. It is easier to build mathematically on a secure foundation of calculating skill.

(b) Algebra: Symbols are Time-savers

No doubt many people recall algebra at school as a series of mysterious manipulations with letters having in many cases neither purpose nor meaning. Algebra is, in fact, a form of mathematical shorthand enabling statements to be made as concisely as possible. You may like to think that algebra arises from the laziness of mathematicians who dislike the idea of starting each new problem from the beginning. To avoid this they try to group together similar kinds of problem so that a start may be made from a general result applicable to all problems of the same type.

The area of a rectangle provides a familiar example: if the length of a rectangle is 6 in. and its breadth is 4 in., its area, which is obtained by multiplying length by breadth, is 24 sq. in. In algebra we generalize this result and say that if the length of the rectangle is l in. and its breadth b in., then its area, A sq. in., is $l \times b$ sq. in.

In symbols, $A = lb$.

We call the statement $A = lb$ a formula. Formulae enable us to express briefly what might take a whole paragraph to explain in words. The algebraic statement $A = lb$ applies not to a particular rectangle but to all rectangles. When we use this formula for calculating we replace the letters in the formula by the actual values. This is called substituting in the formula. Suppose, for example, that a rectangular room is 15 ft. long and 12 ft. wide, to use the formula we substitute these values for l and b respectively.

Thus $A = lb$

$$= 15 \times 12 \text{ sq. ft.} = 180 \text{ sq. ft.}$$

Notice that in the formula we have written $l \times b$ without the multiplication sign, and this is a common practice in the language of algebra. When the formula is translated into figures the multiplication sign reappears. It is important, also, when symbols are used, to say what they stand for. Notice, too, in substituting in the simple formula $A = l \times b$ that l and b are measured in the same units. If, for example, l is given in feet and b in yards, then we need to express both in feet (or yards) before substituting, to obtain a sensible result. Hundreds of examples of familiar formulae occur in text-books of mathematics, science, engineering, building and other practical subjects. Let us consider one or two of these to illustrate first this business of substitution:

(1) The volume V of a circular cylinder is given by the formula
$$V = \pi r^2 h$$
where r = radius of the base, h = height, and $\pi = \frac{22}{7}$. Have a good look at the formula before we substitute any values in it, to consider the meaning of the symbols. You will probably recognize πr^2 as the formula for the area of a circle which forms the base of the cylinder. What the formula states, then, is that the volume of the cylinder is equal to the area of its circular end multiplied by its height. What a lot of writing is saved by algebraic shorthand! What is the meaning of r^2 in the formula? It means $r \times r$ or rr, and must not be confused with $2r$, which is $2 \times r$. This is a common mistake to which reference will be made later. Let us find the volume of a cylinder of which the base radius is 7 in. and the height is 10 in.

$$\text{Here } V = \pi r^2 h$$
$$= \frac{22}{7} \times 7 \times 7 \times 10 \text{ cu. in.}$$
$$= 1{,}540 \text{ cu. in.}$$

(2) The horse-power of a steam engine is given by the formula
$$\text{h.p.} = \frac{PLAN}{33{,}000}$$
where P = steam pressure in pounds per sq. in., L = length of stroke in ft., A = area of piston head in sq. in., and N = number of piston strokes per min.
Find the h.p. of an engine in which $P = 110$, $L = 1\frac{1}{2}$, $A = 30$, and $N = 60$. It should be 9.

(3) The time which a pendulum takes to swing from side to side depends on its length and not, strangely enough, on how far it is displaced from its central position. The formula for its swing is

$$T = 2\pi \sqrt{\frac{l}{g}}$$

where T = time in sec., l = length in ft., g (the acceleration

due to gravity) $= 32$ ft. per sec. per sec., and $\pi = \frac{22}{7}$.
Find the time of swing of a pendulum which is 2 ft. long.

$$\text{Substituting, } T = 2 \times \frac{22}{7} \times \sqrt{\frac{2}{32}} \text{ sec.}$$

$$= 2 \times \frac{22}{7} \times \sqrt{\frac{1}{16}}$$

$$= \frac{44}{7} \times \frac{1}{4}$$

$$= 1\frac{4}{7} \text{ sec.}$$

These few brief examples of substitution will suffice. The method is similar for all formulae and once the substitution is correctly made the rest is pure arithmetic.

MAKING YOUR OWN FORMULA

We can often construct formulae for ourselves from the written details of the problem. An old recipe for making tea is to use one spoonful of tea for each person and "one for the pot"! Let us construct a formula for the number of spoonfuls when n people are to have tea. Clearly, spoonfuls $(S) = n + 1$. It is easy to check this. When $n = 5$ then $S = 6$; that is, 5 people use 6 spoonfuls, and so on. The tea might be a bit strong as the number of persons is increased!

Here is an example where constructing a formula may in the end save time and trouble. Suppose we wish to find the sum of all the numbers 1, 2, 3, . . . up to 100. Let S represent the required sum. Then $S = 1 + 2 + 3 + 4 + \ldots + 98 + 99 + 100$. Notice that pairs of numbers at equal distances from each end add up to 101 : $(100 + 1)$, $(99 + 2)$, $(98 + 3)$, and so on. How many pairs will there be altogether? Yes, fifty. So the total sum will be given by

$$S = 50 \times 101 = 5,050$$

We can use the method to find a formula for the sum of the first n whole numbers: 1, 2, 3, . . . $(n - 2)$, $(n - 1)$, n. Using pairs at equal distances from each end as before, we have:

$$\text{1st pair} = n + 1$$
$$\text{2nd pair} = (n - 1) + 2 = n + 1$$
$$\text{3rd pair} = (n - 2) + 3 = n + 1$$

and so on. Each pair totals $n + 1$. How many pairs are there altogether? As there are n numbers to begin with and we are grouping them in twos there will be just $\frac{1}{2}n$ pairs, each totalling $(n + 1)$. Total sum (S) therefore will be $S = \frac{1}{2}n(n + 1)$. Try the formula on the first five hundred numbers.

A triangle ABC has sides of length a, b, c (Fig. 15). Write down formulae for its perimeter (distance round it) and the sum of its

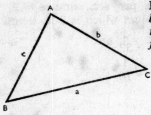

FIG. 15. *What formula can be found for the perimeter of this triangle? What is the formula for the sum of its angles?*

FIG. 16. *The box below, which is lidless, is formed from the metal sheet on the left. How can its volume be expressed in terms of the dimensions given?*

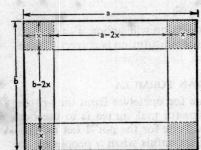

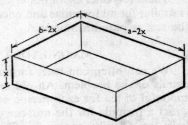

angles. Clearly, if P is the perimeter, then $P = a + b + c$. Also, the sum of the angles of any triangle is 180°, and so $A + B + C = 180°$. These are the two formulae required.

Consider the following problem. A sheet of metal, a in. long and b in. wide, has small squares of sides x in. cut from each corner. The edges are then turned up to form a shallow lidless box. Neglecting overlap, what is the formula for the volume of the box? The diagram (Fig. 16) shows the dimensions of the resulting box. You will see that the volume V is given by the formula

$$V = (a - 2x)(b - 2x)x \quad \text{[length × breadth × depth]}.$$

If $a = 16$ in., $b = 10$ in. and the sides of the squares removed are 1 in., then

$$V = (16 - 2) \times (10 - 2) \times 1 \text{ cu. in.}$$
$$= 14 \times 8 \times 1 \text{ cu. in.} = 112 \text{ cu. in.}$$

Note the use of brackets in the formula to ensure that the right quantities are multiplied together.

TRANSPOSING THE FORMULA

A formula is not always in the most convenient form for calculation. For example, the volume V of a cone is given by

$$V = \tfrac{1}{3} \pi r^2 h$$

where $r =$ the radius of the base and $h =$ the height. We might wish to find the height of a cone of which the volume and radius are given.

44

Suppose $V = 66$ cu. in. and $r = 3$ in. Taking $\pi = \frac{22}{7}$ we can substitute in the formula directly:

$$66 = \frac{1}{3} \times \frac{22}{7} \times 3 \times 3 \times h$$

$$\text{or } 66 = \frac{66}{7} h$$

and therefore h must be 7 in.

A better way to solve this same problem would be to rearrange the formula before substitution to obtain an expression for h in terms of the other letters. Such a rearrangement is called transposition and h becomes the subject of the formula. Remember that a formula is really an algebraic statement of equality. It is reasonable to suppose that if we operate in the same way on both sides of this equality then the sides will remain equal.

$$V = \tfrac{1}{3}\pi r^2 h$$
$$\text{or } 3V = \pi r^2 h \quad \text{(Multiplying both sides by 3)}$$
$$\text{or } \frac{3V}{\pi r^2} = h \quad \text{(Dividing by } \pi \text{ and by } r^2\text{)}$$

Now substitute $V = 66$, $r = 3$, $\pi = \frac{22}{7}$ in this revised form of the formula and we get $h = 7$ as before.

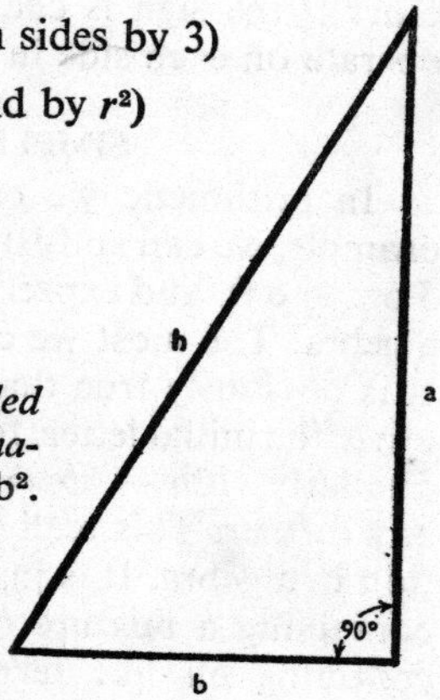

FIG. 17. *Because this is a right-angled triangle we can use the theorem of Pythagoras to produce the equation* $h^2 = a^2 + b^2$.

The well-known theorem of Pythagoras concerning the sides of a right-angled triangle states that the square on the hypotenuse (h in Fig. 17) equals the sum of the squares on the other two sides containing the right-angle (a and b), or, in symbols, $h^2 = a^2 + b^2$. Rearrange this to find a formula for a.

Subtract b^2 from each side, or, what amounts to the same thing, transpose b^2 and change its sign: $h^2 - b^2 = a^2$.

Take the square root of each side: $a = \sqrt{h^2 - b^2}$
This, of course, cannot be simplified further unless numerical values are given to h and b. In the case of a formula where the quantity to be found is contained under the square root sign, it is usually necessary at some stage of the working to square both sides. For example, the diameter, d, of rivets to be used for joining boiler plates of thickness t in. is given by the formula

$$d = 1\cdot2\sqrt{t}.$$

First isolate $\sqrt{t}$ by dividing each side by 1·2.

That is, $\sqrt{t} = \dfrac{d}{1\cdot2}$

Square both sides to obtain t:

$$t = \frac{d^2}{1\cdot2^2} = \frac{d^2}{1\cdot44}$$

(Remember to square both denominator and numerator of the fraction.)

Enough has now been said about the transposition of formulae to enable us to summarize our rules. Here they are:

We can multiply or divide both sides of a formula or equation by the same number without upsetting the equality. Any number or quantity can be added to or subtracted from each side or, what amounts to the same thing, can be transferred from one side to the other if the sign is changed ($+$ to $-$, $-$ to $+$). In short, we must operate on each side in the same way.

SIMPLE PROCESSES OF ALGEBRA

In arithmetic we can add or subtract similar quantities. For example, we can add 10 in. to 7 in. to obtain 17 in., but we do not add 5 oz. to 6 ft. and expect to arrive at a sensible result. It is the same in algebra. The most we can do is to put similar expressions together. It is obviously true that 4 apples $+$ 3 apples $=$ 7 apples, and if we use a, the initial letter, for apples this can be written as $4a + 3a = 7a$. Similarly, $10b - 6b = 4b$. We cannot, however, simplify $7a + 4b$ any further. This really exhausts the rules for addition and subtraction in algebra. It is just as simple as that! If we have an expression containing a mixture of terms we simplify it as far as possible by collecting all like terms together and writing the answer in its simplest form.

For example:

$$6a + 9b + 7c - 4a + 2b - 5c = 2a + 11b + 2c.$$

This is as far as we can go.

Similarly, we may simplify $2x^2 + 7x + 5 + 3x^2 - 2x + 1$ by recognizing that x^2, x and the plain numbers are three different kinds of quantity and must be totalled separately. This leads us to the result $5x^2 + 5x + 6$. As in arithmetic, too, we can do addition by arranging like quantities under each other and totalling each column separately. For instance, add $6a^2 + 2ab + 5b^2$ to $3a^2 - 4ab - 3b^2$. Setting this out as an addition sum:

$$
\begin{array}{r}
6a^2 + 2ab + 5b^2 \\
3a^2 - 4ab - 3b^2 \\
\hline
9a^2 - 2ab + 2b^2
\end{array}
$$

46

Notice that when quantities to be added contain minus signs, due regard must be paid to the signs. How, then, do we arrive at the result $-2ab$ by adding $+2ab$ to $-4ab$? If for the moment we regard $+$ as putting something in and $-$ as taking something out, then the net result of putting 2 in and taking 4 out is that we take 2 out. We shall return to this again later.

Subtraction is best done by regarding it as the opposite of addition. Instead of subtracting one expression from another, the sign of the second expression can be changed and it can be added. Each pair of similar terms can be dealt with as for addition. Instead, therefore, of writing

$$\text{from } 6x^2 - 10xy + 4y^2$$
$$\text{take } 3x^2 + 7xy - 3y^2$$

we can write

$$\text{to } \quad 6x^2 - 10xy + 4y^2$$
$$\text{add } - 3x^2 - 7xy + 3y^2$$

The answer is $3x^2 - 17xy + 7y^2$

In order to master this idea you should write down and add and subtract a variety of expressions for yourself. It is well worth the trouble.

We have already seen in the formula for the area of a rectangle that $l \times b$ is written lb (or bl). Similarly, $x \times y \times z$ is written xyz, $2a \times 3b$ is written $6ab$, and $4a \times 3b \times 2c$ is written $24abc$. In the last two cases the numbers are multiplied first and then the letters written down, preferably in alphabetical order. The number in front of the letters is usually referred to as the coefficient. Multiplication in algebra is very easy for, apart from the numbers, we never actually do it!

By the multiplication rule, $a \times a = aa$
and $a \times a \times a = aaa$.

The expressions aa and aaa are written in shorthand form as a^2 and a^3 respectively, and are referred to as "a squared" and "a cubed." Similarly, a^4 means $aaaa$ and is read as "a to the fourth power." The little number to the right and above the letter shows how many times the letter is to be multiplied by itself. It is called an index, and such terms as a^2, a^3, and a^4, are known as "powers" of a. Thus, $6a^2 b^3$ means $6 \times a \times a \times b \times b \times b$.

To multiply two powers of the same number is a simple matter. For example, $a^3 \times a^4$ means $aaa \times aaaa$, which is $aaaaaaa$ (7 factors) or a^7. All we need to do is to add the indices. Notice, however, that $a^3 \times b^4 = a^3 b^4$, which cannot be simplified further.

Here are a few examples just to fix the idea:

$$4a^2 \times 3a^5 = 12a^7$$
$$2a^3b^2 \times 4ab^3 = 8a^4b^5 \text{ (Note that } a \text{ is really } a^1)$$
$$3x^2yz \times 2xy^3z^2 = 6x^3y^4z^3.$$

Division is the reverse of multiplication. To divide powers of the same number one by the other the indices are subtracted:

$$a^5 \div a^2 = \frac{aaa\cancel{a}\cancel{a}}{\cancel{a}\cancel{a}} = a^3, \text{ and so on.}$$

If there are numerical coefficients the division is actually carried out:

$$6x^4 \div 2x^2 = 3x^2$$
$$15l^3m^4 \div 5lm^3 = 3l^2m.$$

HOW TO MANIPULATE PLUS AND MINUS SIGNS

One important idea remains to be explored before we can make further progress. It is usually in algebra that we meet for the first time the use of negative numbers; that is, numbers with a minus sign in front of them such as -2, $-6x$, $-a^2$. The plus and minus signs in arithmetic are instructions to add or subtract respectively, but in algebra we often use them rather differently; $-$ is regarded as the reverse of $+$. Any number with a $+$ sign before it is a gain, increase or asset, while any number with a $-$ sign before it is a loss, decrease or debt. Or, again, if $+$ indicates measurement along a scale in one direction then $-$ indicates measurement along the scale in the opposite direction. Here are some examples of the $+$ and $-$ signs used in this way:

If $+10°$ means a temperature of $10°$ above zero, then $-10°$ means a temperature of $10°$ below zero.

If $+1,000$ means 1,000 ft. above sea-level, then $-1,000$ means 1,000 ft. below sea-level.

If $+100$ means A.D. 100 then -100 means 100 B.C.

If $+6$ means 6 paces forward, then -6 means 6 paces backward.

If $+5$ means an asset of £5, then -5 means a debt or loss of £5.

These numbers with a sign attached are called directed numbers, those with a $+$ sign being positive and those with a $-$ sign negative numbers. In order to work with them it is necessary to know what to do with such expressions as $-4+5-3$, or $(-6)+(-3)$, or $6 \times (-4)$, or $(-4) \times (-5)$. This is not particularly easy to learn and it can only be done by working numerous examples until the ideas are firmly grasped. We have yet to learn the rules before we can play the game. Look at this scale:

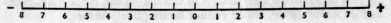

48

Displacements to the right of the zero are positive numbers and those to the left are negative. The scale might have been arranged vertically like this:

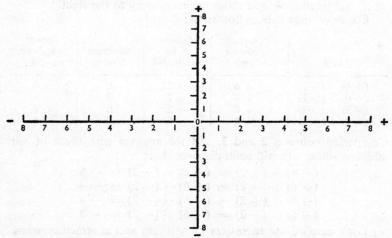

Positive numbers are upward displacements and negative numbers are downward displacements from zero.

If these two scales are superimposed we get the two axes normally used in drawing graphs:

We shall be using these axes in a moment, but if you turn to the section on graphs you will see many examples of their use. Refer to the horizontal scale. To add + quantities, move to the right; to add — quantities, move to the left. Here are some addition sums:

Sum	Starting point on scale	Amount to be added	Direction L or R	Answer (end point on scale)
(+ 6) + (+ 2)	+ 6	+ 2	R	+ 8
(+ 6) + (− 2)	+ 6	− 2	L	+ 4
(− 6) + (+ 2)	− 6	+ 2	R	− 4
(− 6) + (− 2)	− 6	− 2	L	− 8

If you examine columns 2, 3 and 5 you will see that these can be written:

$$+ 6 + 2 = + 8$$
$$+ 6 - 2 = + 4$$
$$- 6 + 2 = - 4$$
$$- 6 - 2 = - 8$$

In addition, therefore, we may write down each number with its own sign and omit the + sign linking them together as in column 1. Thus, $(+ 5) + (− 3) + (− 6) + (+ 2)$ may be written $+ 5 − 3 − 6 + 2 = − 2$. Check this on the scale by starting at $+ 5$, moving three places to the left, then six more places to the left, then two places to the right. You will finish on − 2. If subtraction can be regarded as the reverse of addition then we can say that:

subtracting + quantities means moving to the left;
subtracting — quantities means moving to the right.

Consider these subtraction sums:

Sum	Starting point on scale	Amount to be subtracted	Direction L or R	Answer (end point on scale)
(+ 6) − (+ 2)	+ 6	+ 2	L	+ 4
(+ 6) − (− 2)	+ 6	− 2	R	+ 8
(− 6) − (+ 2)	− 6	+ 2	L	− 8
(− 6) − (− 2)	− 6	− 2	R	− 4

Comparing columns 2 and 3, and the answers with those of our addition sums, you will soon discover that:

$$(+ 6) + (+ 2) = (+ 6) - (- 2) = + 8$$
$$(+ 6) + (- 2) = (+ 6) - (+ 2) = + 4$$
$$(- 6) + (+ 2) = (- 6) - (- 2) = - 4$$
$$(- 6) + (- 2) = (- 6) - (+ 2) = - 8$$

Look carefully at these sets of addition and subtraction sums. You will see that if we make all the subtraction signs into addition signs and then change the signs of the quantities to be subtracted the two sets are identical. Thus, a simple rule for subtraction is that we should reverse the sign of the quantity to be subtracted and add it instead. We have already shown that in addition we can dispense with the addition sign and treat each quantity in accordance with its appropriate sign.

At first sight, a sum like this might look terrifying:

$$(+8) + (-4) - (+6) - (-8) + (-3)$$

But it is really all very simple. First change all the subtraction signs to addition, at the same time remembering to change the sign of the quantity to be subtracted.

$$= (+8) + (-4) + (-6) + (+8) + (-3).$$

Now drop all the addition signs and deal with each quantity with its sign attached:

$$+8 \quad -4 \quad -6 \quad +8 \quad -3$$

What is the answer? $+3$ is right.

Normally the intermediate steps are not set down. Competence in dealing with directed numbers is acquired by practice until the processes are automatic. You will probably need to do many examples before you have acquired the technique.

You may feel we have dwelt too long on this subject of directed numbers, especially as we have not yet considered multiplication and division. We will deal with them now.

Imagine a train speeding northwards at a steady thirty-five miles per hour and passing through a town O exactly at noon. Let the hours after the train leaves O be regarded as positive quantities and the hours before it reaches O, that is before noon, as negative quantities. Similarly, let distances north of O be positive; then distances south of O will be negative. O is the zero position on both time and distance scales. Using this convention we will draw a diagram (graph) showing the train's progress (Fig. 18). On our scales one square on the horizontal (time) axis represents one hour and one square on

Fair Shares

Tom, Dick and Harry inherited their father's estate, which consisted entirely of eleven cows. The will said they were to have $\frac{1}{2}$, $\frac{1}{4}$ and $\frac{1}{6}$ respectively. They were flummoxed to know how to do it, so they consulted Gaffer Brown. "Easy," he said. He brought over his own cow and put it with the eleven. After he had given each son his share, his own cow was left. Who received more than his fair share?

Solution on page 444

the vertical (distance) axis represents twenty miles. To plot the points which will represent the route of the train mark points vertically above and below the hours on the time scale at distances which show how far the train is from O at that time. Distances to the north will be upwards and distances to the south will be downwards. You will soon realize that since the train is travelling at a constant speed the graph will go up equal distances in equal times and the resulting points will lie in a straight line. There is no need to plot all the points. Two will do. Let velocity northwards (35 m.p.h.) be positive (+) and remember that distance = speed × time, or expressed in symbols, $s = vt$, where s = distance in miles, v = speed in miles per hour, and t = time in hours.

Position of the train at A:

$$s = vt = (+ 35) \times (- 4)$$
$$= - 140 \qquad\qquad \text{(140 miles south of O)}$$

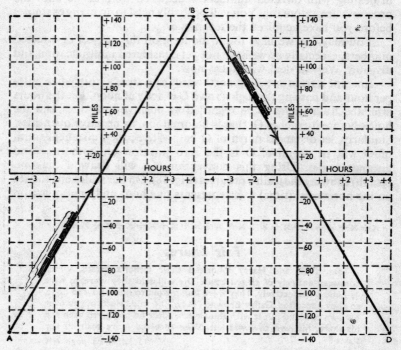

FIG. 18. *Graph showing northward progress of train from A to B.*

FIG. 19. *Southward progress of train travelling from C to D.*

Position of the train at B:
$$s = vt = (+\,35) \times (+\,4)$$
$$= +\,140 \qquad \text{(140 miles north of O)}$$

Now consider the train on its return journey travelling southwards. A graph can be drawn representing the journey (Fig. 19). Let velocity southwards (35 m.p.h.) be negative.

Position of train at C:
$$s = vt = (-\,35) \times (-\,4)$$
$$= +\,140 \qquad \text{(140 miles north of O)}$$

Position of train at D:
$$s = vt = (-\,35) \times (+\,4)$$
$$= -\,140 \qquad \text{(140 miles south of O)}$$

Examine these four multiplications carefully. When quantities with opposite signs are multiplied, what is the sign of the answer? When quantities with similar signs are multiplied what is the sign of the answer? No doubt you will soon spot the fact that like signs when multiplied produce a + sign and unlike signs when multiplied produce a − sign.

Remember that though this rule has been derived for multiplication it can easily be shown to hold also for division. Do not confuse it with the results for addition and subtraction. Having mastered (we hope) the rule of signs, we can be more ambitious in our manipulations with algebraic expressions. Let us extend our experience of multiplication by introducing brackets. $5 \times (6 + 7)$ means that the whole of the quantity within the bracket is to be multiplied by 5. Simplified, it is 5×13. Another method is to multiply each term in the bracket by 5 and then collect the resulting quantities together. Thus $5 \times (6 + 7)$ becomes $30 + 35$, or 65 as before. This second method is the one normally used in algebra since the bracketed quantity cannot usually be simplified. What is $a\,(x + y)$? The bracket is in its simplest form already. Multiply each term by a: the answer is $ax + ay$.

Below are some examples to illustrate this point:
$$a\,(a + b) = \quad a^2 + ab$$
$$-\,a\,(a + b) = \quad -\,a^2 - ab$$
$$-\,2x\,(x - y) = -\,2x^2 + 2xy$$
$$6\,(p - 3q) - 4\,(2p - q) = 6p - 18q - 8p + 4q$$
$$= -\,2p - 14q.$$

Check this for yourself, remembering the rule of signs, and then make up many more examples for practice.

How can we multiply an expression like $x + 5$ by an expression like $x + 3$? A diagram suggests how this is done (Fig. 20). Draw a rectangle $x + 5$ units long and $x + 3$ units wide (x can be any

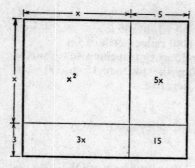
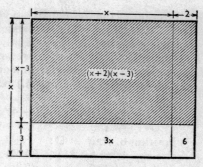

FIG. 20. *This illustrates the result of multiplying* $(x + 5)$ *by* $(x + 3)$.

FIG. 21. *Area of shaded portion is* $(x + 2)(x - 3)$, *or* $x^2 - x - 6$.

convenient length). Split the rectangle up by lines as shown. It is divided into a square and three rectangles.

$$\text{Total area} = x^2 + 5x + 3x + 15$$
$$= x^2 + 8x + 15.$$

Also, area of rectangle = length × breadth = $(x + 5)(x + 3)$.

$$\therefore (x + 5)(x + 3) = x^2 + 8x + 15.$$

Look at the diagram another way. The two upper portions, x^2 and $5x$, are obtained by multiplying out $x(x + 5)$ and the two lower portions by $3(x + 5)$.

$$\therefore \text{Total area} = (x + 3)(x + 5)$$
$$= x(x + 5) + 3(x + 5)$$
$$= x^2 + 5x + 3x + 15$$
$$= x^2 + 8x + 15.$$

Thus $(x + 5)$ is multiplied by each term of $x + 3$ in turn and the result simplified by collecting similar quantities together (in this case x's only). Similar arguments can be applied to $(x + 2)(x - 3)$ illustrated in Fig. 21. In this case the area required (shaded) is the area of the largest rectangle less the areas of the two rectangles $3x$ and 6.

$$\text{Area required} = (x + 2)(x - 3)$$
$$= x^2 + 2x - 3x - 6$$
$$= x^2 - x - 6.$$

Put in a slightly different way this can be stated as: Area required = total area — area of bottom strip

$$= x(x + 2) - 3(x + 2)$$
$$= x^2 + 2x - 3x - 6 \text{ (note two unlike signs)}$$
$$= x^2 - x - 6.$$

Each term of $(x + 2)$ is multiplied by each term of $x - 3$ and the result simplified. This is just like arithmetic: when two numbers are

54

multiplied together each figure of one is multiplied by each figure of the second and the result simplified. We can do the same in algebra; it is not necessary to draw diagrams all the time.

Multiply $(2a - 3b)$ by $(3a + 2b)$. Here is the whole thing set down for you as in arithmetic:

$$\begin{array}{r} 2a - 3b \\ 3a + 2b \\ \hline 6a^2 - 9ab \\ + 4ab - 6b^2 \\ \hline 6a^2 - 5ab - 6b^2 \end{array}$$

Due regard must be paid to the signs of the multipliers.

This is really all there is to algebraic multiplication; but there are two special cases of multiplication which are worth remembering since they are met with so often. The first is any expression multiplied by itself; this is called a perfect square. Take $(a + b)^2$ as a typical example and multiply it out. This result can be remembered as "the first quantity squared, plus twice the product of the two quantities, plus the second quantity squared."

Now try working out $(a - b)^2$. If you have used the rule concerning signs correctly you should find that the answer is $a^2 - 2ab + b^2$, which differs from the first result only in the sign of the $2ab$.

These results are very useful in enabling us to square quite readily any expression consisting of two terms. What is $(2x + 3y)^2$? Here the a of the standard form is replaced by $2x$ and the b by $3y$. Substituting these in the result above we have:

$$(2x + 3y)^2 = (2x)^2 + 2 \times 2x \times 3y + (3y)^2$$
$$= 4x^2 + 12xy + 9y^2.$$

An expression like $(3p - 4q)^2$ can be worked in a similar manner. Try it for yourself.

These formulae are also useful in calculating the squares of some numbers.

For example $199^2 = (200 - 1)^2$
$$= 40,000 - 400 + 1 = 39,601$$
or $(5{\cdot}01)^2 = (5 + {\cdot}01)^2$
$$= 5^2 + 2 \times 5 \times {\cdot}01 + ({\cdot}01)^2$$
$$= 25 + {\cdot}1 + {\cdot}0001 = 25{\cdot}1001$$

With a little practice you should be able to square such numbers "in your head."

The second useful case of multiplication consists of expressions of the form $(a + b) \times (a - b)$, which equals $a^2 - b^2$.

Thus, $(4x + 3y)(4x - 3y) = (4x)^2 - (3y)^2$
$$= 16x^2 - 9y^2$$

All examples like this can be treated in a similar fashion.

55

The reverse process of this last form of multiplication is often very useful in simplifying and shortening numerical calculation. This means that we start with the difference between two squares (as $a^2 - b^2$) and put it back into the form of its original factors $[(a + b) (a - b)]$.

Calculate $401^2 - 399^2$. This looks a formidable piece of work until we write down

$$401^2 - 399^2 = (401 + 399) (401 - 399)$$
$$= 800 \times 2 = 1600$$

Here is a second example to illustrate the usefulness of this result. The formula for the cross-sectional area of a circular pipe is $\pi R^2 - \pi r^2$, where R = the outer radius and r the inner radius (Fig. 22). Find the area of a cross-section of a pipe of outside radius 5·35 in. and inside radius 4·65 in.

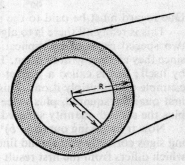

Area $= \pi R^2 - \pi r^2$
$= \pi(R^2 - r^2)$
$= \pi(R + r) (R - r)$

Substituting the values given for R and r and taking $\pi = \frac{22}{7}$, you will find the answer is 22 sq. in.

Fig. 22. *Area of shaded portion is* $\pi R^2 - \pi r^2$, or $\pi(R + r) (R - r)$.

Complicated division is seldom met with in practice and one example to illustrate the method must be sufficient. Divide $x^3 + 2x^2 - 5x - 6$ by $x^2 - x - 2$. Set out like a normal division sum in arithmetic:

$$
\begin{array}{r}
x + 3 \\
x^2 - x - 2) \overline{)x^3 + 2x^2 - 5x - 6} \\
\underline{x^3 - x^2 - 2x} \\
3x^2 - 3x - 6 \\
\underline{3x^2 - 3x - 6} \\
\end{array}
$$

Since x^3 divided by x^2 is x, multiply $x^2 - x - 2$ by x and subtract, leaving $3x^2 - 3x$. Next bring down the $- 6$. Now x^2 into $3x^2$ goes 3 times; multiplying $x^2 - x - 2$ by 3 we find the division is exact.

USING ALGEBRA TO SOLVE PROBLEMS

Having considered very quickly the basic processes of algebra we can begin to apply what we have learnt to the solution of problems. It is in its application to problems that algebra proves most useful. Many problems lead to simple equations, and an easy example will give us a start with these.

56

A man is three times as old as his son. In ten years' time he will only be twice as old. What are their ages now? How do we set about solving problems such as this? There are really only two things to do. Call one unknown quantity x and then build up in algebraic form the facts that are given, so that two things that are equal can be made into an equation.

Suppose the son's age now is x years, then the father's age must be $3x$ years (three times as old). In ten years' time the son will be $x + 10$ years and his father $3x + 10$ years. Now we are told that the father will be twice his son's age then. Expressing this fact in symbols instead of words:

$3x + 10 = 2(x + 10)$
$3x + 10 = 2x + 20$ (removing brackets)
$3x = 2x + 20 - 10$ (subtracting 10 from each side)
$3x - 2x = 10$ (subtracting $2x$ from each side)
or $x = 10$ years

Father's age $= 30$ years.

In ten years the father will be forty years old and the son twenty. Do these figures fit the facts? If so, our solution is the correct one. You will see that our manipulation of the equation is identical with the manipulation of a formula. The methods are the same, and there are no new rules. Provided we operate equally on both sides of the equation, the equation remains true. A few easy examples will soon illustrate the idea.

(1) If $4x = 12$
          $x = 3$ (divide each side by 4)

(2) If $\dfrac{x}{4} = 5$
          $x = 20$ (multiply both sides by 4)

(3) If $\dfrac{2x}{3} = 4$
        $2x = 12$ (multiply each side by 3)
          $x = 6$ (divide each side by 2)

(4) If $2x + 4 = 9$
        $2x = 5$ (subtract 4 from each side)
          $x = 2\frac{1}{2}$ (divide each side by 2)

(5) If $3x - 5 = 7$
        $3x = 12$ (add 5 to each side)
          $x = 4$ (divide each side by 3)

(6) If $4(x + 3) = 3(x + 6)$
    $4x + 12 = 3x + 18$ (multiplying brackets)
        $4x = 3x + 6$ (subtracting 12 from each side)
          $x = 6$ (subtracting $3x$ from each side)

(7) $\frac{1}{4}(x-3) + \frac{1}{3}(2x-1)$ $= 2$
Then $3(x-3) + 4(2x-1) = 24$ (multiplying each side by
                                 12 to remove the fractions)
$$3x - 9 + 8x - 4 = 24$$
$$11x = 37 \quad \text{(adding 13 to each side)}$$
$$x = 3\tfrac{4}{11}.$$

Sometimes the unknown quantity may be in the denominator of a fraction but this presents no real difficulty.

(8)   If $\dfrac{3}{5} = \dfrac{4}{x}$

Then $3 = \dfrac{20}{x}$ (multiply each side by 5)

$\quad\quad 3x = 20$ (multiply each side by x)

$\quad\quad x = 6\dfrac{2}{3}$ (divide each side by 3).

There are other arrangements of simple equations which need simplification before a solution can be found. You will see that in all cases we rearrange our equation until finally the unknown number is on one side of the equation and the known number on the other. All simple equations ultimately become like $ax = b$, whence $x = \dfrac{b}{a}$.

The find-the-number kind of puzzle is very popular and is usually easy to solve after the facts have been sorted out and an equation found. Find a number which if 8 is added to it produces the same result as if 4 were taken from twice the number. The equation is $x + 8 = 2x - 4$, which gives $x = 12$. The answer should always be checked by substituting it in the equation to see if it satisfies it. Putting $x = 12$ in this example,

Left-hand side of equation $12 + 8$ $= 20$
Right-hand side of equation $2 \times 12 - 4 = 20$.

The equation is true if $x = 12$, which is therefore the correct solution.

Here is another number problem. The difference between two numbers is 3. Three times the smaller number is 2 more than the sum of the numbers. Find the numbers.

Let $x =$ smaller number
Then $x + 3 =$ larger number
$$3x - 2 = x + 3 + x$$
$$3x - 2 = 2x + 3$$
$$x = 5 \text{ (smaller number)}$$
$$x + 3 = 8 \text{ (larger number)}$$

Three times the smaller number is 15; the sum of the two numbers is 13; the difference 2. Do these numbers satisfy the problem?

58

You can make up hundreds of number puzzles for yourself and you will come across them often in newspapers, magazines and puzzle books.

A car travels 40 miles in the same time as a second car, travelling 5 m.p.h. faster, does 50 miles. What are the speeds?

Let S = speed of slower car in m.p.h.

Then $S + 5$ = speed of faster car

Remembering that $\dfrac{\text{distance}}{\text{speed}}$ = time, we have

$$\frac{40}{S} = \frac{50}{S + 5}$$

from the fact that the time taken is the same. This is a rather more difficult equation than we have met with so far. Divide both sides by 10 and multiply both sides by S:

$$4 = \frac{5S}{S + 5}$$

Multiply both sides by $S + 5$:

$$4(S + 5) = 5S$$
$$4S + 20 = 5S$$
$$20 = S$$
$$S = 20 \text{ m.p.h.}$$

40 miles at 20 m.p.h. takes 2 hours.

50 miles at 25 m.p.h. takes 2 hours.

The answers fit the facts of the case. You may have noticed that clearing the equation of fractions is equivalent to saying $40 \times (S + 5)$ and $50 \times S$ are equal.

$$\frac{40}{S} \bowtie \frac{50}{S + 5}$$

This is known as cross-multiplying and is a very useful device when two fractions are equal.

SIMULTANEOUS EQUATIONS

Not all problems lead to simple equations in one unknown. What, for instance, is the answer to the problem "find two numbers the sum of which is 10"? Obviously there is no single solution, since hundreds of possible answers spring readily to mind—$6 + 4$, $1\frac{1}{2} + 8\frac{1}{2}$, $1\cdot6 + 8\cdot4$, $12 + (-2)$, and so on. The possibilities are infinite. If x represents one of the two numbers and y the other we can say $x + y = 10$, but this alone does not enable us to find unique values for x and y. Our information is inadequate. If in addition to stating that the sum of the two numbers is 10 we add that their difference is 2 we can make progress. Common sense suggests that only the numbers 6 and 4 satisfy these facts. Writing down the facts symbolically produces two equations:

$$(1)\ x + y = 10$$
$$(2)\ x - y = 2$$

While there are thousands of values of x and of y which will satisfy these equations separately there is only one value of x and one value of y which will make them both true at the same time. They are therefore called simultaneous equations. By guesswork (or common sense) $x = 6$ and $y = 4$. How can we solve algebraically?

The method is simple. Add equations (1) and (2): $2x = 12$ ($+ y$ and $- y$ added give $0y$), and so $x = 6$. Substitute this value for x in either equation:

$$6 + y = 10$$
$$y = 4.$$

Check these answers by substituting in the equation not already used: $6 - 4 = 2$. The equations are satisfied.

The method commonly employed in solving simultaneous equations is to eliminate (get rid of) one of the unknowns. Here is an example:

$$(1)\ 2x + 3y = 17$$
$$(2)\ 3x - 2y = 6.$$

Adding or subtracting the equations as they stand will not result in the elimination of either of the unknowns, since there are unequal numbers of each in the two equations. But we can readily produce the same number of x's (or y's):

Multiply equation (1) by 3: $6x + 9y = 51$
Multiply equation (2) by 2: $6x - 4y = 12$

Subtract (change signs and add): $13y = 39$
$$y = 3$$

Substitute this value for y in equation (1):
$$2x + 9 = 17$$
so $x = 4$

Check in equation (2): $3 \times 4 - 2 \times 3 = 6$. These answers are correct.

This method of solving simultaneous equations is easy to understand and operate. Look up some examples and practise for yourself; you will become proficient only by doing so.

QUADRATIC EQUATIONS

Earlier on we saw that the result of multiplying $(x + 3)$ by $(x + 5)$ was $x^2 + 8x + 15$. An expression such as this, in which the highest power of the unknown is the square (x^2), is called a quadratic. a^2, $p^2 + 5$, $l^2 - 5l + 6$, are all examples of quadratic expressions. Many practical problems or the substitution of values in formulae

60

lead to quadratic equations in which the unknown quantity occurs squared either alone or in combination with a first degree term and a number. We solve a quadratic equation every time we use the theorem of Pythagoras. What, for instance, is the length of the hypotenuse of a right-angled triangle in which the two shorter sides are 5 in. and 12 in. ? (Fig. 23).

If h is the hypotenuse,

$$h^2 = 5^2 + 12^2$$
$$= 25 + 144$$
$$= 169$$
$$h = \sqrt{169}$$
$$= 13 \text{ in.}$$

The quadratic equation is $h^2 = 169$, or $h^2 - 169 = 0$. Is $h = 13$ the only answer? You will remember from the rules of signs that $- 13 \times - 13 = + 169$. Hence $h = - 13$ is also a possible solution

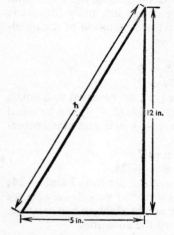

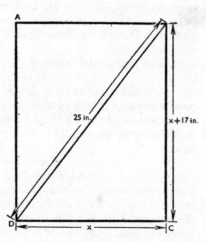

FIG. 23. *Knowing the lengths of the other two sides, we can find* h.   FIG. 24. *The same formula also helps us to find the value of* x *in this case.*

of the question. It is not, however, an acceptable answer to the problem, since we are finding the length of a side of a triangle. It would be safe to say that while $h = + 13$ and $- 13$ are solutions to the quadratic equation $h^2 = 169$, we select the answer $+ 13$ as the only one applicable to this problem.

Consider a second example. The diagonal of a rectangle is 25 in. and one side is 17 in. longer than the other (Fig. 24). What are the lengths of the sides? If the short side is x in. long, then the longer side is $x + 17$ in. By the theorem of Pythagoras,

$$25^2 = x^2 + (x + 17)^2$$
$$625 = x^2 + x^2 + 34x + 289$$
$$= 2x^2 + 34x + 289$$

Transfer 625 to the other side: $0 = 2x^2 + 34x - 336$

Dividing by 2, $\quad 0 = x^2 + 17x - 168$.

It would be difficult to guess the answer to this or ever to arrive at it by common sense. A method of solving it is needed. You will recall that $x^2 + 8x + 15$ was the result of multiplying $(x + 3)$ by $(x + 5)$. Can we find two single expressions which when multiplied produce $x^2 + 17x - 168$?

Consider $(x + a)(x + b)$. The product is $x^2 + (a + b)x + ab$. In our example $a + b$ is 17 and ab is 168. We want to find two numbers which add to 17 and multiply to -168. By experiment these are found to be $+ 24$ and $- 7$. Thus $x^2 + 17x - 168$ is the same as $(x + 24)(x - 7)$. This process of putting the expression back into the two factors from which it was originally formed is known as factorizing. How does it help in the solution of the quadratic equation?

Let us argue a bit about it.

$$x^2 + 17x - 168 = 0$$

is the same as $(x + 24)(x - 7) = 0$.

Now a product (result of multiplication) cannot be equal to 0 unless one of the multipliers is 0, and hence $(x + 24)(x - 7)$ can be equal to zero only when $x + 24 = 0$ or when $x - 7 = 0$, and never otherwise.

$$\text{If } x - 7 = 0, x = 7$$
$$\text{and if } x + 24 = 0, x = -24.$$

The roots (answers) of the quadratic equation are thus 7 and $- 24$; in the particular example from which we started we can only accept the answer 7 in. for the shorter side of the right-angled triangle. None the less, $- 24$ is also a solution to the equation.

How Many Jumps?

In the centre of a circle 9 ft. in radius is a frog. It begins to jump in a straight line to the circumference of the circle. Its first jump is 4 ft. 6 in., its second 2 ft. 3 in., and it continues to jump half the length of the preceding jump. How many jumps does the frog make to get out of the circle? Solution on page 444

We have discovered a method of solving a quadratic equation. Bring all the terms to one side of the equation and equate to 0; factorize (if possible) the quadratic expression, and solve the two simple equations which result. One objection to this method is that not all such expressions can be split into factors. We must therefore seek a method which can be applied to all quadratics. The method depends on the fact that we can readily solve an equation like $(x - 1)^2 = 25$. Taking the square root of each side,

$x - 1 = + 5$ or $- 5$ (remember the two possible square roots). This is equivalent to the two separate statements:

(1) $x - 1 = + 5$, whence $x = 6$
(2) $x - 1 = - 5$, whence $x = - 4$

$x = + 6$ and $- 4$ are the two roots of the original equation. Really, you see, it is again the method of reduction to two simple equations. Let us examine this method when applied to some examples:

Solve $\qquad\qquad x^2 - 4x + 3 = 0.$
Transpose the 3. $\qquad x^2 - 4x = - 3$
Add 4 to each side. $x^2 - 4x + 4 = - 3 + 4$
That is, $\qquad\qquad (x - 2)^2 = 1.$
$\qquad\qquad\qquad x - 2 = + 1$ or $- 1$
$\qquad\qquad\qquad\qquad x = 3$ or $1.$

The trick lies in adding 4. Why 4? you may ask. To answer that question you should multiply out a few expressions like $(x + 3)^2$, $(x - 5)^2$, $(x + 8)^2$, $(x + a)^2$. You will discover that in every case in these perfect squares the final number is the square of half the coefficient (multiplier) of x. Take the last case, $(x + a)^2$.

$$(x + a)^2 = x^2 + 2ax + a^2.$$

Coefficient of x is $2a$. Half of this is a. Squaring this produces a^2, the last term of the expression.

Looking at this process in the reverse direction, we should see that if we are given x^2 and the x term we can complete the whole quadratic expression as a perfect square by halving the coefficient of x, squaring the number so obtained, and adding it on.

Solve $x^2 + 5x + 6 = 0.$
Rearrange: $x^2 + 5x = - 6$
Add $\left(2\tfrac{1}{2}\right)^2$ to each side: $x^2 + 5x + \left(\dfrac{5}{2}\right)^2 = - 6 + \dfrac{25}{4}$
which is $\left(x + \dfrac{5}{2}\right)^2 = \dfrac{1}{4}$
Taking the square roots, $x + \dfrac{5}{2} = + \dfrac{1}{2}$ or $- \dfrac{1}{2}$
$\qquad\qquad\qquad x = - 2$ or $- 3$

Notice what happens if there is more than one x^2.

Solve $2x^2 - 7x + 3 = 0$.

Divide *first* by 2 (the coefficient of x^2):

$$x^2 - \frac{7x}{2} + \frac{3}{2} = 0.$$

Transpose $\frac{3}{2}$:

$$x^2 - \frac{7x}{2} = \frac{-3}{2}$$

Add $\left(\frac{7}{4}\right)^2$ (the square of half coefficient of x):

$$x^2 - \frac{7x}{2} + \left(\frac{7}{4}\right)^2 = \frac{-3}{2} + \frac{49}{16}$$

$$\left(x - \frac{7}{4}\right)^2 = \frac{25}{16}.$$

Taking the square roots, $x - \frac{7}{4} = +\frac{5}{4}$ or $-\frac{5}{4}$

$$x = \left(\frac{7}{4} + \frac{5}{4}\right) \text{ or } \left(\frac{7}{4} - \frac{5}{4}\right) = 3 \text{ or } \tfrac{1}{2}.$$

Can we generalize this method to obtain a formula applicable to all quadratic equations? It can be done and we shall now proceed to do it.

By giving values to a, b and c the equation $ax^2 + bx + c = 0$ can be used to represent *all* quadratic equations with one unknown. Let us use the method of perfect squares on this.

$$ax^2 + bx + c = 0$$

Divide by a:

$$x^2 + \frac{bx}{a} + \frac{c}{a} = 0$$

Transpose $\frac{c}{a}$ and add to each side $\left(\frac{1}{2} \cdot \frac{b}{a}\right)^2$:

$$x^2 + \frac{bx}{a} + \left(\frac{b}{2a}\right)^2 = \frac{-c}{a} + \frac{b^2}{4a^2}$$

$$\left(x + \frac{b}{2a}\right)^2 = \frac{+b^2 - 4ac}{4a^2}$$

The fractions $\frac{-c}{a} + \frac{b^2}{4a^2}$ have been put over a common denominator.

Take the square roots: $x + \frac{b}{2a} = \pm \sqrt{\frac{b^2 - 4ac}{4a^2}}$

$$= \pm \frac{\sqrt{b^2 - 4ac}}{2a}$$

Transpose $\frac{b}{2a}$: $x = \frac{-b}{2a} + \frac{\sqrt{b^2 - 4ac}}{2a}$, or $\frac{-b}{2a} - \frac{\sqrt{b^2 - 4ac}}{2a}$

or, writing the results together, $x = \frac{-b \pm \sqrt{b^2 - 4ac}}{2a}$.

We have arrived at a formula which gives the two values of x that satisfy the equation $ax^2 + bx + c = 0$. Does it look frightening? It is not so in practice. All we have to do is to substitute in it the values of a, b and c for any particular equation, bearing in mind the appropriate signs, and then calculate the two values required.

Solve: $2x^2 - 11x + 12 = 0$.

Comparing this with our standard equation $ax^2 + bx + c = 0$, we see that $a = +2$, $b = -11$, $c = +12$. Substituting in the formula,

$$x = \frac{-(-11) \pm \sqrt{(-11)^2 - 4 \times 2 \times 12}}{2 \times 2}$$

$$= \frac{+11 \pm \sqrt{121 - 96}}{4}$$

$$= \frac{11 \pm \sqrt{25}}{4}$$

$$= \frac{11 \pm 5}{4}$$

$$= \frac{16}{4} \text{ or } \frac{6}{4} \text{ (taking first the } + \text{ and then the } - \text{ sign)}$$

$$= 4 \text{ or } 1\tfrac{1}{2}.$$

These values can be tested by substituting in the original equation.
If $x = 4$: $2(4)^2 - 11(4) + 12 = 32 - 44 + 12$
$$= 0.$$

If $x = \frac{3}{2}$: $2\left(\frac{3}{2}\right)^2 - 11\left(\frac{3}{2}\right) + 12 = 4\tfrac{1}{2} - 16\tfrac{1}{2} + 12$
$$= 0.$$

Each value satisfies the equation.

Remembering this formula is very useful since it relieves us from starting from scratch each time and illustrates how we can often sum up a process in a general rule which can then be applied to all examples of the same type.

Having learnt how to solve a quadratic equation, let us consider some further problems. A carpenter uses the following formula when he wishes to make an arch of radius r, height h and span $2s$:

$$r = \frac{s^2 + h^2}{2h}$$

What is the height of the arch, of span 6 ft., which can be cut from a circle of radius $3\tfrac{1}{4}$ ft.? Substituting in the formula the given values,

$$3\tfrac{1}{4} = \frac{9 + h^2}{2h}$$

or $6\tfrac{1}{2}h = 9 + h^2$ (multiplying by $2h$)

$$h^2 - \frac{13h}{2} + 9 = 0.$$

You will find that $h = 4\frac{1}{2}$ ft. or 2 ft. Both answers are positive and either could satisfy the needs of the problem. Which one is the carpenter likely to use? Why? The diagram (Fig. 25) may suggest which is the more likely arch.

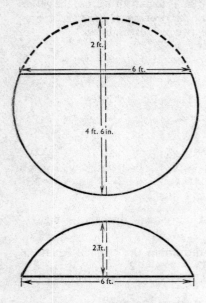

FIG. 25. *Two arches each spanning 6 ft. can be cut from the circle. There is little doubt which would be used for the arched doorway.*

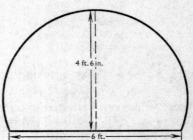

One equation of motion is $s = ut + \frac{1}{2}at^2$. Find t when $u = 64$ ft. per sec., $s = 960$ ft. and $a = 32$ ft. per sec. per sec. Substituting in the equation the given values and then simplifying it you should get $t^2 + 4t - 60 = 0$. The answer is $t = -10$ or 6. For a practical answer we should doubtless take $t = 6$ sec. though $t = -10$ sec. might also do if the minus sign indicated time before a certain zero hour! Verify that the answers satisfy the original equation by substituting these values in it.

The two quadratics solved above resulted from substitution in established formulae. Often it is necessary to build up the quadratic equation from the facts of the problem. A number puzzle will illustrate this need. Find two consecutive positive integers (whole numbers) such that the sum of their squares is 265.

If n is taken for the smaller number, then $n + 1$ will be the number next above it.

$$\text{So} \quad n^2 + (n + 1)^2 = 265$$
$$n^2 + n^2 + 2n + 1 - 265 = 0 \quad \text{(squaring } n + 1)$$
$$2n^2 + 2n - 264 = 0$$
$$n^2 + n - 132 = 0 \quad \text{(dividing by 2)}.$$

66

Using the formula for quadratic equations, $a = 1, b = 1, c = -132$, you will find that $n = 11$ or -12. Rejecting the -12, the positive integers required are 11 and 12. Test these for yourself.

A piece of wire 28 in. long is cut into two parts each of which is bent into the form of a square (Fig. 26). The sum of the areas of the two squares is 25 sq. in. What are the lengths of the sides of the two squares?

Let one piece of wire be $4x$ in. long. (This is to enable us to bend it into a square of side x in. and so avoid fractions.) Then the second piece is $(28 - 4x)$ in. long.

One square has a side of x in.

The second square has a side of $\frac{1}{4}(28 - 4x)$ in., or $(7 - x)$ in. The sum of their areas is 25 sq. in., so

$$x^2 + (7 - x)^2 = 25$$

which you should be able to solve yourself. The sides of the squares are 4 in. and 3 in. The pieces of wire are 16 in. and 12 in. Do these measurements fit the facts?

Problems in speed often lead to quadratic equations. If a car had covered the 210 miles from A to B at an average speed of 5 m.p.h. faster than it did, the time for the journey would have been one hour less. What was its speed?

Let x = car's speed in miles per hour, then

$x + 5$ = increased average speed in miles per hour.

Time of journey at original speed = $\dfrac{210}{x}$ hours.

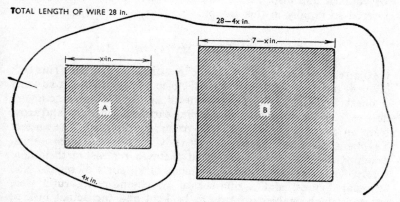

FIG. 26. *The piece of wire forming the two squares is* 28 *in. long and the combined areas of the squares is* 25 *sq. in. From the facts given in the drawing we can find by algebra the lengths of the sides of the squares.*

Time of journey at increased average speed $= \dfrac{210}{x + 5}$ hours.

From the facts of the case,

$$\frac{210}{x} - \frac{210}{x + 5} = 1.$$

The equation must first be simplified by clearing the fractions. Multiply each side by x and then by $x + 5$:

$$210 (x + 5) - 210x = x (x + 5)$$
$$\text{becomes } x^2 + 5x - 1050 = 0.$$

By the formula, $x = \dfrac{-5 \pm \sqrt{25 - 4 \times 1 \times (-1050)}}{2}$

$$= 30 \text{ or } - 35.$$

The original speed is therefore 30 m.p.h. The negative answer does not meet the needs of the practical problem. Verify that the answer is correct.

You may feel that it is rather artificial that all the examples given have worked out exactly. So it is. The quantity under the square root sign will not always come to a perfect square. It may be necessary to obtain approximate answers by using square-root tables or logarithms. This does not affect the method but only complicates the arithmetic and we have been more concerned here with the method than heavy numerical calculation.

Engineering, building, science and mechanics all provide numerous examples of quadratic equations. You may ferret out many of these for yourself and also practise the elementary processes of algebra covered so rapidly in this section.

(c) Geometry: Lines, Shapes and Angles

GEOMETRY has been defined as the investigation of space. This task involves not only the study of solid objects but also of flat surfaces (planes), lines, angles and shapes of all kinds. The name geometry derives from two Greek words meaning earth measurement and arose from an essentially practical need to survey the land. The ancient Egyptians living on the banks of the Nile suffered almost annual flooding, and circumstances forced them to remeasure their land yearly. This required the measurement of all sorts of regular and irregular figures, and a number of rough-and-ready rules were evolved which enabled records to be kept and the actual task of remeasuring to be carried out expeditiously.

Subsequent civilizations improved this primitive geometry until the Greek mathematician Euclid, who lived in the third century B.C., gathered all the accumulated knowledge together in his famous books. Euclid's geometry consisted of a number of self-evident facts (axioms) from which truths about geometrical shapes can be shown to follow (theorems). These are presented in a logical sequence so that each can be made dependent on what has gone before.

The value of a geometrical truth increases as we understand what it is about and appreciate its importance in practical everyday applications. Look around you as you read this. You will see everywhere examples of lines, angles, rectangles, squares, circles, curves and solid figures of all shapes and sizes. Nature offers many wonderful examples of geometrical shapes, from the complex designs of leaves and petals and the beautiful patterns of snowflakes and frost crystals to the simplicity of the hexagonal cell of the bee. Men, too, build the houses in which they live in various geometrical forms.

Geometry should be regarded as essentially practical and useful; many people are discouraged from studying it because so frequently the facts, most of which seem self-evident, lie buried in a mass of words. The straight line and the circle are the basis of elementary geometry (Euclid), and our brief survey of the subject will be largely confined to them.

With some elementary drawing instruments—ruler, compasses, set squares, and protractor—many things can be discovered by drawing and measurement and many obvious facts verified. We shall begin our study of geometry by considering lines and angles and then proceed to such familiar shapes as triangles and circles.

WHAT YOU SHOULD KNOW ABOUT ANGLES

Look at the hands of a clock or watch, the spokes of a wheel, or the legs of a pair of compasses. In Fig. 5 on page 10 you will see that the angle between the hands of the large clock and the angle between those of the watch, with its much shorter hands, are the same: the size of an angle does not depend on the length of its arms. We may

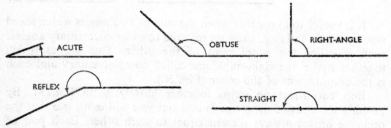

Fig. 27. *Angles are named in this way according to their size.*

think of an angle being formed when a straight line turns about a point in its own length; the amount of turn will determine the amount of angle. This is the way in which an angle is usually measured. In one hour the minute hand of a clock makes one complete revolution and the angle turned through is 360 degrees (units of angle).

Fig. 27 shows how angles are named according to their size. If you bolt two Meccano strips loosely together by their end holes you can form any of these angles for yourself. Or if you can get hold of a carpenter's folding rule you may use the jointed sections of the rule for the same purpose (Fig. 28). A knowledge of angles is essential to engineering, surveying, architecture and navigation. The compass is a great help in studying angles (Fig. 29).

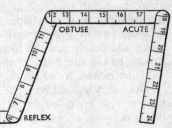

FIG. 28. *Angles of all kinds can be formed with a folding rule.*

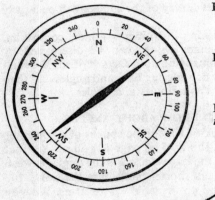

FIG. 29. *A compass is a very useful instrument for studying angles.*

FIG. 30. *Angles* x *and* y *are supplementary, while angles* a *and* b *are complementary.*

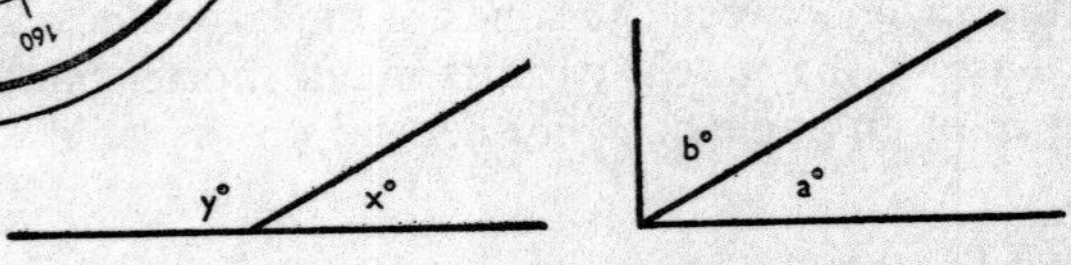

It is useful to know that when the sum of two angles which stand side by side is 180 deg., they are referred to as supplementary angles: each is called the supplement of the other. Two angles which together make one right-angle are called complementary and each is the complement of the other (Fig. 30).

Bolt two Meccano strips together loosely as in Fig. 31. By pushing the ends of the strips in and out you will easily see that the opposite angles always remain equal to each other. Each pair of angles formed when two straight lines cross are called vertically

FIG. 31. *Whatever their size, the vertically opposite angles are always equal.*

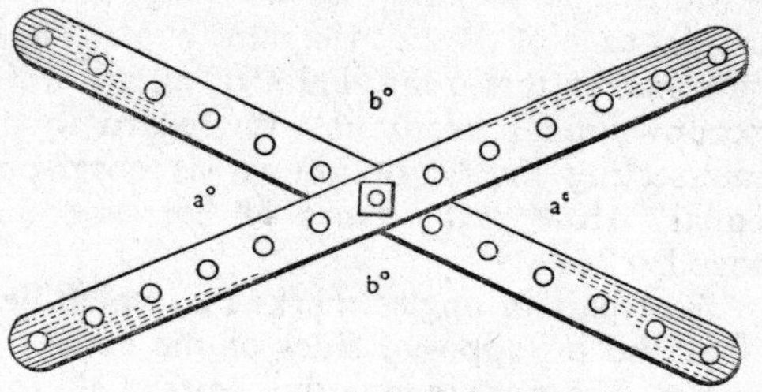

opposite angles; what we have discovered is that vertically opposite angles are equal.

By far the commonest angle is the right-angle; it is formed when one line is perpendicular to another. There are doubtless hundreds of examples of right-angles around you now. It is often important to ensure that a surface is horizontal or vertical or that a corner is square. A builder, for example, finds a spirit level, a plumb-line, and a large set-square useful for this purpose, while a draughtsman may use a T-square and set-squares. You will find it interesting to discuss with different craftsmen the methods they use to obtain right-angles.

WHEN LINES ARE PARALLEL

The term parallel is readily understood. Railway lines, whether curved or straight, run side by side always keeping the same distance apart, and are hence parallel. The furniture, walls, floor and ceiling of the room in which you are sitting provide numerous examples of pairs of parallel lines. Now look at the line in which the ceiling meets the wall facing you; then look at the line in which the floor meets the wall to your left or right. These lines can never meet. But they are not parallel. They do not lie in the same plane (or flat surface). Parallel straight lines, therefore, are straight lines lying in the same plane which do not meet however far they are extended at either end.

The geometry of a five-barred gate will tell us nearly all we need to know about parallel lines (Fig. 32). The five horizontal bars are

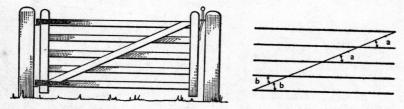

FIG. 32. *The geometry of a five-barred gate. The angles marked a are corresponding angles; those marked b are alternate. They are all the same size. How many pairs of each are there here?*

71

obviously all parallel and the diagonal bar from corner to corner crosses each of these at the same angle. The simplified diagram of the gate makes this clear. Pairs of angles like those marked *a*, which occupy similar positions with regard to the parallel lines and the intersecting lines, are known as corresponding angles. Are they equal? How many pairs of corresponding angles are there altogether?

The pair of angles marked *b*, which lie inside a pair of parallel lines and on opposite sides of the cutting line, are called alternate angles. There are many other pairs of alternate angles in the diagram. Can you find them all? You will probably see easily enough that the angles *a* and *b* are the same size.

The most useful fact to remember about parallel lines which will assist further progress in geometry is that when a set of parallel lines is crossed by another straight line angles of *two* sizes only are formed and these two sizes are supplementary.

TALKING OF TRIANGLES

One of the most important of all geometrical figures is the triangle, which, as its name implies, is a figure having three angles. You could make one by taking three Meccano strips (not necessarily of the same length) and bolting them loosely together at the corners. Can you change its shape without bending or breaking one of its sides? You will discover that it forms a rigid frame. This is not true for a four-sided figure, as you can prove for yourself by constructing one from Meccano strips (Fig. 33). Provided the corners are loosely jointed, the four-sided frame can easily be pushed into various shapes. The fact that the triangle is a rigid structure is of tremendous importance when bracing is required in cranes, bridges, pylons, derricks, doors, gates, shelf supports, furniture construction, and so on.

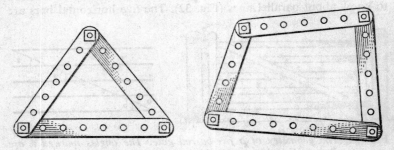

FIG. 33. *A triangle forms a rigid frame, but a four-sided figure does not.*

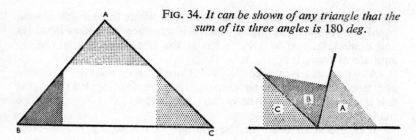

FIG. 34. *It can be shown of any triangle that the sum of its three angles is* 180 *deg.*

Keep your eyes open for examples of the practical applications of this important property of a triangle.

It is obviously possible to draw an unlimited number of triangles of all sizes and shapes. Draw a few fairly large triangles. Using a protractor, measure the angles of each triangle and find their sum. What do the angles of a triangle add up to? Your totals should all be about 180 deg., since this is the sum of the three angles for all triangles. This can be shown in another way. Draw a triangle and cut off its corners. Fit the pieces together as shown in Fig. 34. Do the three angles form a straight line? It is possible to establish this truth

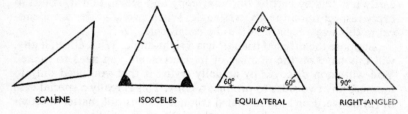

| SCALENE | ISOSCELES | EQUILATERAL | RIGHT-ANGLED |

FIG. 35. *The four members of the triangle family. The scalene triangle has all its sides and all its angles different; the isosceles has two equal sides and two equal angles; the equilateral has all its sides equal and all its angles equal; the right-angled triangle has one angle of* 90 *deg.*

in a theorem by extending one side of a triangle and drawing from the same vertex (corner) a line parallel to the side opposite that vertex. You will see at once that the three adjacent angles so formed are bound to be equal to the three angles forming the triangle. The whole "proof" can be seen in the mind's eye.

The triangle has three sides; these may all be of different lengths, two sides may be equal, or all three sides may be the same. The triangle family is shown in Fig. 35. You should discover for yourself by constructing various triangles that when two sides are equal so are the angles opposite those sides, and that when three sides are all equal so are the three angles. Such triangles are known as isosceles and equilateral respectively. What is the size of each angle in an equilateral triangle?

A set-square is a triangle. What angle have all set-squares in common? Obviously the right-angle. They are right-angled triangles; this is a specially useful form of the triangle to which reference will be made later.

It is useful to think of the triangle as having six parts—three angles and three sides. If you were set the problem of copying a given triangle exactly, how many of these would you need to measure? Draw any large triangle on a sheet of paper and set about making an exact copy of it, using the smallest number of measurements. You should discover, as the result of your experiment, that the triangle can be reproduced exactly if you measure

    (1) The three sides; or
    (2) Two sides and the angle between them; or
    (3) One side and any two of the angles.

Your copy should be an exact duplicate of the original triangle. In (3) you must be sure to get the angles in the right order. You can easily test this by cutting out your copy and seeing that it will fit in every respect upon the given triangle. When two triangles are identical in this way they are said to be *congruent*.

Suppose the original triangle has a right-angle. What effect, if any, will this have on the number of measurements you need to make? You will soon discover by actually trying it that you need only to measure any two sides to produce a copy. This is really a special case of (2) above. For a right-angled triangle it does not matter whether the two sides measured contain the right-angle or not.

How's Your Geometry?

(1) Where on earth could you find a triangle of which each angle is 90 deg.?

(2) Construct two lines at right-angles, a circle, two semicircles on the same line, a triangle with two sides produced, three-quarters of a circle repeated once, and a circle. Place these seven figures in a row. The answer will soothe your nerves.

(3) At what time are the hands of the clock pointing in exactly opposite directions, each towards a minute division line?

Solutions on p. 444

Let us consider a practical application of congruency, since you may well think that our discussion so far has been largely theoretical.

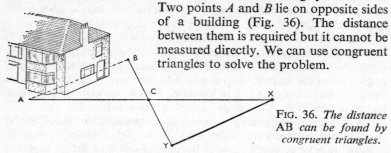

Two points *A* and *B* lie on opposite sides of a building (Fig. 36). The distance between them is required but it cannot be measured directly. We can use congruent triangles to solve the problem.

FIG. 36. *The distance* AB *can be found by congruent triangles.*

Choose any point, *C*, from which the points *A* and *B* can be seen and from which it is possible to measure the distances *AC* and *BC* with a chain or tape. Place a stick in the ground at *C* and find a point *X* in line with *A* and *C* and such that *AC* equals *CX*. Similarly, find a point *Y* in line with *B* and *C* so that *BC* equals *CY*. The diagram helps to make this clear. Measure *XY*. This is equal to *AB*. This method depends on one of the cases of congruency—can you say which it is?

Here is a method for finding the width of a river by means of congruent triangles. Choose a point *X* on your side of the river, opposite some permanent object *O* on the other bank. Turn through a right-angle at *X* and measure any convenient distance along the bank to *Y*. Continue along the bank to *Z*, so that *XY* and *YZ* are equal, making sure that *X*, *Y* and *Z* are in a straight line. Turn inland

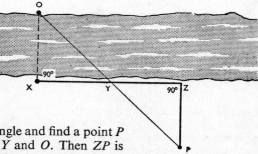

FIG. 37. *Applying congruent triangles to find the width of a river.* OX = PZ.

at *Z* through a right-angle and find a point *P* which is in line with *Y* and *O*. Then *ZP* is equal to the width of the river. You will see from Fig. 37 that two right-angled congruent triangles are involved.

It was stated earlier that we should return to the right-angled triangle. Many centuries ago it was known that the triangle in which the sides were 3, 4, and 5 was right-angled. This fact was made use of by the surveyors of ancient Egypt for land measuring and building. A rope knotted to form lengths of 3, 4 and 5 was used when a right-angle was required (Fig. 38). One other important property of a right-angled triangle has also been known for thousands of years. It was Pythagoras, in the sixth century B.C., who first proved that in any right-angled triangle the square on the side opposite to the right-angle (called the hypotenuse) is equal to the sum of the two squares on the sides containing the right-angle. This truth may be suggested to you if you look at the floor pattern of tiles in Fig. 39.

We need not be concerned here with the geometrical proof of this relationship between the sides of a right-angled triangle, but an interesting way of checking it is by cutting out and fitting together the pieces as suggested in Chapter 1. This important truth, known as Pythagoras's Theorem, enables us to calculate the length of the third side of a right-angled triangle if we know the length of any two of its sides. The use of this rule can best be illustrated by an example: *A* and *B* are two points on opposite sides of a pond (Fig. 40), and the distance *AB* is required but cannot be measured directly. From *A* set out any convenient line *AX* and determine the point *C* on *AX* such that *ACB* is a right-angle. You will think of ways to do this. Measure *AC* and *BC*. If *AC* is 15 yd. and *BC* is 36 yd., how long is *AB*?

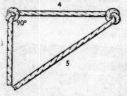

FIG. 38. *The ancient Egyptians used a knotted rope in this way to form a right-angle.*

FIG. 39. *A pattern of triangular tiles illustrates in a simple way the theorem of Pythagoras that in a right-angled triangle the square on the hypotenuse is equal to the sum of the squares on the other two sides of the triangle.*

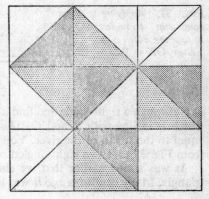

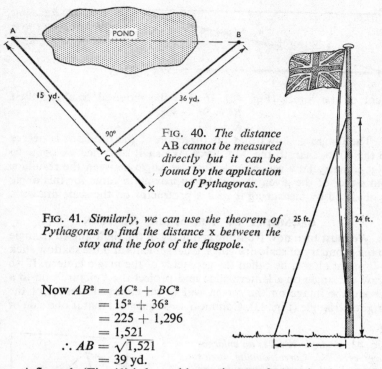

FIG. 40. *The distance AB cannot be measured directly but it can be found by the application of Pythagoras.*

FIG. 41. *Similarly, we can use the theorem of Pythagoras to find the distance* x *between the stay and the foot of the flagpole.*

Now $AB^2 = AC^2 + BC^2$
$= 15^2 + 36^2$
$= 225 + 1,296$
$= 1,521$
$\therefore AB = \sqrt{1,521}$
$= 39$ yd.

A flagpole (Fig. 41) is braced by a wire stay fastened to it at 24 ft. from the ground. If the stay is 25 ft. long, how far out from the foot of the pole is the stay fastened into the ground? If x is the required distance, then

$$x^2 + 24^2 = 25^2$$
$$\text{or } x^2 + 576 = 625$$
$$\therefore \quad x^2 = 49$$
$$x = \sqrt{49} = 7 \text{ ft.}$$

A well-known fact in mechanics is that if two forces acting at a point at right-angles to each other are represented in size and direction by two sides of a rectangle (drawn to scale), then a single force equivalent to them, known as the resultant, can be represented by the diagonal of the same rectangle. This clearly enables us to find the value of the resultant by scale drawing, but it can also be found by calculation by applying Pythagoras's theorem.

Two forces of 9 lb. and 40 lb. act at right-angles to each other. What is the value of their resultant? The diagram shows the arrange-

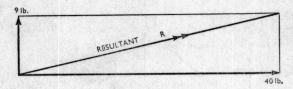

FIG. 42. *Resultant of two forces acting at right-angles.*

ment of the forces (Fig. 42). If R is the required resultant then
$$R^2 = 9^2 + 40^2$$
$$\therefore R = 41.$$

The diagram shows that the direction of the resultant is nearer to the 40-lb. than to the 9-lb. force. We shall see when we come to trigonometry how we can calculate the angle between the resultant and either of the given forces. An approximate value for this angle is obtained by measuring it with a protractor on the scale drawing.

GEOMETRY OF THE MAGIC LANTERN

We must turn now from the geometry of the right-angled triangle to the geometry of scale drawings, enlargements and the shadow stick —it might almost be called the geometry of the magic lantern. If we draw a triangle on a lantern slide and project the "picture" on to a screen, the image on the screen will be an enlarged version of the original triangle (Fig. 43). Common sense suggests that if one side of

FIG. 43. *Triangle XYZ is an enlargement of* ABC. *Corresponding angles are equal and corresponding sides are proportional. The triangles are similar.*

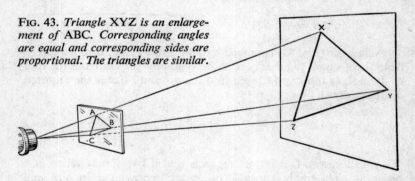

our original triangle is magnified twenty times then the other sides likewise will be magnified twenty times. We do not expect the angles to be changed but that all corresponding measurements of length will be in proportion.

The triangles have the same shape, corresponding angles are equal, and one triangle is a larger version of the other. Such triangles are said to be *similar*. The principle of similarity is not restricted to

78

triangles. If, for example, we examine a specimen under the micro-scope the image seen is similar in every way to the original object.

Every time an architect or engineer makes a scale drawing, or a photographer makes an enlargement, or we use field glasses or a telescope, this principle is realized. It was well known to the ancient mathematicians who used it to measure the heights of the Pyramids. If a stick is fixed upright in the ground there will come a time, when the sun is 45 deg. above the horizon, at which the stick's shadow will be equal to the height of the stick itself. If the shadows of build-ings, trees or cliffs are measured at this same moment their heights can be determined, since they too will be equal to their shadows

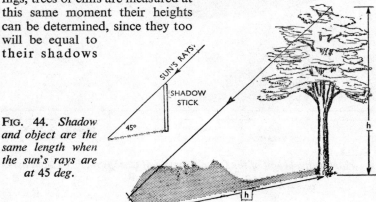

Fig. 44. *Shadow and object are the same length when the sun's rays are at 45 deg.*

(Fig. 44). But waiting for the sun to be at an angle of 45 deg. in the sky is too inconvenient and wearisome! Such measurements could only be made on certain days of the year. The principle of similarity suggests that the height of the tree (H_t) is as many times the height of the shadow stick (H_s) as the shadow of the tree (L_t) is greater than the shadow of the stick (L_s). In mathematical language this can be written:

$$\frac{H_t}{H_s} = \frac{L_t}{L_s}$$

Centuries ago the method was used to measure the height of the Great Pyramid of Cheops. This massive monument has a square base, of which each side is 764 ft. long. The side of the base can be measured directly but the height cannot. The height was found about 600 B.C. by the use of the shadow stick. In the diagram (Fig. 45) a section ABC through the centre of the pyramid is shown and near it is a verti-cal pole LM. AD is the vertical height of the pyramid. The shadows CE and MN of pyramid and pole respectively are measured at the same moment. Suppose the pole 8 ft. high casts a shadow 10 ft. long,

79

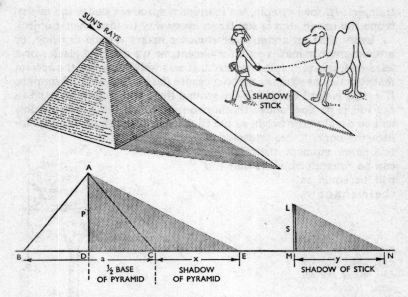

FIG. 45. *How the height of the Great Pyramid of Cheops was measured many centuries ago. By similar triangles,* $\dfrac{P}{S} = \dfrac{\frac{1}{2}a + x}{y}$.

and the length of the shadow of the pyramid at this time is 218 ft.: from these measurements and the size of the base of the pyramid the height of the pyramid can readily be calculated, using the similar right-angled triangles ADE and LMN.

$$\text{Length } DE = DC + CE$$
$$= 382 \text{ ft.} + 218 \text{ ft.} = 600 \text{ ft.}$$
$$MN = 10 \text{ ft.}$$
$$\therefore DE = 60 \times MN$$

By similarity, height of pyramid $AD = 60 \times LM$
$$= 60 \times 8 \text{ ft.} = 480 \text{ ft.}$$

This is the same as using the relationship $\dfrac{H_p}{H_s} = \dfrac{L_p}{L_s}$

Another way of arriving at the same result would be to argue that since the height of the pole is $\frac{8}{10}$ of the length of its shadow, then the height of the pyramid is $\frac{8}{10}$ of the total length of its shadow added to half its base. Taking $\frac{8}{10}$ of 600 ft. we obtain an answer 480 ft. as before.

In essentials the same method could be used to determine the height of any inaccessible object (though we should generally find it easier by trigonometry). In geometry, as in other branches of mathematics, we usually learn more by doing and measuring than by reading and theorizing. Two useful and easily constructed pieces of apparatus for practical work are the home-made shadow stick and the geometric square.

TRY A LITTLE PRACTICAL WORK

Fig. 46 illustrates the design for the shadow pole. A piece of wood about 12 in. long and 3 in. wide and $\frac{1}{2}$ in. thick is fixed (by screws or suitable joint) at right-angles to the end of a baseboard about 30 in. long. The baseboard is marked in inches and tenths of an inch starting from the bottom of the upright piece. Spirit-level and plumb-line add to the accuracy with which the instrument can be used.

Here is an example of how to use the shadow pole. An electric lamp standard casts a shadow 25 ft. long (Fig. 47). At the same time the shadow of the 12-in. shadow stick on the baseboard is 15 in. Calculate the height of the lamp standard.

Height of stick $= \frac{12}{15} \left(\text{or } \frac{4}{5} \right)$ of its shadow.

$\therefore$ Height of standard $= \frac{4}{5}$ of its shadow

$= \frac{4}{5}$ of 25 ft. $= 20$ ft.

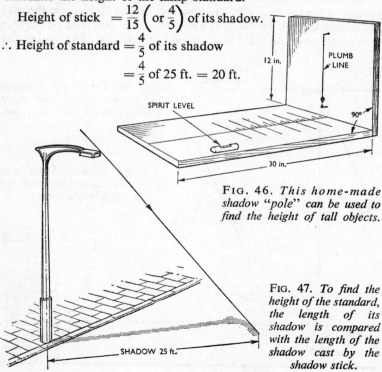

FIG. 46. *This home-made shadow "pole" can be used to find the height of tall objects.*

FIG. 47. *To find the height of the standard, the length of its shadow is compared with the length of the shadow cast by the shadow stick.*

81

The geometric square is another instrument which is based on the principle of similar triangles and can be used for calculating heights as in Fig. 48. Make a square board, *ABCD*, with each side 12 in. long (thick cardboard would do but soon wears out). Divide two sides *BC* and *CD* into twelve equal parts and number the parts from 1 to 12 as in the diagram. From the corner *A* suspend a small plumb-bob by a fine thread. When using the instrument you should ensure that it is held vertically so that the plumb-line can hang freely. So long as the top edge *AD* is horizontal the plumb-line will coincide with *AB*. When *AD* is tilted the plumb-line will swing freely over the scale but remain vertical. You may like to discover from the diagram why the angle between the edge *AB* and the plumb-line is the same as the angle between the top edge *AD* and the horizontal. If you are using the edge *AD* to sight the top of a distant object, then the two angles referred to above are also equal to the angle of elevation of the top of this object.

Suppose the height of a distant wall is to be found using the geometric square (Fig. 49). The observer stands 50 ft. from the wall and sights the top of the wall along the edge *DA*. The plumb-line then hangs over the third division on the scale *BC*. The instrument

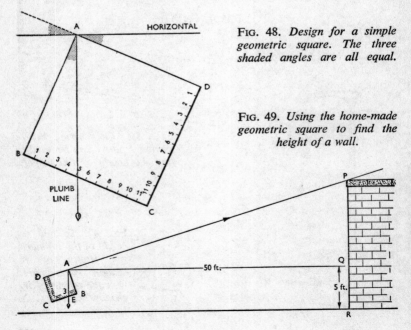

FIG. 48. *Design for a simple geometric square. The three shaded angles are all equal.*

FIG. 49. *Using the home-made geometric square to find the height of a wall.*

itself is held 5 ft. from the floor. From this information we can calculate the height of the wall. In the figure the triangles ABE and PQA are right-angled and the angles BAE and PAQ are equal. Hence the third angles are equal and the triangles are similar.

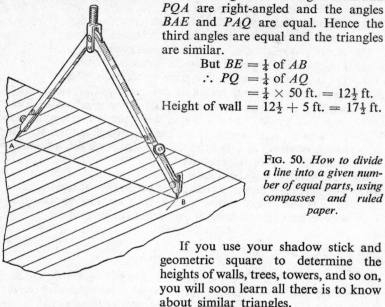

But $BE = \frac{1}{4}$ of AB
$\therefore PQ = \frac{1}{4}$ of AQ
$= \frac{1}{4} \times 50$ ft. $= 12\frac{1}{2}$ ft.
Height of wall $= 12\frac{1}{2} + 5$ ft. $= 17\frac{1}{2}$ ft.

FIG. 50. *How to divide a line into a given number of equal parts, using compasses and ruled paper.*

If you use your shadow stick and geometric square to determine the heights of walls, trees, towers, and so on, you will soon learn all there is to know about similar triangles.

The principle of similar triangles can be used to divide a line into any number of equal parts. For example, divide a line 4 in. long into eleven equal parts. If you use a piece of ruled paper the job is almost half done before you start. Set your compasses to a radius of 4 in. Then, with the point A on one ruling, describe an arc of a circle to cut the eleventh ruling (at B). Join AB by a line. It will be divided by the rulings into eleven equal parts as seen in Fig. 50.

OTHER GEOMETRICAL FIGURES

The next logical step is to consider figures with four sides. Any four-sided figure is called a quadrilateral. It has already been stated that a quadrilateral is not a rigid framework. In order to become so it needs a diagonal cross member, and this has the effect of dividing it into two connected triangles. Hence the fact that a door made of vertical boards on a rectangular frame needs a diagonal member to make it rigid.

In Fig. 51 is shown the quadrilateral family with some of its most important members. You may feel that many of the theorems about four-sided figures are obvious. Here are some which you can either verify for yourself by drawing and measurement or which you may like to try to prove, using some of the facts about lines, angles and triangles described earlier in this chapter.

(1) The angles of any quadrilateral add up to 360 deg. (Draw a diagonal and divide it into two triangles.)

(2) The opposite sides of a parallelogram are equal.

(3) The opposite angles of a parallelogram are equal.

(4) The diagonals of a parallelogram bisect each other.

(5) The diagonals of a rectangle are equal. (Carpenters and bricklayers frequently have to make rectangles out of four lengths of wood. To be sure that the figure *is* a rectangle and not a parallelogram they measure the two diagonals with a length of string or a lath. If the two diagonals are not equal some adjustment is necessary.)

(6) All the sides of a rhombus are equal.

(7) The diagonals of a rhombus bisect each other at right-angles. (This is also true of a square. How, then, do the diagonals of a square differ from those of any other rhombus?)

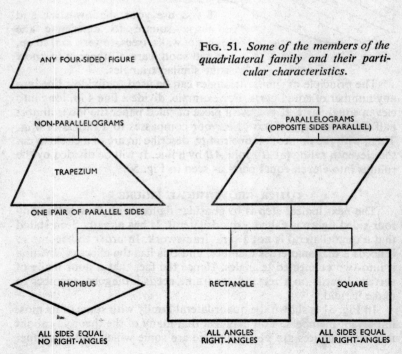

FIG. 51. *Some of the members of the quadrilateral family and their particular characteristics.*

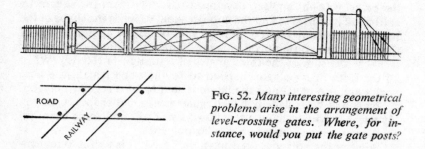

RAILWAY

FIG. 52. *Many interesting geometrical problems arise in the arrangement of level-crossing gates. Where, for instance, would you put the gate posts?*

Have you ever found yourself waiting to pass over a level-crossing which looked like the one in Fig. 52? If so, have you wondered why the railway engineer who designed it went to all the trouble and expense of making one gate much longer than the other, instead of having equal gates which would have been easier to make and mount? Draw one pair of parallel lines (the road) crossing another pair (the railway). See if you can decide where to put the gate posts. Remember that the gates when closed must completely bar the road and when open must fence off the railway. There are a number of interesting problems connected with these gates. Which determines the combined length of the two gates—the width of the road or the width of the railway? What shape is the quadrilateral contained by the four gate posts? Which gate turns through the acute angle and which through the obtuse? Why is this? How is it that the two ends of the gates arrive at the same point together since they have different lengths and turn through different angles? It is surprising how many queries can arise out of what you may have taken for granted.

The commonest of the many-sided figures (polygons) are the hexagon (six angles), which is the shape of the cell in the honeycomb;

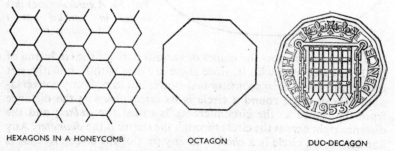

HEXAGONS IN A HONEYCOMB   OCTAGON   DUO-DECAGON

FIG. 53. *Three common polygons: six-sided, eight-sided and twelve-sided.*

85

the octagon (eight angles), developed naturally from the square by cutting off its corners; and the duo-decagon, which is the shape of the bronze threepenny bit. To find the sum of all the angles of any of these polygons you simply divide the figure into triangles and use the fact that the sum of the three angles of a triangle is 180 deg. When all the sides of a polygon happen to be the same length, the base angles are also equal and the figure is said to be a regular polygon.

Nuts and bolts usually have regular hexagonal shapes. Can you say why? If you examine a few flowers you will find some beautiful petal arrangements based on regular polygons.

Some of the polygons are shown in Fig. 53. It is useful to remember the names of these shapes.

GEOMETRY OF CIRCLES

We must now finish with shapes made from straight lines alone, and turn to the circle and to the circle combined with straight lines. These shapes play a prominent part in almost all forms of machinery. You will probably agree that the circle in the form of wheels of all kinds has brought untold benefit and progress to mankind.

Circles can be drawn in many ways. A gardener marks out a circular flower bed using a couple of pegs and a piece of rope, and this is how circles were marked out in the sand centuries ago. Fig. 54 shows this being done. A similar method could be used on paper using a pin, pencil, and piece of string or thread, but it is much more convenient to use compasses.

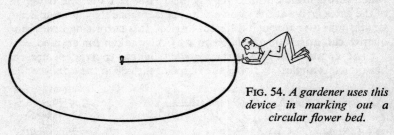

FIG. 54. *A gardener uses this device in marking out a circular flower bed.*

It is useful to know the names of various parts of the circle and of the lines associated with it, since these are met with frequently, not only in this book or in geometry text-books but in ordinary conversation. The distance round a circle is its *circumference*; the distance from the centre to the circumference is called the *radius*; and the distance right across the circle through the centre is the *diameter*. Any line across the circle is a *chord* and any part of the circumference is called an *arc*. A chord divides the circle into two *segments* and a

86

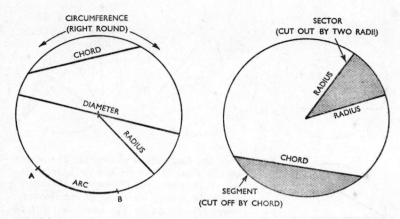

"slice" taken out of the circle is known as a *sector*. These names are in common usage in connexion with circles and are easy to remember once you are familiar with their meanings (Fig. 55).

Many of the theorems concerning circles you may regard as obvious, though a great deal of space in geometry text-books is devoted to proving them. For our purpose a brief list of the most important truths will suffice. You should try to verify them by careful drawing and measurement.

(1) Draw a circle of any size and mark the centre as *O* (Fig. 56*a*). Draw any chord *AB*. From *O* draw a line *OP* at right-angles (perpendicular) to *AB*. Measure *AP* and *BP*. Are they equal? This is our first theorem about a circle. Put briefly it states that the perpendicular from the centre of a circle to a chord bisects the chord. This result enables us to solve an important problem in arch construction, as we shall see in a later chapter. For since the centre of the circle lies on the perpendicular bisector of any chord, the point where any two such bisectors meet is the centre. This construction enables us, therefore, to find the centre of a circle when only an arc is given, and if necessary the circle can then be completed. It also enables us to draw a circle to pass through any three known points (provided they are not all in a straight line). Just mark three points at random and see if you can construct a circle to pass through them. Is this the same problem as drawing a circle round a triangle? Geometry theorems are sometimes useful after all!

(2) A circle, centre *O*, is drawn and three points *A*, *B*, *C*, marked on its circumference (see Fig. 56*b*). The angle *AOB* is the "angle at the

87

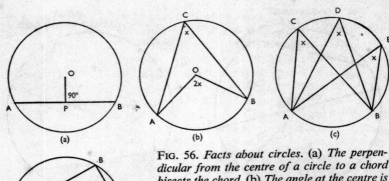

FIG. 56. *Facts about circles.* (a) *The perpendicular from the centre of a circle to a chord bisects the chord.* (b) *The angle at the centre is twice the size of the angle at the circumference.* (c) *Angles in the same segment are equal.* (d) *The angle formed in a semicircle is always a right-angle.*

centre" and the angle *ACB* is the "angle at the circumference." Measure these angles and compare their sizes. You should find that the angle *AOB* is twice as large as the angle *ACB*; the argument, or "proof," in support of this truth is a theorem which is typical of Euclid's geometry. He drew a line from *C* to *O* and beyond to *D*, thus breaking down the picture to give triangles. Knowing a good deal about triangles, we might now see how Euclid argued. From the theorem that all the angles of a triangle make 180 deg., and the theorem that in every isosceles triangle there are two equal angles, we may show that the angle *DOB* is twice as big as the angle *DCB*. You should not have much difficulty in seeing that. But you may not find it easy to put the argument into words which defy contradiction. This is how Euclid argued.

△ *OCB* is isosceles (*OC* and *OB* being radii)

∴ ∠*OCB* = ∠*OBC*

∠*COB* is the supplement of ∠*DOB*

and ∠*OCB* + ∠*OBC* together form the supplement of ∠*COB* (angles of △ make 180 deg.)

∴ ∠*DOB* = ∠*OCB* + ∠*OBC*

= 2∠*OCB*

By similar argument ∠*DOA* = 2∠*OCA*

and combining these

results   ∠*AOB* = 2∠*ACB*.

Thus the angle at the centre is double the angle at the circumference. This is a second useful fact about a circle.

88

(3) A third fact about a circle, which you can reason out from the previous one, is that angles in the same segment are equal. Fig. 56c helps to make this clear. If A and B are two points in a circle, the chord AB will divide the circle into two segments. If any three points C, D, E, are marked on the circle all on the same side of AB (that is, all in the same segment) and are all joined to A and to B, three angles ACB, ADB, and AEB will be formed. This theorem states that these angles are all equal, as will be every other angle drawn in that segment on the same base AB. The method of proof is simply to draw the angle at the centre standing on the same arc AB and to proceed from the fact that each of the three angles is equal to a half of the one at the centre.

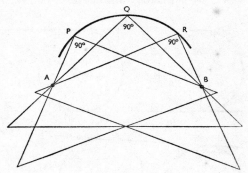

FIG. 57. *Using a set square and two fixed pins (A and B) to draw a semicircle.*

(4) A semicircle is half a circle bounded by a diameter and half the circumference. If the ends A, C, of the diameter are joined to any point B on the circumference, the angle at B is always a right-angle (Fig. 56d). This is usually stated as "the angle in a semicircle is a right-angle." This follows at once from the fact that the angle at the centre (180 deg. in this case) is double the angle at the circumference. The diagram (Fig. 57) shows how we can make use of this result to draw a semicircle using a set square only.

TANGENTS AND CHORDS

The facts about a circle considered so far have been mainly concerned with angles. Those which follow are chiefly about lines which are associated with a circle. A straight line which touches a circle—at one point—is called a tangent to it at that point. For example, the rail on which a wheel stands is a tangent to its tyre. It is fairly obvious that from any point outside a circle two tangents can be drawn to it and that these will be equal in length. There are geometrical methods of constructing tangents to a circle from any point outside it, or of drawing the tangent to a circle at any point on

89

it, but for everyday purposes it is usually sufficiently accurate to place a ruler or other straight edge so that it touches the circle, and then to draw along it.

Here are some facts about tangents, given without proof, which you may care to confirm by drawing.

(1) The tangent at a point on a circle meets the radius at that point at right-angles (Fig. 58a). If TA is the tangent at A and OA the radius, then the angle $TAO = 90$ deg. To test this, place your bicycle on a level road with the valve of one wheel at its lowest point and decide whether the centre of that wheel is then vertically over the valve. Which is the tangent and which the radius in this case?

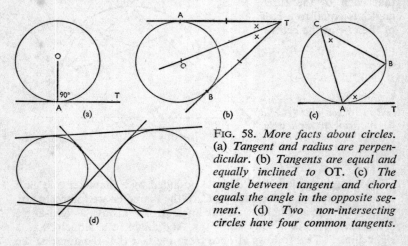

FIG. 58. *More facts about circles.*
(a) *Tangent and radius are perpendicular.* (b) *Tangents are equal and equally inclined to* OT. (c) *The angle between tangent and chord equals the angle in the opposite segment.* (d) *Two non-intersecting circles have four common tangents.*

(2) Two tangents to a circle from a point outside it are inclined at the same angle to the line which joins the point to the centre of the circle (Fig. 58b). If TA and TB are the tangents and O is the centre of the circle, then angle $ATO =$ angle BTO. This result can be used to find the centre of a cylindrical shaft or circular disk. A turner uses a special tool for this purpose. It is made of two pieces of metal firmly fixed together at an angle, and a central blade one edge of which bisects the angle between the metal arms (Fig. 59). To use the instrument, the blade is placed across one end of the shaft, with the arms touching the circumference of its circular end. A line is then ruled or scratched along the edge of the blade (the one which bisects the angle), and this marks one diameter of the shaft. The tool is now moved into another position and a second diameter marked. Where these two diameters meet is the centre of the circle.

90

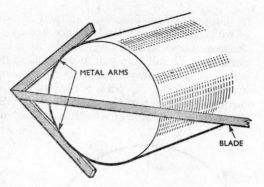

Fig. 59. *A practical application of Fig. 58b. A line drawn along the top edge of the blade marks the diameter of the circular end. When any two diameters are so drawn they intersect at the centre.*

METAL ARMS

BLADE

(3) The angle between the tangent and any chord drawn from its point of contact is equal to any angle in the segment of the circle on the opposite side of the chord from the tangent (Fig. 58c). If TA is the tangent and AB the chord, with ACB any angle in the opposite segment, then angle TAB = angle ACB.

The remaining facts we shall mention about circles are largely concerned with chords.

When two chords of a circle intersect, the products of the parts into which they divide each other are equal (Fig. 60a). If chords AB and CD intersect at O, then $AO \times OB = CO \times OD$. This result holds good even when the point of intersection of the chords is outside the circle (Fig. 60b). Moreover, in this second case with the point O outside the circle, one of the chords, say CD, can become a tangent OC by bringing the points C and D nearer and nearer together until finally they coincide (Fig. 60c). The line OC then touches the circle and the result above becomes $AO \times OB = OC \times OC = OC^2$. This means that the square on the tangent = the product of the parts of the chord.

Fig. 60. (a) *and* (b) *The products of the parts of intersecting chords are equal.* (c) *The tangent squared equals the product of the parts of the chord.*

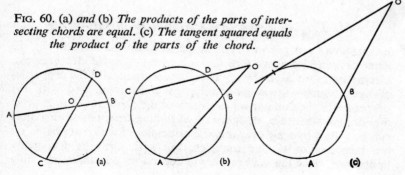

On page 87 we found the method of fixing the centre of a circle of which we were given only an arc. Instead, we might have used the theorem about intersecting chords to calculate the radius of the circle. Fig. 61 will help you to understand this. From *C*, the highest point of the arc, draw a perpendicular *CO* on to *AB*, the base of the arc. Why is *O* the mid-point of the base? If *CO* is extended it will pass through the centre of the circle. Why is this? Suppose *COD* is the diameter of the circle of which *ACB* is an arc, then *AB* and *CD* are intersecting chords, and so

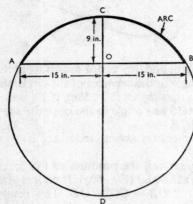

$$AO \times OB = OC \times OD.$$

Substituting the values (in inches) for *AO*, *OB* and *OC*, we have

$$15 \times 15 = 9 \times OD$$
$$9OD = 225$$
$$OD = 25 \text{ in.}$$

Hence the diameter of the circle is 34 in.

FIG. 61. *From a given arc we can find the radius and complete the circle.*

It has been emphasized that geometry is a practical subject having its origins in practical needs. Much has been omitted in this necessarily brief survey. If you wish to study geometry in greater detail you should consult one of the many text-books on the subject. For geometrical material look about you inside and outside your own home, on the streets, and in your office or factory.

(d) Trigonometry: A Development of Geometry

ELEMENTARY trigonometry is at least two thousand years old, the name deriving from two Greek words meaning angle measurement. Geometry, as we have already seen, is concerned with the properties of figures such as triangles, polygons and circles, and with the properties of the familiar solids. Many of the problems of map making, draughtsmanship, design, and of finding heights and distances can be solved by scale drawing, the principles of which are based on the theorems of similar triangles. But scale drawing has many limitations, since the final result will depend on our ability not only to make highly accurate measurements of the distances and angles but to reproduce these on a reduced scale on the drawing board. Errors of measurement, errors in using the instruments, errors in the instruments themselves, and even errors in the drawing paper, can all contribute to the inaccuracy of the final result. In trigonometry we attempt to improve on the methods of drawing by devising methods of calculation rather than of measurement.

Let us consider a method often used by Scouts to find the height of a tree or building (Fig. 62). A baseline of convenient length is marked off from the foot of the tree and one Scout (the observer) kneels or lies at the end of this baseline with his eye to the ground. A scout-pole is moved along the baseline by another Scout until the top of the pole and the top of the tree appear to the observer to be in line. The position of the pole is then marked. The height of the tree is calculated by using the relationship:

$$\frac{\text{height of tree}}{\text{height of pole}} = \frac{\text{distance of observer from tree}}{\text{distance of observer from pole}}.$$

If in the diagram AB represents the height of the tree, CD the pole and O the position of the eye of the observer, then our formula for calculating the height of the tree would become $\dfrac{AB}{CD} = \dfrac{OB}{OD}.$

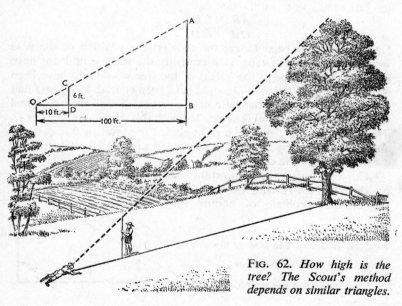

FIG. 62. *How high is the tree? The Scout's method depends on similar triangles.*

Tall Stories?

(1) Take a large sheet of very thin paper (say one-thousandth of an inch thick) and tear it in halves. Putting the two pieces together tear these in halves, and again put the pieces together and tear. If you repeat the procedure fifty times, how high will your stack of paper reach?

(2) If it takes 25 years for one generation to beget the next, what is the greatest possible number of male forebears living in A.D. 1100 from whom a child born in 1950 could claim descent?

Solutions on p. 444

Using the measurements shown, $\dfrac{AB}{6} = \dfrac{100}{10} = 10.$

$$\therefore AB = 60 \text{ ft.}$$

Obviously we are using the fact that the triangles *ABO* and *CDO* are similar (that is to say, they are equiangular and have corresponding sides proportional), but even if we were unaware of this relationship we could still have solved this particular problem by scale drawing. You will doubtless have realized that we are concerned here with two right-angled triangles and that in both the ratio of the vertical side to the horizontal side is 0·6—that is,

$$\frac{AB}{OB} = \frac{CD}{OD} = 0\cdot6.$$

Had the baseline been longer (or shorter) the position of the pole would have been different. Consequently the ratio would not have been 0·6, and although the height of the tree would still have been 60 ft., the angle of sight at *O* would have been altered. It appears that the particular value of the ratio of the vertical side to the horizontal side (0·6 in our example) is associated with this particular angle at *O*, irrespective of the size of the right-angled triangle. In this case the angle is very nearly 31 deg., as you can discover for yourself by making an accurate drawing.

This conclusion is so important that it will be worth while divorcing the mathematics from the original problem of finding the height

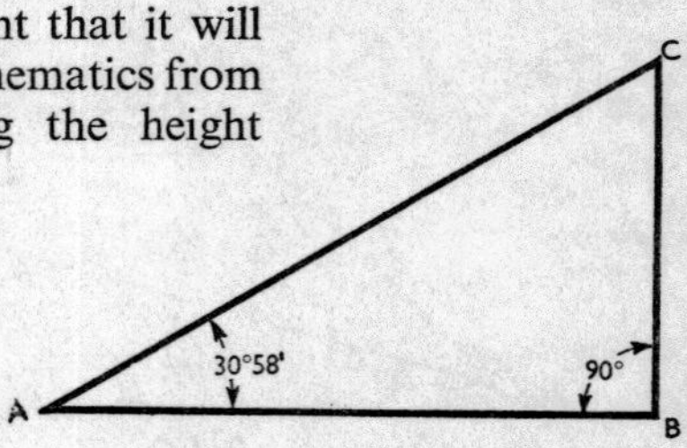

FIG. 63. *Whatever the size of the triangle, the value of the ratio* $\dfrac{CB}{BA}$ *remains unchanged at* 0·6.

of a tree. If ABC is a right-angled triangle (Fig. 63), in which $A = 30° 58'$ and $B = 90°$, then $\dfrac{CB}{BA} =$ is 0·6 irrespective of the size of the triangle. It will be quite simple for you to test the truth of this statement by drawing a few right-angled triangles, measuring the two sides CB and BA in each case, and finding their ratio.

HOW TO USE TANGENTS

Changing the size of the angle A will of course produce a different ratio, but one which is constant for that particular angle. Since the ratio $\dfrac{CB}{BA}$ is a constant number depending only on the value of the angle A we may call it "a function of A" and give it a name. To mathematicians it has long been known as "the tangent of A" and is usually written as tan A.

$$\tan A = \frac{CB}{AB} = \frac{\text{side opposite } A}{\text{side adjacent to } A}.$$

So far we have obtained the tangent of only one angle (tan $30°58' = 0·6$). By means of many very accurate scale drawings we could compile a table showing the value of the tangents of all acute angles. Not only would this prove a long and tedious process but our results could be accurate only within the limitation of the drawings. Fortunately there are better and quicker methods, which need not concern us here, by means of which the values of the tangents may be calculated as accurately as we please, and we shall rely on the tables of tangents so obtained, which are to be found in any book of mathematical tables (Fig. 64). It may, however, be helpful to consoli-

Natural Tangents

De-gree	0'	6'	12'	18'	24'	30'	36'	42'	48'	54'	1'	2'	3'	4'	5'
0	·0000	·0017	·0035	·0052	·0070	·0087	·0105	·0122	·0140	·0157	3	6	9	12	15
1	·0175	·0192	·0209	·0227	·0244	·0262	·0279	·0297	·0314	·0332	3	6	9	12	15
2	·0349	·0367	·0384	·0402	·0419	·0437	·0454	·0472	·0489	·0507	3	6	9	12	15
3	·0524	·0542	·0559	·0577	·0594	·0612	·0629	·0647	·0664	·0682	3	6	9	12	15
4	·0699	·0717	·0734	·0752	·0769	·0782	·0805	·0822	·0840	·0857	3	6	9	12	15
5	·0875	·0892	·0910	·0928	·0945	·0963	·0981	·0998	·1016	·1033	3	6	9	12	15
6	·1051	·1069	·1086	·1104	·1122	·1139	·1157	·1175	·1192	·1210	3	6	9	12	15
7			·1263	·1281	·1299	·1317	·1334	·1352	·1370	·1388	3	6	9	12	15

FIG. 64. *Part of a table of tangents. By using such tables of trigonometrical ratios you can cut out a good deal of the donkey work of calculation. Books of mathematical tables contain other aids of this kind.*

95

date our ideas on tangent ratio by producing, for a limited range of angles, a "home-made" tangent table. Fig. 65 suggests how this can be done and gives some of the tangents obtained. Compare these with the accurate results obtained from the tangent tables.

An understanding of the tangent is our first step in trigonometry and we can make immediate use of it in the solution of a practical problem by calculation.

To determine the height of a chimney stack (Fig. 66) a theodolite is set up at a distance of 150 ft. from the base of the stack. The

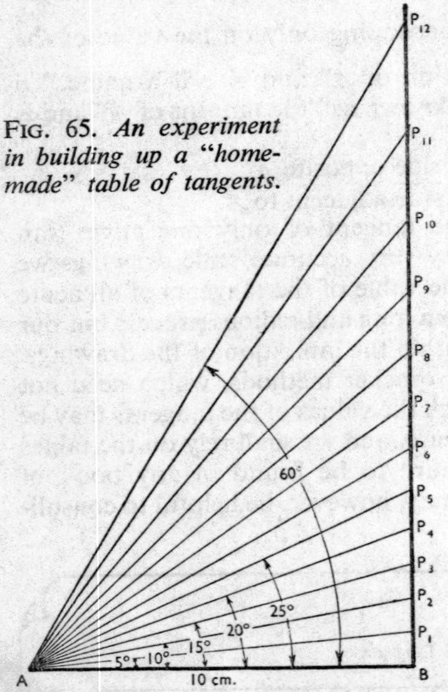

FIG. 65. *An experiment in building up a "home-made" table of tangents.*

Angle	AB (side adj.)	BP (side opp.)	$\tan A = \dfrac{BP}{AB}$
5°	10 cm.	0·9 cm.	0·09
10°	,,	1·75	0·175
15°	,,	2·7	0·27
20°	,,	3·6	0·36
25°	,,	4·7	0·47
30°	,,	5·8	0·58
35°	,,	7	0·7
40°	,,	8·4	0·84
45°	,,	10	1·0
50°	,,	11·9	1·19
55°	,,	14·3	1·43
60°	,,	17·3	1·73

instrument is 4 ft. 6 in. above ground-level and the angle of inclination of the top of the stack is found to be 39 deg. Let us find the height of the stack.

Using the fact that $\dfrac{AB}{150} = \tan 39°$

$$AB = 150 \times \tan 39°$$
$$= 150 \times 0·8098 \text{ (value from tables)}$$
$$= 121·5 \text{ ft.}$$

Height of stack $= 121·5$ ft. $+ 4·5$ ft. $= 126$ ft.

96

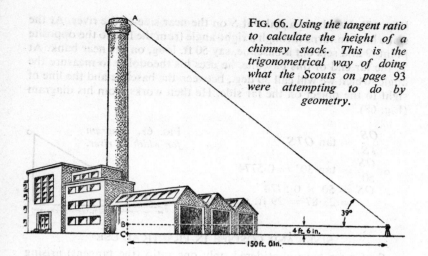

FIG. 66. *Using the tangent ratio to calculate the height of a chimney stack. This is the trigonometrical way of doing what the Scouts on page 93 were attempting to do by geometry.*

Note that the height of the instrument (4·5 ft.) has been added in this case. You will realize, too, the practical difficulties of measuring the distance from the theodolite to *C*, which is somewhere inside the buildings.

A similar method can be used to find a width or a length which is on the ground instead of vertical. For example, a surveyor wishes to find the distance between two points on opposite banks of a river

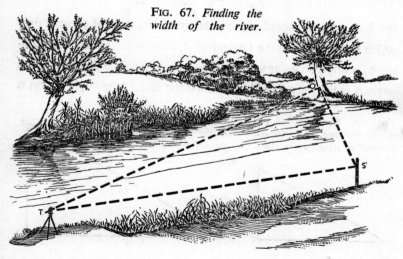

FIG. 67. *Finding the width of the river.*

(Fig. 67). He places a stake at S on the near side of the river. At the stake he then turns through a right-angle from the line to the opposite point O and sets out a baseline, say 50 ft. long, on the near bank. At T, the far end of this baseline, he uses his theodolite to measure the angle, which we will call 30 deg., between the baseline and the line of sight to the object on the far side. He then works from his diagram (Fig. 68).

$$\frac{OS}{TS} = \tan OTS$$

$$\text{or } \frac{OS}{50} = \tan 30° = 0\cdot5774$$

$$\therefore OS = 50 \times 0\cdot5774$$
$$= 28\cdot87 = 29 \text{ ft. approx.}$$

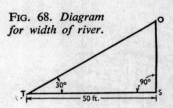

FIG. 68. *Diagram for width of river.*

SINES AND COSINES IN PRACTICAL USE

So far we have considered only one ratio (the tangent) arising from the right-angled triangle containing our angle. Look at the triangle ABC in Fig. 69. You will see that the side opposite the angle A has been called a, and so on. This is a convenient system which saves much time. Now let us compare this triangle with $A^1B^1C^1$ in Fig. 70. If the corresponding angles are equal—that is, if $A = A^1$, $B = B^1$, and $C = C^1$—then the corresponding sides are in proportion and the following ratios are always constant:

$$\frac{a}{b} = \frac{a^1}{b^1}, \quad \frac{a}{c} = \frac{a^1}{c^1}, \quad \frac{b}{c} = \frac{b^1}{c^1}$$

We have already noted the constancy of the first of these ratios, which we have called the tangent of A. Similarly, $\frac{a}{c}$ and $\frac{b}{c}$ are constant for any particular value of the angle A. Another function of the angle A is the ratio $\frac{a}{c}$, which is called the sine of the angle A and is

FIG. 69. *Right-angled triangle showing conventional method of naming the sides.*

FIG. 70. *Because the angles of the two triangles agree, the sides are in proportion.*

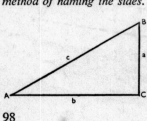

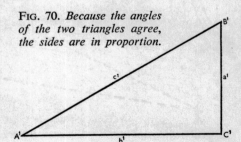

98

usually written sin A. The ratio $\dfrac{b}{c}$ is called the cosine of the angle A and is usually written cos A.

To assist in memorizing these ratios we can write them out in full, thus:

$$\sin A = \frac{\text{side opposite } A}{\text{hypotenuse}}$$

$$\cos A = \frac{\text{side adjacent to } A}{\text{hypotenuse}}$$

Find a few 60-deg. set-squares, measure the lengths of their edges and so calculate sin 60° and tan 30° from each. What do your results prove?

You can test the constancy of the sine and cosine by drawing an angle of any size (say 40 deg.) and adding a series of perpendiculars from one arm of this angle on to the other arm as in Fig. 71. (You will see that this produces a series of similar right-angled triangles.) The

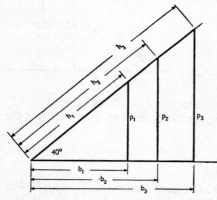

FIG. 71. *The perpendicular (P) divided by the corresponding hypotenuse (h) is the same for each position of P. Similarly, the base (b) divided by the corresponding hypotenuse (h) is also constant for each length of b.*

lengths of successive perpendiculars divided by the corresponding hypotenuses produce a constant answer, which is the sine of 40 deg.

Similarly, successive base lengths divided by corresponding hypotenuses give a constant answer, which is the cosine of 40 deg. Try this for yourself. You should find that sin 40° is about 0·64 and cos 40° about 0·77.

$$\sin 40° = \frac{p_1}{h_1} = \frac{p_2}{h_2} = \frac{p_3}{h_3} = 0·64 \text{ approx.}$$

$$\cos 40° = \frac{b_1}{h_1} = \frac{b_2}{h_2} = \frac{b_3}{h_3} = 0·77 \text{ approx.}$$

We can now apply these two new ratios, the sine and the cosine, to practical calculations to illustrate their use.

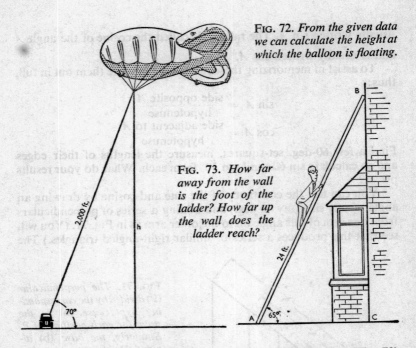

FIG. 72. *From the given data we can calculate the height at which the balloon is floating.*

FIG. 73. *How far away from the wall is the foot of the ladder? How far up the wall does the ladder reach?*

2,000 ft.

70°

h

24 ft.

65°

A

B

C

The crew of a barrage balloon let out 2,000 ft. of cable (Fig. 72). If the cable is inclined at 70 deg. to the ground at what height is the balloon floating?

$$\frac{h}{2,000} = \sin 70°$$

$$\therefore h = 2,000 \sin 70°$$

$$= 2,000 \times \cdot 9397 \text{ (value from tables)} = 1,879\cdot4 \text{ ft.}$$

The balloon is therefore at 1,880 ft. approximately.

A 24-ft. ladder rests against a wall, making an angle of 65 deg. with the horizontal (Fig. 73). How far up the wall does it reach? How far is the foot of the ladder from the wall? *BC* is the height of the ladder up the wall and *AC* the distance of the foot of the ladder from the wall.

$$\frac{BC}{24} = \sin 65° = \cdot9063$$

$$\therefore BC = 24 \times \cdot9063 = 21\cdot75 \text{ ft.}$$

$$\frac{AC}{24} = \cos 65° = \cdot4226$$

$$\therefore AC = 24 \times \cdot4226 = 10\cdot14 \text{ ft.}$$

You will possibly notice now that sin 65° has the same value as cos 25°, since both are measured in the above example by $\frac{BC}{24}$. This is easily seen from the right-angled triangle in Fig. 74.

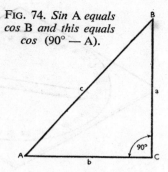

FIG. 74. *Sin* A *equals* *cos* B *and this equals* *cos* (90° — A).

$$\sin A = \frac{a}{c} \qquad \cos B = \frac{a}{c}$$

But $A + B = 90°$, since C is $90°$.

That is, $B = 90° - A$

$\therefore \sin A = \cos (90° - A)$

For this reason it is not necessary to have separate tables for sines and cosines, since tables of sines can be used for finding cosines. The trigonometrical ratios of some of the more familiar angles, 30, 60 and 45 deg., can be found without reference to the tables, using a square or an equilateral triangle:

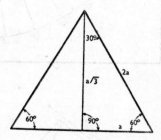

$$\sin 45° = \frac{a}{a\sqrt{2}} = \frac{1}{\sqrt{2}}$$

$$\cos 45° = \frac{a}{a\sqrt{2}} = \frac{1}{\sqrt{2}}$$

$$\tan 45° = \frac{a}{a} = 1.$$

$$\sin 60° = \frac{a\sqrt{3}}{2a} = \frac{\sqrt{3}}{2} = \cos 30°$$

$$\sin 30° = \frac{a}{2a} = \tfrac{1}{2} = \cos 60°$$

$$\tan 60° = \frac{a\sqrt{3}}{a} = \sqrt{3}$$

$$\tan 30° = \frac{a}{a\sqrt{3}} = \frac{1}{\sqrt{3}}$$

It has been possible to deal only very briefly with the main trigonometrical ratios, the sine, cosine and tangent, and you should make yourself thoroughly familiar with these and their use in easy calculations before attempting to study the subject further. One of the most interesting and practical ways of doing this is to construct some simple measuring instruments and with them to carry out some elementary surveying and the determination of heights and distances.

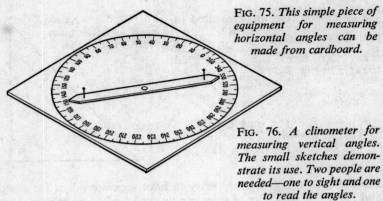

FIG. 75. *This simple piece of equipment for measuring horizontal angles can be made from cardboard.*

FIG. 76. *A clinometer for measuring vertical angles. The small sketches demonstrate its use. Two people are needed—one to sight and one to read the angles.*

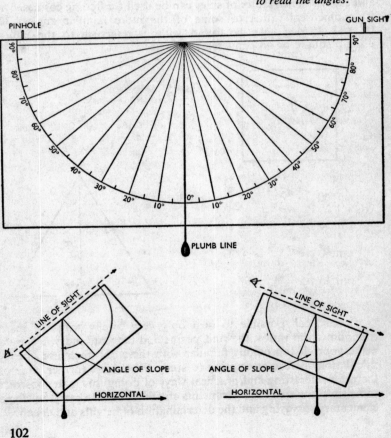

PINHOLE

GUN SIGHT

PLUMB LINE

LINE OF SIGHT

ANGLE OF SLOPE

HORIZONTAL

LINE OF SIGHT

ANGLE OF SLOPE

HORIZONTAL

102

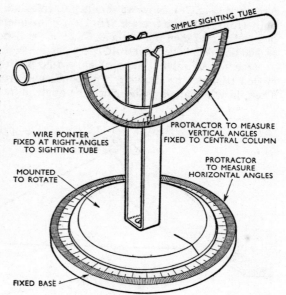

FIG. 77. *With a little patience and ingenuity the instruments opposite may be combined in this way to form an elementary theodolite, with which you can have all the experience you want in practical trigonometry. For vertical angles the tube is inclined on its pivot; for horizontal angles the instrument is rotated.*

SIMPLE SIGHTING TUBE

WIRE POINTER FIXED AT RIGHT-ANGLES TO SIGHTING TUBE

PROTRACTOR TO MEASURE VERTICAL ANGLES FIXED TO CENTRAL COLUMN

MOUNTED TO ROTATE

PROTRACTOR TO MEASURE HORIZONTAL ANGLES

FIXED BASE

You will learn a great deal more from this than if you confine yourself to a theoretical study of trigonometry from text-books, and you will realize far more readily what a practical subject it can be. Figs. 75–77 suggest the design of some simple equipment for use in practical trigonometry. You will not find it difficult to make.

WHEN THE TRIANGLE HAS NO RIGHT-ANGLE

It is not always possible in a practical situation, nor is it essential, to obtain a right-angled triangle for calculating the distance of an inaccessible point or the height of an inaccessible object. So far we have considered only triangles containing a right-angle and we shall now turn to the more general problem of solving (that is, finding the missing parts of) triangles which have no right-angles. We must approach the problem in a common-sense way and ask ourselves whether the information we have about the triangle to begin with is sufficient to enable us to draw it. If the problem can be solved by drawing then it is reasonable to expect that it may be solved by trigonometry.

Let us take an example. From two points A and B on the coastline, at a distance c apart, observations were made of a buoy C out at sea, and the angles made by the directions AC and BC with AB were measured (Fig. 78). Now we shall try to calculate the distance of the buoy from A. In the triangle ABC, since the angles at A and B have been measured then the angle at C is known also, since $A + B + C$ = 180 deg. We have to find AC.

One way of solving the problem would be to produce two right-angled triangles by drawing a perpendicular from A to BC (AD). Then, in the triangle ADB, since the angle at D is 90 deg. we have

$$\frac{AD}{c} = \sin B$$

$$\text{or } AD = c \sin B.$$

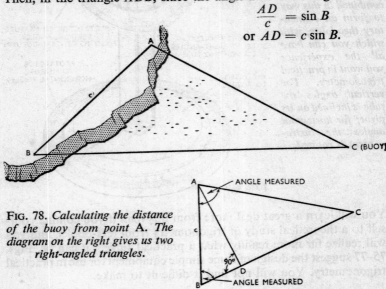

FIG. 78. *Calculating the distance of the buoy from point* A. *The diagram on the right gives us two right-angled triangles.*

We have thus found the length of AD, because c and B are known. Using this information in the triangle ADC, we have

$$\frac{AD}{AC} = \sin C, \text{ or } AC = \frac{AD}{\sin C}$$

and this enables us to find AC, since AD and C are known. You can discover for yourself that by using cosines (or tangents) in the two right-angled triangles the length of BC also can be calculated. It is possible therefore by converting it into two right-angled triangles to solve a triangle completely when one side and two angles are already known. Can we obtain a formula for doing this?

We have shown that $AD = c \sin B$ and also that $AD = AC \sin C$. Therefore $c \sin B = AC \sin C$, which may be written $c \sin B = b \sin C$.

Rearranging this, $\dfrac{\sin B}{b} = \dfrac{\sin C}{c}$.

104

It is not difficult to extend the formula to
$$\frac{\sin A}{a} = \frac{\sin B}{b} = \frac{\sin C}{c}.$$

This formula, usually called the sine rule, is what we need to enable us to solve our triangle when we know two angles and one side, though we have yet to discover what to do if one of the angles is obtuse. It can also be used to solve the triangle if we know two sides and one angle (provided it is not the angle enclosed between the two sides), though in this case two different triangles can sometimes be obtained. You can test this for yourself by drawing some triangles in which two sides and one angle are given.

It is useful to have a formula for solving the triangle when we know the lengths of two of its sides and the angle included between them. There is such a formula known as the cosine rule, and we will see how it is obtained.

Suppose, in Fig. 79, the angle A and the sides b and c are known. We wish to find a formula for calculating the third side a and if possible the angles B and C. A perpendicular p from C to AB produces two right-angled triangles and divides the side c into two parts x and $c - x$.

Now $a^2 = p^2 + (c - x)^2$ (Pythagoras)
and $p^2 = b^2 - x^2$

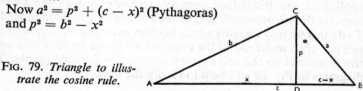

Fig. 79. *Triangle to illustrate the cosine rule.*

We are not concerned with p since it does not enter into our original triangle, and we replace p in the first equation so that
$$a^2 = b^2 - x^2 + c^2 - 2cx + x^2$$
$$= b^2 + c^2 - 2cx.$$

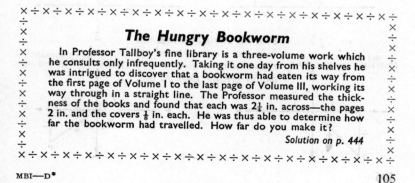

The Hungry Bookworm

In Professor Tallboy's fine library is a three-volume work which he consults only infrequently. Taking it one day from his shelves he was intrigued to discover that a bookworm had eaten its way from the first page of Volume I to the last page of Volume III, working its way through in a straight line. The Professor measured the thickness of the books and found that each was $2\frac{1}{4}$ in. across—the pages 2 in. and the covers $\frac{1}{8}$ in. each. He was thus able to determine how far the bookworm had travelled. How far do you make it?

Solution on p. 444

Now $\dfrac{x}{b} = \cos A$ (from the right-angled triangle)

Therefore $x = b \cos A$.

Putting in this value of x, we have
$$a^2 = b^2 + c^2 - 2bc \cos A.$$
This gives a value for a from known values of b, c and A. It may be shown by similar argument that
$$b^2 = a^2 + c^2 - 2ac \cos B$$
$$\text{and } c^2 = a^2 + b^2 - 2ab \cos C.$$
By rearrangement, the formula we found above becomes
$$\cos A = \frac{b^2 + c^2 - a^2}{2\,bc}.$$
This enables us to find an angle (each angle in fact) when the three sides of the triangle are known.

FUNCTIONS OF LARGE ANGLES

The sine and cosine rules, together with the simple trigonometrical ratios, can be used to solve many problems which occur in surveying, mechanics, navigation, engineering and other branches of applied science. But before attempting a few easy examples we shall consider the trigonometrical functions of angles greater than 90 deg. To do this we may imagine a rotating arm sweeping out angles of any size and then make use of the conventions about positive and negative directions on the axis as normally used in drawing graphs. The diagrams in Fig. 80 will help to clarify the idea.

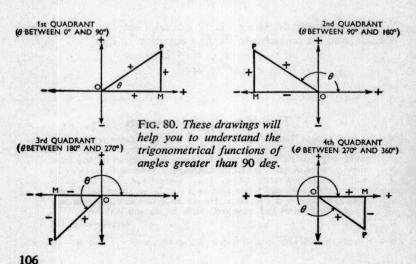

FIG. 80. *These drawings will help you to understand the trigonometrical functions of angles greater than 90 deg.*

106

Whatever the position of the rotating radius *OP* in the course of one complete revolution from its initial position along the positive horizontal scale, a perpendicular *PM* is dropped on to the horizontal scale to form the triangle *OPM*. The distance *OP* is always regarded as positive, but *PM* and *OM* will sometimes be regarded as positive and sometimes as negative depending on the position of *OP*—the diagrams will help to explain this. The three trigonometrical ratios are then defined as:

$$\tan \theta = \frac{\text{perpendicular}}{\text{base}} \quad \left(\frac{PM}{OM}\right)$$

$$\sin \theta = \frac{\text{perpendicular}}{\text{radius}} \quad \left(\frac{PM}{OP}\right)$$

$$\cos \theta = \frac{\text{base}}{\text{radius}} \quad \left(\frac{OM}{OP}\right)$$

These ratios are true whatever the size of the angle, due regard being paid to the sign of each of the two directions. You will see that these are in accord with previous definitions except that only in the first quadrant is the angle, swept out by the radius, contained in the triangle. Forgetting for a moment the angle θ and any signs attached to *OP*, *OM*, *PM*, and considering only the triangle *POM*, we see that in fact $\frac{PM}{OM}, \frac{PM}{OP}, \frac{OM}{OP}$ measure the three trigonometrical ratios of the base angle *inside* the triangle. If θ is known then this base angle is also known. Clearly it will always be acute and the value of its trigonometrical ratios can therefore be found from the tables.

We now have sufficient information to determine the values of the trigonometrical functions of angles of any size. The position of *P* will determine the sign of the trigonometrical function and the base angle of the triangle will enable its value to be found. It all sounds horribly complicated but is comparatively simple in practice. Consider a few examples:

(1) *What is cos 120°?*

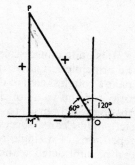

$$\cos 120° = \frac{OM \text{ (negative)}}{OP \text{ (positive)}},$$

which is negative.

Also, from the triangle *OPM*,

$$\frac{OM}{OP} = \cos 60°$$

$$= 0 \cdot 5$$

$$\therefore \cos 120° = -0 \cdot 5.$$

(2) *What is sin 225°?*

$$\sin 225° = \frac{PM \text{ (negative)}}{OP \text{ (positive)}},$$

which is negative.

Also, from triangle *OMP*,

$$\frac{PM}{OP} = \sin 45°$$

$$= 0.7071$$

$$\therefore \sin 225° = -0.7071.$$

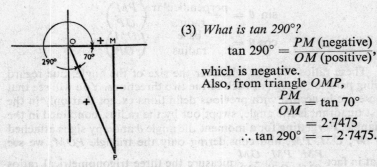

(3) *What is tan 290°?*

$$\tan 290° = \frac{PM \text{ (negative)}}{OM \text{ (positive)}},$$

which is negative.

Also, from triangle *OMP*,

$$\frac{PM}{OM} = \tan 70°$$

$$= 2.7475$$

$$\therefore \tan 290° = -2.7475.$$

In the diagram below these results have been generalized.

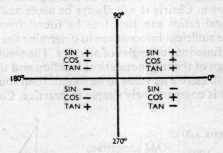

It is quite unnecessary to try to memorize these results, since once the principle is understood it is comparatively quick and simple to make a rough sketch to determine both the sign of the trigonometrical ratio and the value of the angle to be looked up in the tables. It is possible, of course, to have angles greater than 360 (or 720 deg., etc.), but clearly successive rotations of the radius produce only repetitions of a single revolution, and 360 deg. (or multiples of it) can be subtracted without affecting the trigonometrical values.

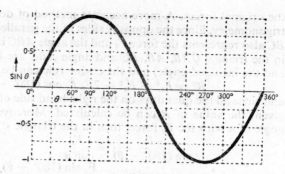

FIG. 81. *Graph of sin θ as θ increases from 0 to 360 deg.*

We now have sufficient values to see how the trigonometrical functions vary as the angle varies between 0 and 360 deg. A graph summarizes the whole matter. Fig. 81 is a graph of sin θ against θ.

Check some sample readings from this sine curve with values obtained for the same angles by calculation.

The sine curve occurs frequently in engineering mathematics and serves many useful purposes. You will find it interesting to plot similar curves for the cosine and tangent and thus obtain a more comprehensive view of these trigonometrical functions.

PARALLELOGRAM OF FORCES

We shall now return to the sine and cosine rules. A very useful rule in mechanics is one which concerns two forces which are acting on the same object; like two horses pulling the same truck, or two men the same garden roller. If these forces are inclined at an angle to each other they can be replaced in effect by a single force equivalent to them according to the law known as the Parallelogram of Forces. This states that if two forces can be represented in size and direction by two adjacent sides of a parallelogram then the corresponding diagonal will represent a force equivalent to them (that is, their resultant).

If, in Fig. 82, forces F_1 and F_2 are known and also the angle θ between them, a scale drawing of the parallelogram $ABCD$ will enable us to find the resulting force R and the angles this makes with

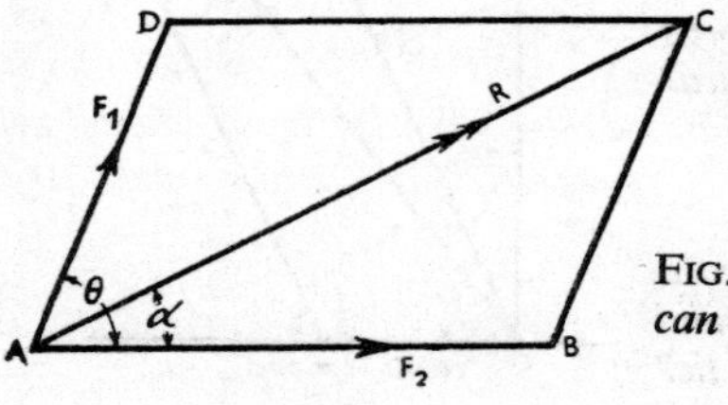

FIG. 82. *The resultant of the two forces can be found by scale drawing or, more accurately, by trigonometry.*

the original forces. A more accurate method of doing this is to use trigonometry. Since the opposite sides of the parallelogram are equal, BC also represents the force F_1 and the angle ABC is $180° - \theta$. Then, in the triangle CAB, AB, BC and angle ABC are known (two sides and the included angle) and the cosine rule can be used. This gives:

$$R^2 = F_1{}^2 + F_2{}^2 - 2F_1 F_2 \cos (180° - \theta)$$

and since all the quantities on the right-hand side of this equation are given, the value of R can be calculated. Moreover if R makes an angle of α with the F_2 force, then in the triangle CAB

$$\frac{R}{\sin (180° - \theta)} = \frac{F_1}{\sin \alpha}$$

$$\text{or } \sin \alpha = \frac{F_1 \sin (180° - \theta)}{R}.$$

As R has already been calculated, the use of the sine rule leads to a value for the angle α.

Let us consider an example. A hawser passes round a bollard: the two straight portions of the hawser are inclined at 40 deg. to each other and are tensions of $\frac{1}{2}$ ton and $\frac{3}{4}$ ton. What force does the hawser exert on the bollard? (Fig. 83.) If R is the resultant force, then

$$R^2 = (\tfrac{1}{2})^2 + (\tfrac{3}{4})^2 - 2 \times \tfrac{1}{2} \times \tfrac{3}{4} \times \cos 140° \text{ (cosine rule)}$$
$$= \cdot 25 + \cdot 5625 - \cdot 75 \times (- \cdot 7660)$$
$$= \cdot 8125 + \cdot 5745 = 1 \cdot 3870$$
$$\therefore R = \sqrt{1 \cdot 3870} \text{ tons} = 1 \cdot 18 \text{ tons.}$$

You will see here the need to extend the trigonometrical ratios at least to angles greater than 90 deg. From previous work, cos $140° = - \cos 40°$.

Here is another example. An aeroplane is flying on a course of 25 deg. at an air speed of 300 m.p.h. Wind is 12 m.p.h. from the west.

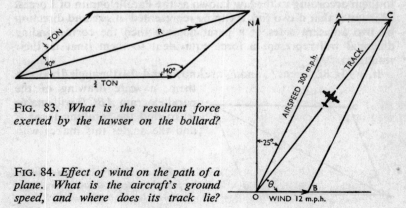

FIG. 83. *What is the resultant force exerted by the hawser on the bollard?*

FIG. 84. *Effect of wind on the path of a plane. What is the aircraft's ground speed, and where does its track lie?*

110

Find its ground speed and track (that is, its path over the ground). The aeroplane is subject to two velocities, 300 m.p.h. along its course and 12 m.p.h. in the direction of the wind. Its resultant velocity and direction are produced by the combination of these (Fig. 84). OC is the resultant of OA and OB. Using the triangle OBC,

$$OC^2 = (300)^2 + (12)^2 - 2 \times 12 \times 300 \cos 115°.$$
$$= 90,000 + 144 - 7,200(-0·4226) [\cos 115° = -\cos 65°]$$
$$= 90,144 + 3,043 = 93,187$$
$$\therefore OC = 305·2 \text{ m.p.h.}$$

Using the sine rule, $\dfrac{305·2}{\sin 115°} = \dfrac{300}{\sin \theta}$

$$\therefore \sin \theta = \frac{300 \times \sin 115°}{305·2}$$
$$\theta = 63°.$$

The track is determined by the angle which the actual path of the plane makes with the north and is the complement of θ, or 27 deg.

CIRCULAR MEASUREMENT OF ANGLES

Angles are normally measured in degrees, minutes and seconds. To obtain degrees the circle has to be divided into 360 parts, each of which is called a degree. The number 360 is really quite arbitrary, though it is very useful in practice as it has many factors and can easily be divided into parts—30, 60, 45, 90, and so on. Moreover, we are so accustomed to it that we should find it rather odd if it were changed.

A second method of measuring angles is known as circular measure and is especially useful for questions connected with speed. It is important to remember that an angle is "amount of turn," and circular measure connects this conception of angle with the actual rotation of a circle. If two circles of radii R and r rotate once, points on their circumference will travel distances of $2\pi R$ and $2\pi r$ respectively. Both have turned through the same angle but because of the differing radii the circumferences have travelled different distances. The 2π factor is present for both and indeed all circles; the angle turned is the same for all. The full turn then may be regarded as 2π units of angle and these units are named radians. It is easy to discover how large one radian is, since

$$2\pi \text{ radians} = 360°$$
$$1 \text{ radian} = \frac{360°}{2\pi} = \frac{180°}{\pi} = 57·3°.$$

The radian is therefore a very much larger unit than the degree.

There is another way of looking at the radian. Since 2π radians are one complete turn, one radian will be $\frac{1}{2\pi}$ of a complete turn. In a

111

circle of radius R, one radian will have an arc of $\frac{1}{2\pi} \times 2\pi R$, which is an arc of length R. One radian therefore is the angle subtended at the centre of a circle by an arc equal in length to the radius. This is made clearer in Fig. 85. An arc of length $2R$ will subtend an angle of two radians and an arc of length nR will form an angle of n radians at the centre.

The two main facts that we know about radians can be remembered in this way:

(1) Angle in radians $= \dfrac{\text{arc}}{\text{radius}}$

(2) π radians $= 180°$

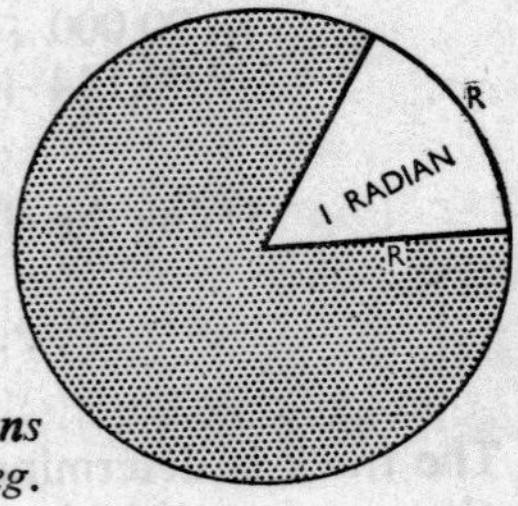

FIG. 85. *Angles may be measured in radians instead of degrees. One radian is* 57·3 *deg.*

For the mathematician, measurement in radians is the most natural to use since it leads to the simplest results. Although the degree remains the unit of practical measurement of angles, the radian is essential in more advanced mathematics and in many important aspects of electrical and mechanical engineering.

(e) Graphs turn Numbers into Pictures

ONE of the most informative, effective and interesting ways of presenting a table of mathematical quantities or of showing the relationship between two varying quantities which depend on each other is the numerical picture or graph. Not only do vivid images remain in the memory longer than bald statements of fact but it is usually far easier to see from a graph how a set of values is changing than to extract the same information from a table of figures.

Most of us are familiar in these days with various forms of graph, which often appear in our newspapers and magazines, on notice boards and advertisement hoardings. Many official publications contain graphs designed to attract our attention to important national statistics which we should hardly pause to consider if they were presented only on page after page of dull tables of figures. Engineers and scientists use graphs not only to picture the results of their experimental work but to obtain additional information and to derive laws. Factory output is often shown by means of graphs; a graph at the head of a patient's bed in hospital shows how his temperature is changing; a barometer with pen attached can often be

112

seen in the window of a jeweller's shop recording changes of air pressure continuously in the form of a barograph.

One of the simplest ways of comparing numbers is by little pictures or pictographs. These tell us facts in a quick and interesting way. Fig. 86 illustrates how these little pictures can be used to present facts. Each small drawing of a motor-car represents 10,000 cars. By examining the pictographs we see at once that output was increased nearly one and a half times between 1932 and 1936 but that in 1940 and 1944 the number of cars being produced was considerably reduced. What probably happened to the factory during these years? By 1948 output had grown until it reached more than twice its pre-war figure. Thus the pictures not only present the figures in a manner which is calculated to capture the attention but may even challenge us to deduce reasons for the changes shown.

THE VALUE OF PICTOGRAPHS

You will often find pictographs in the newspapers, usually in advertisements, in magazines and in Government publications and National Savings posters. Look out for them and consider whether they provide an effective way of presenting the facts. Although pictographs are often attractive to look at they are not particularly easy to draw; often one little picture has to represent a large number of units and it is difficult to tell what fraction is represented by part of a little picture. We could, of course, make drawings of little men and women to represent, say, the number of people employed in the cotton industry at various times, or drawings of little houses to show the number of houses built annually over a period of years. The

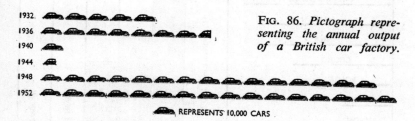

FIG. 86. *Pictograph representing the annual output of a British car factory.*

REPRESENTS 10,000 CARS

possibilities for this form of simple pictograph are almost unlimited and no doubt many more examples will spring readily to mind.

In our pictograph each little drawing or symbol represented a number of similar things such as motor-cars, people and houses. We could, of course, have a pictograph of a somewhat different kind in which each picture represented only one thing, say a river or moun-

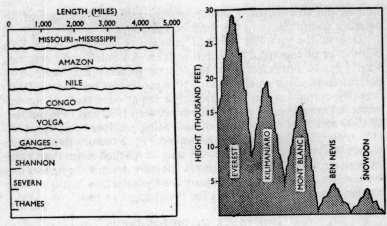

FIG. 87. *Lengths of rivers and heights of mountains compared pictorially.*

tain or building, which we wished to compare in some way with other similar things. The idea is illustrated in Fig. 87, which suggests how we can compare some of the rivers and mountains of the world in graphic form.

Of course, our graphs do not really show the shapes of the rivers

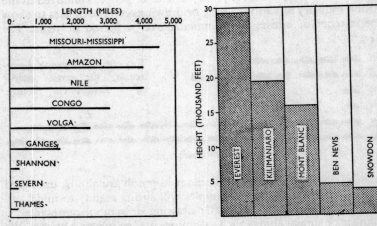

FIG. 88. *Straight lines only are sufficient for comparing rivers.*

FIG. 89. *The heights of mountains compared by means of a column graph.*

or mountains but only provide a simple method of comparing them in a pictorial form. Although it may be interesting to represent facts in this way it is far from convenient; all that is really required is a straight line, upright or across, and this will present the facts equally well, as you can see from Fig. 88.

COLUMN GRAPHS

Since the shapes of the mountains in our mountain graph bear no resemblance to actuality it would serve the purpose equally well to draw a line across each column at the level of each mountain top. It is useful, though not essential, to shade or colour each column so that the complete graph may be more easily seen and the heights more easily compared. Such an arrangement, seen in Fig. 89, is usually called a column graph. Although the columns of our graph

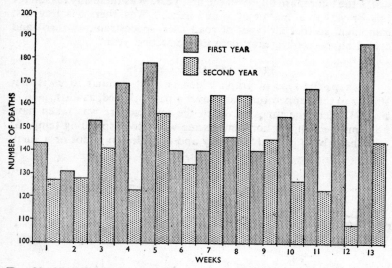

FIG. 90. *Use of the column graph to compare the number of road deaths in Great Britain during corresponding quarters of two successive years.*

represent mountains they could represent a thousand and one things —rainfall, population, imports and exports over a period of years, production figures, road accidents, and so on.

The column graph also offers a very useful method of comparing quantities occurring over a period of time with similar quantities occurring over some other period—as, for example, in comparing

115

the number of road deaths in each month of one year with those in corresponding months of some other year. The number of people killed in road accidents in Great Britain during each week of the last quarters of two successive years are shown in the table:

Week:	1	2	3	4	5	6	7	8	9	10	11	12	13
First year ..	143	131	153	169	178	140	140	146	140	155	167	160	187
Second year ..	127	128	141	123	156	134	164	164	145	127	123	108	144

These facts are represented graphically in Fig. 90. As you see from the graph, it is helpful to use contrasting shading (or colours) for the separate years so that comparison can be seen at a glance. But while the graph readily indicates the differences in corresponding weeks of each of the two years it cannot offer an explanation of these differences. It can be seen, for instance, that on all but three of the thirteen weeks the figures are higher in the first year. Was there any reason for this or was it a matter of pure chance? Was there a safety first campaign, so that all types of road user—pedestrian, motorist and cyclist alike—took greater care in the second year?

POINT-AND-LINE GRAPHS

Perhaps the type of graph which is most familiar to us is that similar to the temperature chart over a patient's bed, as illustrated in Fig. 91. Here the times at which the temperature was taken have been marked on the horizontal scale while corresponding temperatures have been plotted vertically and recorded by a dot or a small

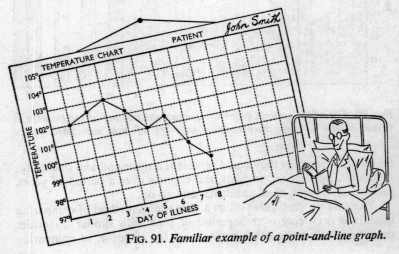

FIG. 91. *Familiar example of a point-and-line graph.*

116

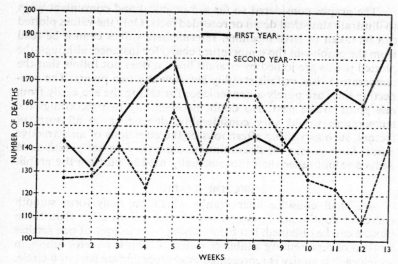

FIG. 92. *Road deaths again compared. The data of Fig. 90 is here presented as a point-and-line graph, simplifying comparison of the two sets of figures.*

cross. In order that the doctor, who is a very busy man, can see at a glance how the patient's temperature is rising or falling, these recordings have been made by the nurse in the form of a point-and-line graph.

The results could have been shown equally well by a series of upright lines or by a column graph. What is the advantage of the method used here? Notice that as there is no likelihood of the temperature falling below 95 deg. it is unnecessary to show all the temperature scale from 0 deg. upwards. Such a graph is another illustration of the way a graph presents a general impression. If the lines continue upwards the doctor may decide there is cause for alarm; if the general tendency is downwards towards the normal temperature he may feel that the patient is well on the way to recovery; or, if it fluctuates in a particular way, he may be assisted in his diagnosis.

Like the column graph, the point-and-line graph may be used conveniently to compare two sets of corresponding figures. In Fig. 92 the road deaths in the last quarters of the two years previously compared in a column graph are shown as point-and-line graphs. You may consider this the better method since the points at which one graph is above (or below) the other is more easily seen.

The graphs considered so far are practical and convenient ways to illustrate statistical detail or recorded facts. Only the values plotted can be taken to have meaning. Intermediate values cannot be read from the graph—in the temperature chart, for instance, although the plotted points are joined by straight lines, it does not follow that the temperature rises or falls steadily between any two points. The connecting lines are purely a convenience for taking the eye easily from one point to the next. No doubt between any two recordings the temperature would vary considerably, depending on all sorts of factors, such as visiting afternoons or the attentions of an attractive nurse! Such graphs are discontinuous since they do not permit us to deduce values other than those actually used in plotting the graph.

SECTOR GRAPHS

We shall consider later graphs which normally form smooth curves or continuous lines and from which values other than those plotted can be obtained, but before doing so let us look at one further method of representing a table of statistics. This is a sector graph, in which each quantity is represented as an appropriate part of a circle. The table below (taken from a National Savings poster) shows how much various sources contributed towards each £1 of the money collected for the National Revenue in a single year.

Income Tax and Surtax	Death Duties and Profit Tax	Alcohol	Purchase Tax	Tobacco	Entertainment and Betting	Miscellaneous Sources
7s. 9d.	2s. 5d.	2s. 0d.	1s. 7d.	3s. 0d.	0s. 4d.	2s. 11d.

Fig. 93 illustrates how these details can be represented in a sector graph. A complete circle is taken to represent £1 and sectors of it are drawn proportional to the amounts under each heading. Income Tax and Surtax, for example, constitute $\frac{93}{240}$ of the total, and the angle at

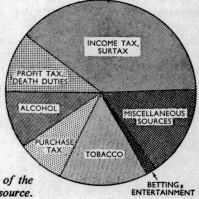

FIG. 93. *Sector graph: proportions of the national revenue drawn from each source.*

118

the centre of its sector is $\frac{93}{240}$ of $360° = 139\frac{1}{2}°$. Other angles can be calculated similarly and the graph completed.

You will find many interesting examples of sector graphs in official pamphlets which are published to bring home to us the nation's economic situation.

CONTINUOUS STRAIGHT-LINE GRAPHS

We shall be concerned in the remainder of this section with graphs in which a mathematical relationship exists between the quantities plotted on two scales. Such graphs, which are normally in the form of straight lines or smooth curves, are continuous and enable us to read from them values other than those plotted.

Let us consider a few examples of this type of graph. We know, for instance, that the freezing point of water is 0 on a Centigrade scale and 32 on a Fahrenheit

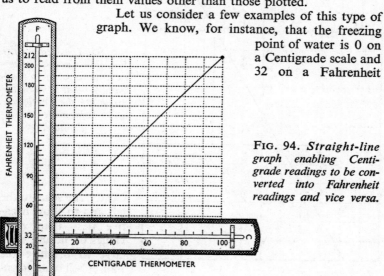

FIG. 94. *Straight-line graph enabling Centigrade readings to be converted into Fahrenheit readings and vice versa.*

scale, and that the corresponding boiling points are 100 and 212 deg. respectively. It is a simple matter, therefore, to construct a graph showing the relationship between the two scales. It will only be necessary to plot two points and complete the graph by joining them (Fig. 94). From the graph it is apparent that 50° C. is equivalent to 122° F.; the graph can thus be used as a sort of ready reckoner for converting Centigrade readings into Fahrenheit readings and vice versa. You can easily draw for yourself other conversion graphs of this type and use them as a short method of calculation.

Examination of the Centigrade-Fahrenheit graph will soon reveal that it does not tell all the story. Temperatures of less than 0° C. and 32° F. do occur, as we all realize, in the depths of winter, when the wireless often reports so many "degrees of frost." Temperatures lower even than 0° F. occur in many of the colder regions of the world. To complete our graph, therefore, we need to extend our scales (or axes as they are usually called) to include values on both which are less than zero. It seems common sense to continue the

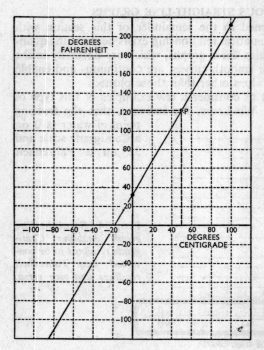

FIG. 95. *The Centigrade-Fahrenheit graph extended to show sub-zero readings. At what point on the graph are the Centigrade and Fahrenheit values identical?*

Centigrade scale to the left and to show negative (less than zero) values on it, and similarly to produce the Fahrenheit scale downwards for negative values. A more complete picture of the Centigrade-Fahrenheit graph is shown in Fig. 95.

We are thus introduced to a convention used by mathematicians for plotting graphs. Graphs are usually (though not always) drawn by reference to two axes at right-angles (the C. and F. scales in our example). These axes cross at the beginning point or origin. On the horizontal axis distances to the right of the origin are positive while distances to the left are negative. Similarly, on the vertical axis upward measurements are regarded as positive and downward measurements as negative. Every point on our Centigrade-Fahrenheit graph is fixed if we know its horizontal and vertical values—that

120

Mr. Smith's Unusual Clock

The striking mechanism of blind Mr. Smith's clock went wrong. It would only strike up to eleven, and then always returned to one, so that you could never tell what hour it was when it struck. Yet he got used to it and always knew what time it was when he happened to hear it. On Monday morning when I was visiting him it struck ten. He said it was ten o'clock all right and challenged me to call to see him on the next day when I could be sure of finding it striking the right hour. When did I go again? *Solution on page 444*

is, its C. and F. values. The point *P*, for example, is the point having a C. reading of 50° and a F. reading of 122°.

The two values which fix the position of any point are known as its co-ordinates. The co-ordinates of the boiling point and the freezing point of water are therefore 100° C. and 212° F., and 0° C. and 32° F. respectively. See if you can find the point on this graph where the co-ordinates are equal.

Let us return for a moment to the axes of reference. The horizontal axis is often referred to as the *x* axis (though we have called it the

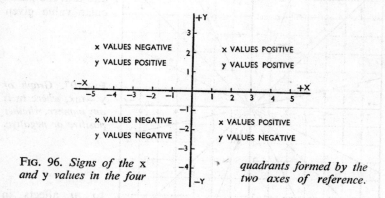

FIG. 96. *Signs of the* x *and* y *values in the four*   *quadrants formed by the two axes of reference.*

Centigrade axis in our example) and the vertical axis is similarly often called the *y* axis (the Fahrenheit axis in our diagram). Fig. 96 shows the signs the *x* and *y* values will have in the four "quadrants" formed by the axes of reference.

If a definite known relationship is always to exist between the *x* and *y* values of a point, then we can plot the "path" which shows this connexion and produce the graph of the relationship. For

121

example, a point may follow a path such that its x value and its y value are always equal to each other; that is, such that $y = x$. This clearly means that the point is everywhere just as far from the x axis as from the y axis. It must therefore lie on a line which bisects the angle between the axes and which makes an angle of 45 deg. with each if the units on each scale are the same. Similarly, the relationship $y = 2x$ produces the line every point of which has a y value which is twice its x value.

In Fig. 97 a number of these lines have been grouped together. If you examine them carefully you will see that they do in fact represent graphically the formulae or laws written against them. Choose any point on any line; see what x is and what y is at the point and see if these values fit the formula indicated. All these graphs have two things in common in that (*a*) they are all straight lines, and (*b*) they pass through the origin. They differ only in the angle they make with the x axis, and examination will show that the effect of changing the number in front of the x (called the coefficient of x) is to alter that angle. It appears that the graph of the relation $y = mx$, where m is any number positive or negative, is a straight line passing through the origin and that the particular value given

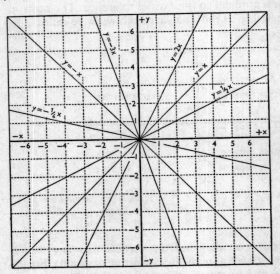

FIG. 97. *Graph of* $y = mx$, *where* m *is any number, whether positive or negative.*

to m affects in some way the slope of the line. Can you deduce by examining the diagram the effect of m (the coefficient of x) having a positive or negative value?

But not all relationships, not even those which lead to straight-line graphs, are as simple as the ones we have considered so far.

122

In our Centigrade-Fahrenheit graph, for example, the line did not pass through the zero point on both scales, since when C. = 0°, F. = 32°. Suppose the equation connecting the x and y values of a point is now $y = 2x + 3$, how can we draw the graph of this relationship? It is very simple. Give a series of values to x, find the corresponding values of y, and then plot these pairs of values on a sheet of graph paper in the usual way. Thus, if $x = 1$, then $2x = 2$ and $y = 5$; similarly, if x is 0, then y must be 3. Find two or three more points. When the points are plotted they will be found to lie on a straight line which is parallel to the line $y = 2x$ but three units above it in the y axis.

Now try to draw the graph of $y = 2x - 3$. Plotting as before, we find a straight line parallel to $y = 2x$ but three units below it on the y scale. Clearly the presence of a constant number in the equation only serves to move the line up or down on the y scale and this is consistent with our previous idea that it is the coefficient of x (2 in this case) alone that indicates the slope of the line. Thus the lines $y = 2x$, $y = 2x + 3$, $y = 2x - 3$ are all parallel; that is, they have the same slope.

We can perhaps now jump to the conclusion that the graph of $y = mx + c$, where m and c are ordinary numbers (either $+$ or $-$), is always a straight line and that the constant number c on the end of the equation indicates where the line cuts the y axis (usually called the intercept on the axis of y).

To sum up:

(1) The graph of $y = mx + c$ is a straight line (m and c are constants which are not affected by changes in the values of x and y).

(2) m, the coefficient of x, determines the slope of the line.

(3) c, the independent constant, fixes the position of the line by indicating where it cuts the y axis (because when $x = 0$, $y = c$).

Although we have spent some time considering straight-line graphs this is fully justified by their importance in many branches of practical and scientific work. If the equation connecting the two quantities (x and y) is known it is a simple matter to draw the graph since we can give any values we please to x and calculate the corresponding value of y. The quantity x is generally known as the independent variable (since we can give any value to it) and y as the dependent variable (since its value will depend on the value assigned to x). From the table of values obtained we can plot the graph in the usual way.

If, on the contrary, a straight-line graph is obtained from the results of an experiment it may be desirable to find the equation connecting the variable quantities from the graph itself. A practical

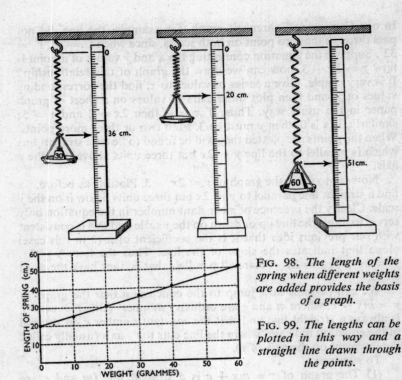

FIG. 98. *The length of the spring when different weights are added provides the basis of a graph.*

FIG. 99. *The lengths can be plotted in this way and a straight line drawn through the points.*

example will show one way in which this can be done. A spiral spring 20 cm. long is hung up and weights added to its lower end (Fig. 98). Its length is noted for each weight added. The table shows the results:

Weight (W) in grammes:	0	10	20	30	40	50	60
Length (l) in cm.:		20	25	30·5	36	41	46	51

When the results are plotted they are found to be almost exactly on a straight line (Fig. 99). It would be unusual if all the points lay exactly on a straight line since the results of practical work are always subject to experimental error. It is clear, however, that the relation between weight (W) and length (l) is of the form $l = mW + c$, since we have decided previously that this is the kind of equation which produces a straight-line graph. By using our graph we can now determine what this equation should be, which is the same as saying that we can find the value of m and c for this particular line. In the graph the best line has been drawn through the points obtained as the result of the experiment.

124

The intercept on the y axis is the value of l when $W = 0$ (that is, when the spring is unloaded), and this is 20. The equation becomes $l = mW + 20$. To find what m stands for we may take any point convenient on the graph other than the actual readings; this is better and more accurate since the line has not been drawn exactly through all the points. When $W = 35$ our graph gives $l = 37\cdot5$, and substituting these two corresponding values in the equation we get $37\cdot5 = 35m + 20$. From this $m = 0\cdot5$ and so the equation connecting l and W should be $l = 0\cdot5W + 20$.

Thus we have worked back from the graph and obtained the law connecting length and loading of this particular spring. We know that c is the natural length of the spring: presumably it depends on its physical properties—material and dimensions. This kind of light that mathematics throws on scientific matters is of immense value. You will find many other examples of this kind of relationship in books of applied science, building and engineering. You should try to find the law connecting F. and C. from the Centigrade-Fahrenheit graph that we were looking at on page 120.

CURVED-LINE GRAPHS

Not all formulae, laws or equations lead to graphs which are straight lines. Consider the squares of the ordinary numbers, for example:

Number: 0 1 2 3   4   5   6   7   8   9 10
Square of number: 0 1 4 9 16 25 36 49 64 81 100

We know that $(-1)^2 = 1$, $(-2)^2 = 4$ and so on, so that the table could be extended to include the negative numbers and their squares also. If we call our number x and its square y then obviously the equation connecting them is $y = x^2$. When plotted this produces the neat smooth curve shown in Fig. 100. Notice that the curve could be used for finding the squares of numbers not plotted, or square roots (each number will have two square roots, one positive and the other negative). You will probably see once again that adding a constant to this equation, so that it becomes $y = x^2 + c$, will not change its

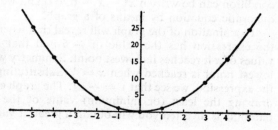

FIG. 100. *Numbers plotted against their squares to produce the graph* $y = x^2$.

shape but only serve to move it up or down on the y axis just as it did the straight line. Similarly, by writing $2x^2$, $4x^2$, $\frac{1}{2}x^2$, the curve is closed in or opened wider. Can you guess what happens if you make the coefficient of x^2 negative? Some of this family of curves, which are called parabolas, are shown in Fig. 101.

An expression like $x^2 - x - 6$ is more complicated, but its graph can be drawn by giving x a series of values and plotting values of the expression (y) against the values of x which gave them. When $x = -5$, for example, the value of y is found to be 24. Similarly,

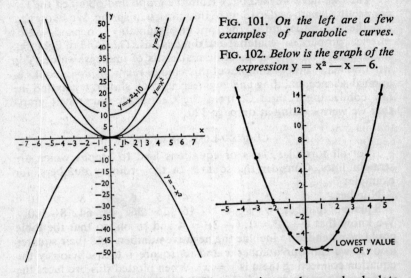

FIG. 101. *On the left are a few examples of parabolic curves.*

FIG. 102. *Below is the graph of the expression* y = x² — x — 6.

LOWEST VALUE OF y

when $x = 4$ the value of y is 6. Give x various values and calculate the corresponding values of y until you have sufficient points to plot the curve shown in Fig. 102. Note that the graph crosses the x axis at two points, where $x = -2$ and $x = +3$. At these two points the value of y and therefore of the expression $x^2 - x - 6$ is zero. This condition can be written $x^2 - x - 6 = 0$ and we have thus solved a quadratic equation by means of a graph.

Examination of the graph will reveal that where $x = 0$ and $x = 1$ the expression has the value of -6 and that between these two values of x it reaches its lowest point. Symmetry will suggest that this lowest point is reached when $x = \frac{1}{2}$. Substituting this value of x in the expression, we see that $y = -6\frac{1}{4}$. The graph enables us to find by drawing the least (or minimum) value of the expression. If the parabola is inverted you will obtain a greatest value instead.

126

Summing up, we can say that the graph of $y = ax^2 + bx + c$ is a parabola and that from it we can determine (*i*) the values of x for which $y = 0$ (if any), (*ii*) the value of x which makes y greatest or least, and (*iii*) the least or greatest value of y. These results may only be approximate and there are methods of doing the same thing more accurately by algebra; but it is often important and useful to be able to learn such facts about a quadratic equation.

A FEW PRACTICAL EXAMPLES

A farmer has 120 yd. of hurdles and wishes to make a rectangular pen of the greatest possible area so that as many sheep as possible can be penned. What should be its dimensions?

The farmer can arrange the hurdles in many ways provided the perimeter is always 120 yd. and each arrangement will produce a different area. Suppose we call the length x yd., then the width is $60 - x$ yd. (since one length and one breadth together measure 60 yd.). The area A is $x (60 - x)$ sq. yd. This is illustrated by Fig. 103. Looking at the expression $x (60 - x)$ or $60x - x^2$ you may decide that its graph is a parabola and that since the sign in front of x^2 is negative the parabola is inverted.

Plot a few points which satisfy the equation $y = 60x - x^2$ and see if you agree with the curve shown in Fig. 104, which shows the greatest area to be 900 sq. yd. and the shape of the pen to be a square.

Let us consider a second problem. A stone is thrown vertically upwards and its height (h ft.) after any time (t sec.) is given by the formula $h = 128t - 16t^2$. What is the greatest height reached and how long is it before the stone returns to its starting point? The

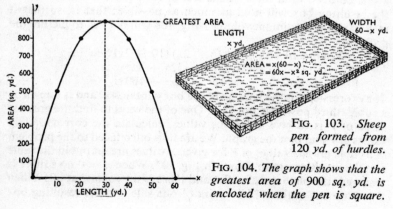

FIG. 103. *Sheep pen formed from 120 yd. of hurdles.*

FIG. 104. *The graph shows that the greatest area of 900 sq. yd. is enclosed when the pen is square.*

127

formula will show that the graph is an inverted parabola. By giving values to t we can calculate corresponding values of h and so draw the curve shown in Fig. 105. The graph tells us all we want to know: the stone obviously returns to its starting point after 8 sec., since the height is again zero at this time. The values of h are symmetrical about the value of 256 ft., which occurs after 4 sec. Our stone takes just as long to go up as to come down (4 sec. each)!

Suppose we put $t = 9$, then $h = 1152 - 1296 = -144$ ft. The conditions of the problem make this value of h impossible unless the stone falls

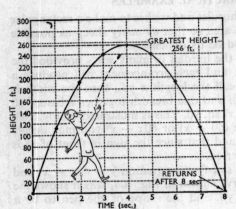

FIG. 105. *Graph of flight of stone according to the formula* h = 128t — 16t².

over the edge of a cliff and we can measure its distance *below* the level of projection.

Not all problems lead to graphs as easy to draw as a parabola. Consider the following problem: a sheet of metal 16 × 10 in. is to have a small square cut out of each corner and the sides turned up to form a shallow rectangular box without a top. Neglecting the overlap at the corners, what must be the size of the square removed so that the resulting box will hold as much as possible; that is, so that it may have the maximum volume? Fig. 106 will help us to picture the problem.

$$\text{Volume of box } V = (16 - 2x)(10 - 2x)x \text{ cu. in.}$$
$$= (160 - 52x + 4x^2)x$$
$$= 4x^3 - 52x^2 + 160x.$$

The expression for the volume of the box contains x^3 and is known as a cubic (third power) expression. One of the ways to find the greatest value of V is to give x various values, calculate the corresponding values of V and plot the graph. We are thus introduced to the problem of a cubic graph. Values of V for given x values are set out in the table and the resulting graph shown in Fig. 107. When $x = 0$ no square is removed, the plate remains flat and there is no volume at all! When $x = 5$ we cut to the middle point of one side and the resulting box

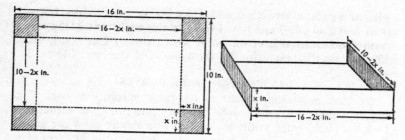

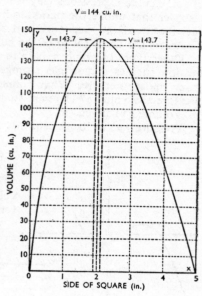

FIG. 106. *The lidless box is formed from a metal sheet 10 × 16 in. and is to have the maximum volume. What is the size of the squares that must be removed from the corners of the sheet?*

FIG. 107. *Graph of the volume of the box according to the formula* $V = 4x^3 - 52x^2 + 160x$. *The highest point on the curve, when* $x = 2$ *in., gives the greatest volume: 144 cu. in. This may be confirmed by giving x the values 1·9 and 2·1 in., when the volume drops in each case to 143·7 cu. in.*

has no width and so its volume is again zero! Do not assume therefore that the best value for V will be when $x = 2\frac{1}{2}$.

Multiply for V $\left\{ \begin{array}{c} \\ \\ \\ \end{array} \right.$

x	0	1	2	3	4	5
$16 - 2x$	16	14	12	10	8	6
$10 - 2x$	10	8	6	4	2	0
V	0	112	144	120	64	0

Volume of box $V = x(16 - 2x)(10 - 2x)$.

The graph suggests that $x = 2$ in. will produce the box of maximum volume. We cannot be sure, however, that the graph does not rise higher somewhere between 2 and 3. By giving x the values 1.9 and 2.1 we find $V = 143.7$ and $V = 143.7$ and this confirms that the graph is falling on either side of the point where $x = 2$. This point, then, will give you the best value for the volume of the box: 144 cu. in.

CUBIC AND OTHER CURVES

We have only studied part of the cubic graph, that part of it lying between $x = 0$ and $x = 5$. This may lead to a false impression of what a cubic graph really looks like. You should draw the graph of some cubic expressions (say $y = x^3 - 2x^2 - 5x + 6$). You may discover that unlike the parabola it has a double bend and that it cuts the x axis at least once and sometimes three times. Fig. 108 illustrates the usual shape of the cubic curve.

Other types of graph remain to be considered. In internal combustion engines and in gas storage cylinders we are dealing with gases under pressure. What connexion, if any, is there between pressure and volume? Here are some actual figures:

Volume (v) in cu. in.: 16 20 24 28 32
Pressure (p) in lb. per sq. in.: 28·75 23·0 19·2 16·4 14·4

If p is plotted against v a curve is obtained which is different from those we have met with so far (Fig. 109). As the pressure increases the volume grows smaller, and conversely as the pressure decreases

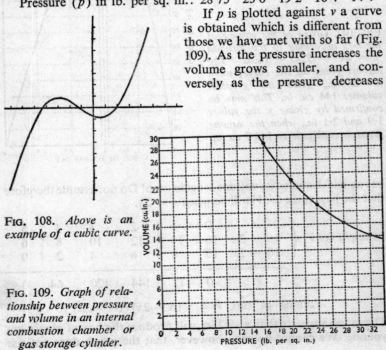

FIG. 108. *Above is an example of a cubic curve.*

FIG. 109. *Graph of relationship between pressure and volume in an internal combustion chamber or gas storage cylinder.*

130

the volume grows larger, provided that in both cases the temperature remains constant. But however great the pressure the volume can never be nothing. Similarly, the pressure is never zero, however great the volume may become. Hence there are no points on this curve for which $v = 0$ or $p = 0$. When pressure is enormous, volume is very small and vice versa, so that the curve continually approaches the axes without ever quite reaching them. The law of the curve is $pv = C$, where C is a constant number. In our example $C = 460$,

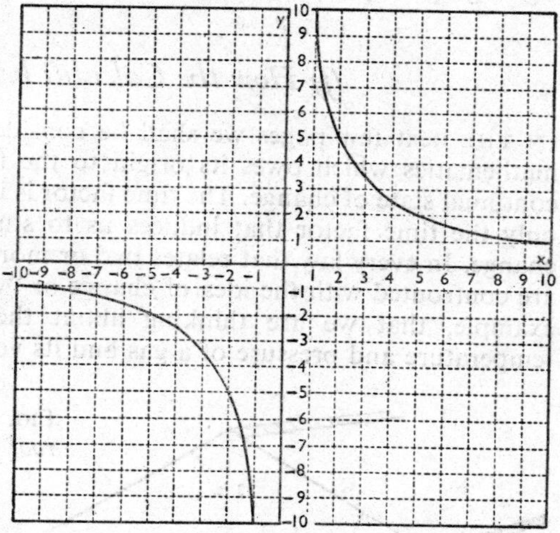

FIG. 110. *Another example of the pressure/ volume type of graph. As one quantity increases the other decreases. In this case* xy = **10.**

as you can easily discover for yourself. The quantities p and v are real, concrete quantities which can be measured and which have positive values—there is, after all, always some volume and the pressure is never negative.

Let us generalize our law for pressure and volume so that it becomes $xy = c$, where the possible values of x and y are not necessarily restricted to positive values only. Here is a table of values for $xy = 10$.

x	1	2	3	4	5 . . . 10	−1	−2	−3	−4	−5 . . . −10
y	10	5	$3\frac{1}{3}$	$2\frac{1}{2}$	2 . . . 1	−10	−5	$-3\frac{1}{3}$	$-2\frac{1}{2}$	−2 . . . −1
xy	10	10	10	10	10 . . . 10	10	10	10	10	10 . . . 10

If both x and y have negative values their product is still positive. Fig. 110 shows that this curve, which is called the hyperbola, has two distinct branches which appear to sit "back to back." The equation $xy = c$ can also be written as $y = \dfrac{c}{x}$ and it expresses the fact that as x grows larger y grows smaller; that is, if x is doubled y is halved, and so on. It is the relationship between two quantities which are in inverse proportion, as for example the connexion between speed of travel and time taken over a particular distance.

Although it is important for engineers, scientists and other specialists to be able to draw graphs and derive laws from them it is more important for ordinary persons to be able to interpret graphs—that is, to understand readily the information that the numerical picture has to tell. You will increase your knowledge and understanding of graphs by looking critically at as many as possible.

(f) How the Calculus helps us

IN THE next few pages we shall be considering a development of mathematics which owes its origin to the fact that nature is in a continual state of change. The time factor is inescapable, but it is not only the time factor that induces us to study the mathematics of change. In every law that relates two or more variable quantities we are confronted with the idea of change or "variation." Suppose, for example, that we are thinking about the relation between the temperature and pressure of a gas and its volume. Observation told

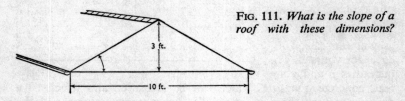

FIG. 111. *What is the slope of a roof with these dimensions?*

Robert Boyle that an increase of temperature results in an increase of pressure or an increase of volume, or both. The variables *p*, *v* and *t* (representing measurements of pressure, volume and temperature) are related by the formula

$$pv = kt$$

where *k* is a constant number. The formula does not contain a time factor, nor does it directly denote change. Yet to the practical man (the meteorologist, for instance), the importance of the formula is that he can *use* it, and in nature a parcel of gas is rarely, if ever, static. The temperature or the pressure or the volume of a parcel of air, or all three, are different from one moment to the next, and he can see in the formula how a change in *t* will affect *p* and *v*.

The mechanical engineer needs to know the effect of an increase of load upon the shape of a beam. The civil engineer needs to know how a change in the design of a bridge will affect its strength. The radio engineer needs to know how an increase of voltage on the grid of a valve affects the current received by the anode.

Mathematically the basis of all their requirements is the notion of variation. The simplest path to a clear understanding of the matter is "the calculus," which investigates the laws of change. What we are now setting out to do, therefore, is to establish rules for studying the effect of an increase in one variable on another related variable. The formula connecting the variables can always be depicted by a graph, and it will help us to look at this as we go along.

The slope of an ordinary roof is dependent on a vertical measurement and a horizontal one. In the case of Fig. 111, you will say at once that it is 3 in 5, and you will see that it is constant from gutter to ridge. You will see that it can therefore be expressed as the tangent of the angle marked.

The surveyor frequently talks of the gradient of a surface as the ratio of vertical rise to distance along the surface, because it is easier for him to put his tape-measure along the gradient than to measure horizontally. He therefore tends to express gradient (or slope) as the sine of the angle.

In mathematics we prefer the builder's approach because our graphs utilize two measurements at right-angles. Whenever we talk of the slope of a line we shall mean the *tangent* of the angle it makes with the horizontal axis. Note that *two* measurements are involved.

Fig. 112 shows that the formula $y = mx + c$ has a straight-line graph and at every point the slope is the same. Test the truth of this statement.

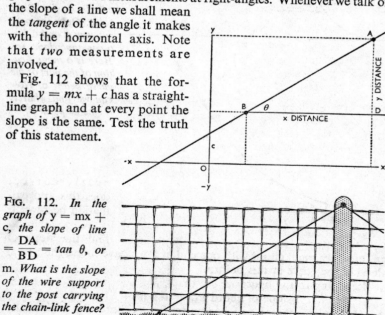

Fig. 112. *In the graph of* y = mx + c, *the slope of line* $= \dfrac{DA}{BD} = tan\ \theta,\ or$ m. *What is the slope of the wire support to the post carrying the chain-link fence?*

Straight-line graphs are all too rare in nature, so we shall now turn to curves and their formulae. In Fig. 113*a* we have a radio engineer's curve. Between points *c* and *d* the curve is straight and its slope is therefore constant. Before we can use the valve we may need to know more about the parts of the curve below *c* and beyond *d*. Let us magnify the first of these (Fig. 113*b*).

Let *P* be any point on the curve and *Q* another point close to *P*. Let *PT* be the straight line which touches the curve (that is, it is the tangent to it) at *P* and which makes an angle θ with the *x* axis. Join *P* and *Q* and call the angle between *PQ* and *PT* α (the diagram makes this clear). We might regard the slope of the chord *PQ* as an approximate measure of the slope of the curve at *P* and the smaller the chord is made the more

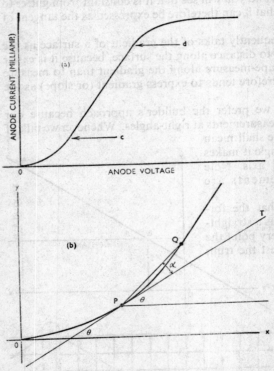

Fig. 113. (a) *Characteristic of a diode valve. Only the part between* c *and* d *has a constant slope.* (b) *Here is a magnification of the part of the curve below* c. *How can we find what is the slope at* P?

nearly correct does this approximation become. If it is possible to find the slope of an infinitely small chord with one end at *P* we have found the actual slope of the curve at this point.

Referring to the figure we see that

slope of chord *PQ* = tan (θ + α).

As *Q* is taken nearer and nearer to *P* the chord *PQ* continually

134

decreases and so does the angle α, so that when the chord becomes infinitely small so does the angle α. Thus the slope of the curve at P reduces to tan θ and this is the same as the slope of the tangent at P.

This provides us with a graphical method of finding the slope, since we can draw the tangent to the curve at the required point and determine the slope of this (tan θ). Normally we have no reliable method of drawing the true tangent to a curve and therefore we can obtain only approximate results.

A practical counterpart to the graphical method is to obtain the slope of a curved object at any point by touching it with a ruler. Fig. 114 suggests how this can be done for a vase and you will no doubt see how the idea can be extended to other curved objects.

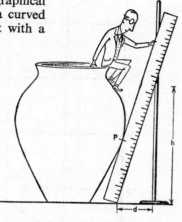

FIG. 114. *The slope of a vase can be found by holding a ruler against it. At* P, *the point of contact, the slope is equal to the fraction* $\frac{h}{d}$.

Just as scale drawing is replaced by the more exact calculations of trigonometry so we must seek a method of *calculating* the slope of the tangent and hence of the curve at any point. For the purposes of discussion we will consider the curve $y = x^2$, since we have already met this and recognize it as a parabola passing through the origin. What is the slope of this curve at the point where $x = 3$? Referring to Fig. 115 you will see that the points where $x = 3$ and $x = 4$ have been joined to give the chord PQ. We can regard the slope of the chord as an approximation to the slope at P and in this case tan $\theta = \dfrac{QM}{PM} = \dfrac{7}{1}$.

Similarly, we can move Q to the point where $x = 3 \cdot 5$, $y = (3 \cdot 5)^2$. The slope now is $\dfrac{(3 \cdot 5)^2 - 3^2}{3 \cdot 5 - 3} \left(\dfrac{\text{perp.}}{\text{base}} \right) = \dfrac{(3 \cdot 5 - 3)\ (3 \cdot 5 + 3)}{(3 \cdot 5 - 3)}$, or

$6 \cdot 5$. Continuing this process, when Q is at the point $x = 3 \cdot 1$, $y = (3 \cdot 1)^2$, the slope becomes $\dfrac{(3 \cdot 1)^2 - 3^2}{3 \cdot 1 - 3}$, or $6 \cdot 1$. Bring Q very close to P so that its co-ordinates are $3 \cdot 001$, $(3 \cdot 001)^2$. The slope is still $\dfrac{\text{vertical distance}}{\text{horizontal distance}}$, or $\dfrac{(3 \cdot 001)^2 - 3^2}{3 \cdot 001 - 3}$, which is $6 \cdot 001$.

135

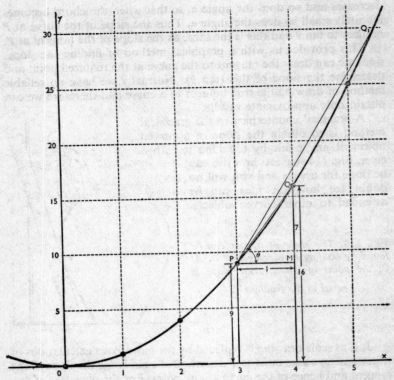

FIG. 115. *Graph of* $y = x^2$. *The slope at* P *is represented very roughly by* PQ_1, *more accurately by* PQ, *and most accurately of all when we move* Q *right down to* P, *so that* PQ *becomes the tangent to the curve at* P.

Setting down these results in tabular form will help towards a clearer appreciation of what is happening:

P		Q		Slope $= \dfrac{\text{Difference of } y}{\text{Difference of } x}$
x value	y value	x value	y value	
3	3^2	4	4^2	$\tan \theta = \dfrac{7}{1} = 7$
3	3^2	3·5	$3·5^2$	$\tan \theta = \dfrac{3·5^2 - 3^2}{0·5} = 6·5$
3	3^2	3·1	$3·1^2$	$\tan \theta = \dfrac{3·1^2 - 3^2}{0·1} = 6·1$
3	3^2	3·001	$3·001^2$	$\tan \theta = \dfrac{3·001^2 - 3^2}{0·001} = 6·001$

It appears that as Q approaches P, the value of the slope of PQ gets nearer and nearer to 6 and that ultimately when Q coincides with P, if we can visualize this happening, the slope of the curve at P will be 6 (that is, the tangent at P makes an angle θ with the x axis such that $\tan \theta = 6$).

Using a similar method and argument we can discover that the slope of the curve when $x = 4$ is 8, and when $x = 2$ it is 4. The results of doing this are collected in the following table:

x value of point	1	2	3	4	5
Slope at this point	1	4	6	8	10

From this table it is easy to see the rule. The slope at any point x, on the curve $y = x^2$, is $2x$, and this is the result we have been seeking. By adopting similar experimental methods we could probably guess the rule for the slope of other curves at any point, but the work is likely to be long and tedious. Is there no more general method of doing it? Such a method does exist and we shall now use it to confirm the result we guessed above that the slope of $y = x^2$ at any point is $2x$.

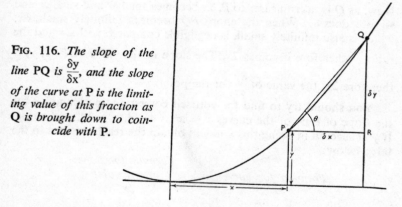

FIG. 116. *The slope of the line* PQ *is* $\dfrac{\delta y}{\delta x}$, *and the slope of the curve at* P *is the limiting value of this fraction as* Q *is brought down to coincide with* P.

In the diagram (Fig. 116) P is a point on the curve with co-ordinates x, y, and Q is a nearby point with co-ordinates $x + \delta x$, $y + \delta y$. The symbols δx and δy, which we are meeting for the first time, are called delta-x and delta-y (from the Greek letter δ) and are used to denote a small change in the value of x (or y). Often in practical life we find it convenient to use the word increment for an extra bit: δx is an increment of x.

From the figure it is clear that the slope of PQ is given by $\tan \theta = \dfrac{\delta y}{\delta x}$. There is nothing new in this, since we have used the ratio

$\dfrac{\text{difference in } y}{\text{difference in } x}$ to express the slope previously.

Now $\qquad y = x^2 \qquad$ (all y values are squares of

and $\quad y + \delta y = (x + \delta x)^2 \qquad$ corresponding x values)

By subtraction $\delta y = (x + \delta x)^2 - x^2$

$\qquad\qquad\qquad = (2x + \delta x)\,\delta x \quad$ (difference of two squares)

$\qquad \therefore \dfrac{\delta y}{\delta x} = 2x + \delta x.$

Now, as Q is taken nearer to P, δx becomes smaller and smaller and so also does δy. When the chord PQ becomes infinitely small, δx, which is also infinitely small, is negligible compared with $2x$ and the ratio $\dfrac{\delta y}{\delta x}$ therefore becomes $2x$. The slope of the curve at $P\,(x,\,y)$ is therefore $2x$, the value of $\dfrac{\delta y}{\delta x}$ for the point.

You should try to find for yourself corresponding formulae for the slope of each of the curves $y = x^3$, $y = x^4$, $y = x^6$, and so on. If you succeed in doing this you will obtain the results set out in the table below:

Formula for curve	Formula for slope at any point
$y = x^2$	$2x$
$y = x^3$	$3x^2$
$y = x^4$	$4x^3$
$y = x^5$	$5x^4$
$y = x^6$	$6x^5$

The law of formation of the gradients of the successive curves is then plain. From x^2 we have x^1, from x^3 we have x^2, and so on. The power of x in the expression for the slope is always one less than the original power. Opposite x^n will appear x^{n-1}. The multiplier in the formula for the gradient is the same as the index of the original power. The law is: If the formula for the curve is x^n then the formula for the slope of the curve at any point on it is nx^{n-1}.

138

Referring back to our method of finding the slope of the curve $y = x^2$, we see that the slope of the chord at P is the value of the fraction $\frac{\delta y}{\delta x}$ at P. The final value of this fraction when ultimately it measures the slope of the curve at P, that is, when δx and δy have been made infinitely small, is written as $\frac{dy}{dx}$. This symbol, which is of great mathematical importance, should be regarded as a unity. It is not $d \times y$, nor should the dx be separated from the dy. This process of finding the slope when the law of the curve is known is called "differentiation." We have established a rule for differentiating x^n. Try to find the slope of $y = ax^2$, $y = ax^3$, and so on. You will soon see that the answers are the same as for the $y = x^2$, $y = x^3$ series, except that they are all multiplied by the constant a. That is, the slope of $y = ax^2$ is $2ax$, of $y = ax^3$ it is $3ax^2$, and so on.

Summing up we may say that if $y = ax^n$ then $\frac{dy}{dx}$ (slope of the tangent at any point) $= nax^{n-1}$.

Make sure you understand this by finding the slope of the curve $y = x^3$ at the points where x has the values 0, 1, 3 and -2. Then sketch the curve roughly and see whether your answers look right.

Fig. 117 shows our own attempt at finding the slope at the point where $x = +1$ on the curve $y = x^5$.

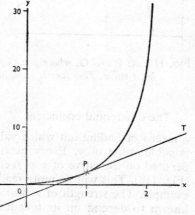

FIG. 117. *For the graph of* $y = x^5$ *the slope* $\frac{dy}{dx} = 5x^4 = 5$ *when* x *is 1. Has the curve a gradient of 5 at P?*

We have used the symbols δx and δy to denote increases in the values of x and y and have regarded the fraction $\frac{\delta y}{\delta x}$ as measuring the average gradient of the graph over the interval between x and $x + \delta x$. Another way of looking at this fraction $\frac{\delta y}{\delta x}$ would be to say that it measures the ratio of the increase in y to the increase in x, or the

139

rate at which y is increasing compared with x over the interval. For example, if $\delta x = 0\cdot1$ and $\delta y = 0\cdot6$, then the average rate of increase of y over this interval is six times as great as x. This conception of rate of change is one of the fundamental ideas of the differential calculus.

In Fig. 113 we depicted the "characteristic" of a diode valve. The characteristics of thermionic valves determine the uses to which they may be put in radio equipment, and the value $\dfrac{dV_a}{dI_a}$ is the internal resistance of the valve. If you turn to a book on radio you will see how important this application of the idea of slope or rate of change becomes. The value of $\dfrac{dy}{dx}$ indicates the rate of change of y with respect to x, not over a small interval but at a point; that is, when the interval has been infinitely diminished.

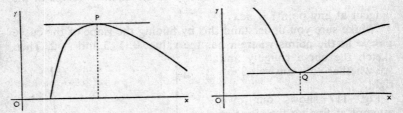

FIG. 118. *At* P *and* Q, *where the slope is zero, the curve has a greatest or least value. This fact is exploited in the beam example below.*

The differential coefficient $\dfrac{dy}{dx}$ can be very useful in providing a means of finding out which value of x gives the greatest or least possible value of y. Every maximum or minimum value of y is denoted on the curve of $y = f(x)$ by a point where the slope is zero (Fig. 118). This will be more readily appreciated by reference to an example. The strength of a beam required for a certain purpose is known to depend on its breadth and depth according to the law

$$S = kbd^2$$

where k is a constant. A tree trunk of 12 in. diameter has to be cut for the purpose. We want to know how broad and deep the beam should be made, and we shall find out without drawing the graph. The first thing to notice is that the strength law as it stands has three variables —S, b and d—and that the last two are interrelated by the fact that the sum of their squares is equal to the square of the diameter of the

140

log (Theorem of Pythagoras). So instead of d^2 we may write $(12)^2 - b^2$ and make the formula

$$S = kb(12^2 - b^2)$$
$$\text{or } S = 144kb - kb^3$$

Now when S is at its greatest value the value of $\dfrac{dS}{db}$ must be zero (that is, the slope of the curve of the formula is zero).

$$\text{If } S = 144kb - kb^3$$
$$\therefore \frac{dS}{db} = 144k - 3kb^2$$

and this is zero when $144k - 3kb^2 = 0$; that is, when $b^2 = 48$, or $b = 6\cdot9$.

This tells us that the dimensions of the strongest beam that can be cut from the log are breadth 6·9 in. and depth 9·8 in. If you think there is any simpler way of solving the problem you are invited to find it.

On page 138 we saw how to find the value of $\dfrac{dy}{dx}$ for a few simple formulae relating y to x, and thereby to dispense with graphs for trying to find the slope at a point on a curve. By building up a reference table of differential coefficients (that is, values of $\dfrac{dy}{dx}$) for many different types of function of x we could save ourselves hours of mathematical drudgery in solving problems. Below we set out a few.

y	$\dfrac{dy}{dx}$
a	0
ax^n	anx^{n-1}
$\sin(ax + b)$	$a\cos(ax + b)$
$\cos(ax + b)$	$-a\sin(ax + b)$
$\tan(ax + b)$	$a\sec^2(ax + b)$

The cost of running a dynamo is related to x, the weight of the armature, and y, the weight of everything else, by the formula $c = 10x + 3y$ and its power is given by the formula $P = axy$. What must the ratio of x to y be if the dynamo is to be run at the greatest possible power for a fixed cost?

We need to know what value of x gives $\dfrac{dP}{dx} = 0$ (that is, slope of curve is zero). If you first express y in terms of x and c and then rewrite the power formula without using y you should get this:

$$P = \frac{ax}{3}(c - 10x)$$
$$\text{or } P = \frac{acx}{3} - \frac{10ax^2}{3}.$$

Now find $\frac{dP}{dx}$ and find out the value of x that makes it zero. Do you agree with the result $x = \frac{c}{20}$? And is y then equal to $\frac{c}{6}$? If these results are correct, the armature must be three-tenths of the weight of the rest of the dynamo. Again you are challenged to find the answer by any other method.

TIME VARIABLES

So far we have not considered the time element as an aspect of change. We will do so now.

We are all familiar with the statement that if a train travels 120 miles in four hours, its average speed is 30 m.p.h. This statement does not imply that the train moves constantly at a steady 30 m.p.h. First it has to get up speed; its speed will vary on different parts of the line, and no doubt the train will stop at intermediate stations. If, however, it had travelled at a constant speed of 30 m.p.h. it would have covered the 120 miles in exactly four hours.

If a body is moving with constant velocity its motion may be represented graphically by measuring time (t) on the horizontal axis of a graph and the corresponding distance

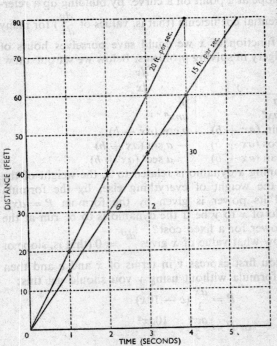

FIG. 119. *Graph of two objects moving at constant velocities along straight paths. In each case* tan θ

$$= \frac{distance\ gone}{time\ taken}$$

= velocity. Thus, the slope of the lines measures velocity.

traversed (s) vertically (Fig. 119). Thus, if an object is moving along a straight path at 15 ft. per sec., it will travel 15 ft. in 1 sec., 30 ft. in 2 sec., and the various points obtained will be in a straight line through the origin. Similarly, if the velocity is 20 ft. per sec. the various points will be on a steeper straight line. In each case the distance gone after any time divided by the interval of time will give the velocity, and this ratio is the gradient of the line $\left(\dfrac{\text{change in } s}{\text{change in } t}\right)$.

In actual experiment the velocity of an object is hardly ever uniform. If you sit in a motor-car and watch the movement of the speedometer you will realize how difficult it is even on a straight and level road for the driver to maintain constant speed.

A body cannot move over any distance in no time, so that we cannot obtain its velocity by observing its position at one single instant. To find its rate of motion we must observe the distance travelled during some interval of time near the given instant, this interval of time being the shortest possible. Hence the term velocity *at any instant* must be regarded as a statement of the average velocity during a very small interval of time including the given instant.

One of the basic problems of the differential calculus is to determine the velocity of an object at any instant if the law connecting the distance and time is known. Knowing the rule implies that the distance/time graph can be drawn and, as you will realize in a moment, we have already learnt the method of finding the velocity. Consider an object falling from rest to earth. Common sense tells us that its speed increases until it hits the ground. The law connecting the distance fallen (s) with the time (t) is $s = 16t^2$. What is the velocity at any moment? Draw the s/t graph by plotting a few points—for example, $t = 1$, $s = 16$; $t = 2$, $s = 64$; and so on (Fig. 120).

To illustrate our point we will find the velocity when t is 2 sec. After 1·5 sec. the distance fallen is 36 ft. and after 2·5 sec. it is 100 ft.

$$\text{Average velocity during the interval} = \frac{\text{distance gone}}{\text{time taken}}$$

$$= \frac{64}{1} = 64 \text{ ft./sec.}$$

$$= \text{slope of chord } PQ.$$

If now the points P and Q are taken nearer and nearer to the point M (when $t = 2$) the average velocity over a smaller interval of time will more nearly represent the velocity at the instant when t is 2 sec. You will probably see that the chord PQ finally becomes the tangent at M and that the velocity at any instant is the gradient of the tangent to the curve at the corresponding point.

The problem of finding the velocity at any instant is therefore the same problem as finding the slope of the curve with which we started this section. We have to differentiate the distance/time relationship to obtain a rule for finding the velocity. You will recall that the symbol for the slope of the tangent was $\frac{dy}{dx}$, and similarly the symbol for the velocity, which is the slope of the distance/time graph, will be $\frac{ds}{dt}$, since we have used s instead of y and t instead of x.

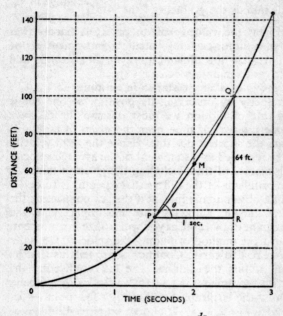

FIG. 120. *Distance/ time graph of a falling object. The slope of the curve at any point is a measure of the velocity at that instant.*

Let us apply the rule to the problem of the object falling freely. In this case $s = 16t^2$; velocity $= \frac{ds}{dt} = 32t$ (compare $y = ax^2$ for which $\frac{dy}{dx} = 2ax$). If we give a value to t, the velocity at any moment is obtained. If $t = 2$, then velocity $v = 64$ ft./sec., and this is a value we could have inferred by finding the average speed in a short interval including the desired instant, say from 1·99 to 2·01 sec. Below are set out the velocities which are obtained at various instants from the rule $v = 32t$.

After t (sec.)	velocity in ft./sec.
1	32
2	64
3	96
4	128

144

Examination of the right-hand column will reveal that the velocity is increasing by 32 ft. per sec. every second. The falling object is thus accelerating uniformly and its acceleration is 32 ft. per sec. per sec. This is the acceleration due to the force which the gravitational pull of the earth exerts on falling bodies.

We can carry our investigation of the motion a further stage by drawing the velocity/time graph (Fig. 121). This is a straight line passing through the origin and having a gradient of 32. You can discover for yourself by similar arguments to those already used that the slope of the velocity/time graph is a measure of the acceleration.

This slope can be represented by $\frac{dv}{dt}$ and if the velocity/time law is known the acceleration can be found by differentiation.

For example: $v = \frac{ds}{dt} = 32t$

Also $\frac{dv}{dt} = d\frac{(32t)}{dt} = 32.$

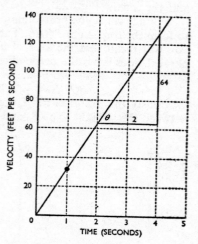

FIG. 121. *Velocity/time graph of a freely falling object. Tan θ =* $\frac{increase\ in\ velocity}{increase\ in\ time}$ = *acceleration* = *32 ft. per sec. per sec.*

Acceleration is sometimes represented by $\frac{d^2s}{dt^2}$, which means that, starting with a formula giving the distance, we differentiate twice to obtain the acceleration.

Differential calculus is concerned with rates of change. If water is running into a trough and if v cu. ft. is the volume of water delivered after any time, t hours, the rate at which the trough is filling is $\frac{dv}{dt}$ cu. ft. per hour. If the water is x ft. deep when the volume is v cu. ft., the rate at which the volume is increasing relative to the depth is $\frac{dv}{dx}$ cu. ft. per foot. The old geometers were more concerned with drawing tangents to curves and finding the areas enclosed by curves than with rate of change in natural phenomena. But these two ideas,

145

tangency and rate, are virtually two aspects of the same idea and in any study of the calculus they should be kept side by side. The calculus is one of the most powerful of mathematical tools; all we are attempting to do here is to give a brief introduction to it. There are many standard text-books on the subject which will enable you to carry your study further.

THE INTEGRAL CALCULUS

Reference was made above to finding the area enclosed by curves, which is one of the problems of the integral calculus. There are a number of ways of doing it which lead to approximate answers. As an example let us consider what area is enclosed by the curve $y = x^2$, the two ordinates (that is, verticals) at $x = 2$ and $x = 4$, and the x axis (Fig. 122).

For a first rough approximation the points P and Q can be joined to form the trapezium $PQRS$. The area of this is $\frac{1}{2} RS (PR + QS)$—you will recall that the area of a trapezium is half the sum of the parallel sides times the perpendicular distance between them.

Now $RS = 2$, $PR = 4$ and $QS = 16$;

$\therefore PQRS = \frac{1}{2} . 2(20) = 20$ sq. units.

Obviously this result is too large, since that part of the trapezium between the straight line PQ and the curve is additional to the area

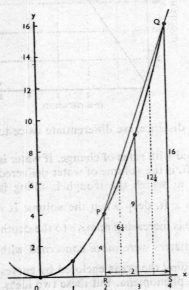

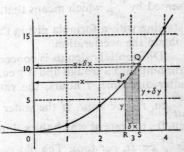

FIG. 122. *In the graph of* $y = x^2$ *on the left, the area enclosed by the curve PQ, the x axis, and the ordinates (verticals) at* x = 2 *and* x = 4, *is roughly that of the trapezium PQRS.*

FIG. 123. *The graph above is also of* $y = x^2$. *We have to find the area of the shaded strip.*

required. A better approximation would be to erect another perpendicular where $x = 3$ and $y = 9$ and regard the area as two trapezia, one with parallel sides 4 and 9 and 1 unit wide, the other with parallel sides 9 and 16 and 1 unit wide. If the area is calculated in this way you will find we have:

Area under curve = 19 sq. units.

A further improvement arises from dividing the area into four compartments and regarding each as a trapezium. According to our calculations the result this time is $18\frac{3}{4}$. Do you agree?

By successive division into smaller sections you will appreciate that a better approximation to the true result can be obtained, though the answer will never be quite exact. Can we tackle this question of finding the area in a more general way?

Let P and Q be two points in the curve $y = x^2$ (Fig. 123) and let the co-ordinates of P be x and y, and those of Q be $x + \delta x$ and $y + \delta y$. When the ordinates are drawn to P and Q the strip $PQRS$ is produced, the top of this strip being bounded by the arc PQ of the curve. If the width δx is small, the strip may be regarded as a trapezium.

$$\text{Area of the strip} = \tfrac{1}{2}(2y + \delta y). \delta x$$
$$= (y + \tfrac{1}{2}\delta y). \delta x$$

If δx is very small, then so is δy and the product of the two becomes negligible. Thus the area of the strip, or δA, $= y. \delta x$.

Now when δx is very small the number of strips is considerably increased and the area of each strip is considerably decreased, but at the same time the quantity $y. \delta x$ represents more exactly the true area of each strip. The final area A is the sum of an infinitely large number of such strips, each of which is infinitely small in area. The process of this summation is represented by the symbol $\int$ and is called "integration" (putting all the parts together).

$\int$ is really an elongated S, the first letter of the word "sum," and arises from the fact that it represents the attempt to calculate an area by finding the limit of the sum of a great number of very small areas. It is written $A = \int y dx$, which is the mathematical way of saying that the area is the sum of all the strips.

$$\text{Now } \delta A = y. \delta x$$
$$\text{or} \quad \frac{\delta A}{\delta x} = y$$

When δx is made infinitely small the fraction $\dfrac{\delta y}{\delta x}$, as we have seen pre-

147

viously, is represented by the symbol $\dfrac{dy}{dx}$ (called a differential co-efficient), that is $\dfrac{dA}{dx} = y$ in the limit when δx is infinitely small.

Therefore A, the area under the curve, is a function of x, which when differentiated with respect to x will give y. To find A we have to carry out the reverse process of differentiation. Previously A was to be found by integration, from which it would appear that integration can be regarded as the reverse of differentiation.

The statement $A = \int y dx$ now not only means that the area is the sum of all the strips but also expresses the question: "What function of x, when differentiated, will produce y?" You will recall that the rule for differentiating a power of x—say x^n—was to multiply by n and reduce the index n by 1, so that if $y = x^n$ then $\dfrac{dy}{dx} = nx^{n-1}$. Since integration is the reverse process, it will be necessary to work backwards and *add* 1 to the index n and then *divide* by the new index. The table below will make this clear.

$$y = \frac{x^2}{2} \quad \frac{dy}{dx} = \frac{2x}{2} = x \quad \therefore \int x dx = \frac{x^2}{2}$$

$$y = \frac{x^3}{3} \quad \frac{dy}{dx} = \frac{3x^2}{3} = x^2 \quad \therefore \int x^2 dx = \frac{x^3}{3}$$

$$y = \frac{x^4}{4} \quad \frac{dy}{dx} = \frac{4x^3}{4} = x^3 \quad \therefore \int x^3 dx = \frac{x^4}{4}$$

You will easily see that this leads to the rule $\int x^n dx = \dfrac{x^{n+1}}{n+1}$, and this is true unless $n = -1$ (a very special case with which it is impossible to deal here).

One point to notice is that the result of differentiating x^3, $x^3 + 5$, $x^3 - 4$, or, in short, $x^3 + c$ (where c is a constant) is in every case $3x^2$, since the differentiation of a constant is zero—that is, it has no rate of change. Hence, in integrating $x^2 dx$ we must write not $\dfrac{x^3}{3}$ but $\dfrac{x^3}{3} + c$, where c is a constant. What this constant is will depend, in particular instances, on the conditions of the problem from which it arises.

One further word before we leave our very brief introduction to this important mathematical subject. It has been shown that the area under a curve is given by $\int y dx$ and if the law of the curve is known—

148

that is, if y can be expressed as a function of x—this integral can be found and the area expressed as a function of x. This represents a general expression for the area, but before the actual value of this area can be found we have to fix its precise boundaries with respect to the axes and this can be done by fixing the initial and final ordinates. In the diagram of $y = x^2$ (Fig. 124) ordinates have been erected at $x = a$ and $x = b$ and these have determined the precise boundaries of the area and fixed the length of the base line. To evaluate this area we take the

formula $A = \int ydx$ and after the

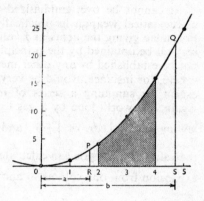

FIG. 124. *Finding the area enclosed by the curve* PQ, *the* x *axis, and the ordinates at* x = a *and* x = b. *When* y = x² *and* a = 2 *and* b = 4, *the shaded area can be determined.*

integration has been performed we substitute first the value $x = b$ and then the value $x = a$ in the resulting expression and find the difference between the two results.

Mathematically this is written $\int_a^b ydx$ and the values b and a are called the upper and lower limits of integration.

One example of this must suffice. We return to the original problem of finding the actual value of the area under the curve $y = x^2$ between the ordinates at $x = 2$ and $x = 4$. In our formula $\int_a^b ydx$ we have $y = x^2$, $a = 2$, $b = 4$.

$$\text{Hence, Area} = \int_2^4 x^2 dx$$

$$= \left[\frac{x^3}{3} + c \right]_2^4$$

$$= \left[\frac{64}{3} + c \right] - \left[\frac{8}{3} + c \right]$$

$$= \frac{56}{3}$$

$$= 18\tfrac{2}{3} \text{ sq. units.}$$

149

You will remember that when the relation connecting distance gone and time taken was known we could differentiate to find $\dfrac{ds}{dt}$, which was a measure of the velocity. Conversely, if the velocity/time law is given the distance/time law can be found by integration. By drawing appropriate diagrams you may argue for yourself that if the velocity/time graph is drawn the area contained by the curve and ordinates at two values of the time is a measure of the distance travelled in that time.

It cannot be over-emphasized that the calculus is a powerful mathematical weapon in practically every field of applied science. Formulae giving the areas and volumes of solids of various shapes may all be obtained by the principle of integration and many could not be established by any other means. The area of the surface of a sphere, for instance, would be very difficult to express in a formula except by summing a series of infinitely narrow circular bands. Again, the work done by a gas expanding in accordance with the law $pv = C$ is $\int p\,dv$, or $\int \dfrac{C}{v}dv$; and if you know how to work out the value of $\int \dfrac{C}{v}dv$ you can calculate the amount of work done in an expansion from one volume to another.

How Old is She?

To baffle your lady friend and find out her age and birthday, ask her to perform the following arithmetical operations:

(a) Multiply by 100 the number of the month in which she was born.
(b) Add the day of the month in which she was born.
(c) Multiply by 2.
(d) Add 8.
(e) Multiply by 5.
(f) Add 4.
(g) Multiply by 10.
(h) Add 4.
(i) Add her age.

Now ask her to tell you the result. From the number announced you subtract 444, then group the digits in the remainder in twos, starting from the right. The first pair of digits will give her age, the second two the day of the month in which she was born, and the last one or two the month.

3

What the Rest of the Book is About

SO FAR we have been thinking about the nature of mathematics and reviewing the basic ideas and processes from which the subject may be developed. For the sake of tidiness we have recognized the traditional division into arithmetic, algebra and geometry. We have seen, however, that in many mathematical situations these three all have a part to play. Geometry, which deals with form and shape, or "spacial relationships," continually employs arithmetic and algebra. Trigonometry is a special kind of mathematics which employs all three. For almost every practical problem outside the bounds of simple trading calculations the mathematical analysis and solution employs algebra and geometry as well as arithmetic. For example, a ball rolling down a hill, a cam-shaft for causing precise movements in a machine, a gadget for opening tins of food (Fig. 1) and an optical instrument such as a telescope each present problems in which algebra and geometry are inseparable.

The remainder of the book is therefore planned in topics which though not essentially mathematical are of mathematical interest. In text-books it is conventional to decorate a mathematical theme with problems and examples from everyday life, industry and science. This is not a text-book. Here the pattern is reversed. We shall look into a variety of topics for mathematical ideas. Thus, instead of discussing our old friends "quadratic equations" and setting a number of "exercises" and "problems" on them we may find ourselves returning to them from time to time in the course of the remaining chapters.

In other words, the remainder of the book has no consecutive order. After this one, the chapters are independent of one another, so the reader should feel at liberty to take them in any order he pleases.

In this chapter we shall consider a few more skills which may be of help later on and then we shall examine carefully some practical problems upon which mathematics throws light.

151

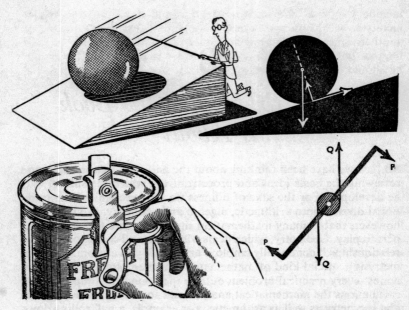

FIG. 1 *The forces at work on the ball (weight, upthrust of floor, friction) are closely allied to the sides of the little triangle which has its vertex at the centre of the sphere, and that is similar to the large triangle. In the case of the tin-opener, the comparatively small forces exerted by the fingers (PP) overcome immense forces (QQ) which oppose the cutting.*

When as infants we first learned to walk vertically we felt mightily pleased with the sensation and perhaps also we experienced the joy of achievement. Later on, whilst still occasionally enjoying walking for its own sake, more often than not we walk as a means to an end. In the course of a contest a champion billiards player will use a great variety of skills with the greatest of ease; intuitively, it seems to the onlooker, he makes the right shot in the best manner, and appears to take it for granted that the balls will come to rest where he is more or less waiting, cue poised, for the next shot. What appears to happen by intuition is the result of many hours of study and practice.

So it is with mathematics. One may become so habituated to certain basic processes, to tricks of procedure, that they are selected and brought into action almost automatically when a big job is under consideration. In this book we do not seek to train people to become proficient mathematicians. If that were our aim the book would include hundreds of exercises which would impart to the reader facility as well as understanding in applying theorems of one kind or another. Since there is any number of text-books that may be used for that purpose, we leave it to the reader to decide whether or not he should practise. A few tricks may be recalled before going on.

USEFUL SHORT CUTS

First, number. It is useful to know the rules of divisibility well. If you can tell at a glance that 1,764 is divisible by 4 and 9, you will also establish quickly in your mind that 147 is also a factor—because it is what you get when you divide 1,764 by 12 (4 × 3)—and thence that 7 is another factor. In no time $2^2 \times 3^2 \times 7^2$ is obtained for the statement of the same number in terms of its prime factors.

The tests of divisibility by 2, 4, and 8 are generally well known. If the number formed by the last two digits is divisible by 4 the whole number is divisible by 4—because the remaining portion is a number of hundreds, each of which is a multiple of 4. Likewise, since one thousand is a multiple of 8, all we have to do to find out if a number is divisible by 8 is to see if the portion formed by the last three figures is so divisible (Fig. 2).

The tests for divisibility by 3 and 9 are interesting. Let a, b, c and d be the digits of a number. We cannot, of course, call the number $abcd$ because that would be read as the product of a, b, c and d. a is the digit denoting thousands, b hundreds, c tens, and d units, so the value of our number is:

$$1,000\,a + 100\,b + 10\,c + d$$

Now if we take away from this $a + b + c + d$, we have left

$$999\,a + 99\,b + 9\,c$$

which is always divisible by 3 and 9 regardless of a, b and c. So if $a + b + c + d$ is divisible by 3 or 9, so also is the number

$$1,000\,a + 100\,b + 10\,c + d,$$

or, for that matter, $1,000\,b + 100\,d + 10\,a + c$ (Fig. 3).

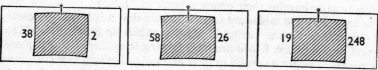

FIG. 2. *Because every* 10 = 5 × 2, *the last digit is sufficient to show that the first number is divisible by* 2, *no matter what is concealed by the cover. Every* 100 = 25 × 4, *so the last two digits show that the second number is not divisible by* 4. *Every* 1,000 = 125 × 8, *so the last three digits alone show that the third number is divisible by* 8.

Divisibility by 6 or 12 depends on divisibility by 2, 3 and 4. The awkward squad are 7 and 11: there are no *easy* tests of divisibility by either of them. The usual test for 11 is to see if the separate sums of alternate digits are equal. For example, 153,582 is divisible by 11 because $1 + 3 + 8 = 5 + 5 + 2$. You will find it interesting to discover the explanation of this test. The secret lies in the following:

$$10 = 11 - 1$$
$$100 = (9 \times 11) + 1$$
$$1,000 = (91 \times 11) - 1$$
$$10,000 = (909 \times 11) + 1, \text{ and so on.}$$

Can you see how this leads to the test of divisibility by 11?

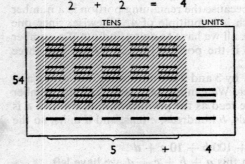

FIG. 3. *Looking at the upper figure we see that if the sum of the digits is not divisible by 3 the number itself cannot be. The lower figure shows that if the sum of the digits is divisible by 9, so is the number.*

Although calculation may be shortened by the use of tricks of various kinds—such as cancelling—it would often become tedious but for the fact that we can consult others who have already had to work out the same sum or whose reference tables set out the answers to all the possible sums of a particular kind. Mathematicians, like everyone else, prefer the quickest route to their destination and so they usually have at their elbow a book of "tables."

Some of these tables are so well known that it is hardly necessary to write them down. The multiplication tables up to 12 times 12, for example. However, if you are often having to multiply together ugly numbers, it might be useful to have at hand tables in which you could quickly find the number in row 1,625, column 5,726, which would be the answer to 1,625 times 5,726. Such tables could easily be made, although in fact the nearest approach to them is the shopkeeper's and clerk's ready-reckoner, which gives the answers to quantities at given prices, like 307 at 5s. 2¾d. or 3 ton 6 cwt. at £3 7s. 8d. per ton.

154

Other tables which could easily be compiled and used, and which in fact *are* often included in "books of mathematical tables," are reciprocals of numbers (for example, $\frac{1}{27}$ and $\frac{1}{53}$, the reciprocals of 27 and 53, are given in decimal form by the table as 0·0370 and 0·0189) and the squares, cubes, square-roots and cube-roots of numbers.

By means of these tables we may obtain such results as $(3\cdot1)^2 = 9\cdot61$, $(18)^3 = 5,832$ and—much more difficult to work out for oneself—$\sqrt{\pi} = 1\cdot77$ and $\sqrt[3]{6} = 1\cdot82$, without any effort.

No directions for the use of these tables are given in this book because a little practice with the tables themselves will usually suffice to give one the necessary facility in using them. The reader is reminded, however, that he should look intelligently at the answer given by the tables to make sure that his fingers and eyes have not wandered over the wrong page of the tables or the wrong lines in the right tables. A moment's thought should be sufficient to reject $\sqrt[3]{23} = 15\cdot16$ as incorrect.

One should also be on one's guard against viewing the tables as being one hundred per cent accurate: there is always some degree of approximation in the last figure. The mathematician usually looks with a measure of mistrust at the last figure on the right as, for instance, when he absent-mindedly uses tables or slide-rule to give him the answer to 2×3 and says to himself "2 times 3; here we are, 5·999; call it 6!"

HOW LOG TABLES HELP

Tables which call for special comment are those giving logarithms and the trigonometrical functions (series, cosines, tangents, and so on, of angles). These are indispensable aids. By means of logarithm tables we can obtain answers provided by all of the tables previously mentioned, and for that reason people who frequently have to perform calculations of all kinds, rather than of one or two specialized kinds, will cheerfully do without all the other tables.

Logarithms exploit the idea embodied in the following statements:

$$a^n \times a^m = a^{n+m}$$
$$a^p \div a^q = a^{p-q}$$

and by means of them processes of multiplication and division may be transferred into the much simpler processes of addition and subtraction respectively.

To work out X times Y, where X and Y may be evil-looking numbers, we use the tables of logarithms to change X into a^x and Y into a^y, the product of which is a^{x+y}, and then we find in the tables which number R (the answer to our calculation) may be represented as a^{x+y}. The values x, y and $x+y$ are called the logarithms of X, Y and R respectively, and a is called the "base" of these logarithms. In "common logarithms," the ones we all use as a labour-saving device, the base is 10.

Ordinary logarithm tables give four-figure logarithms for four-figure (or less) numbers. For more accurate calculation one may use a book of seven-figure logarithms. For less accurate work three-figure logarithms (Fig. 4) may be used.

The beauty of common logarithms—that is, to the base of 10—is that although the four-figure tables give us the logarithms only of numbers between $1 \cdot 000$ and $9 \cdot 999$ we may use the same simple tables for dealing with numbers of *any* size.

Suppose we want the logarithm of 3,427. Although the best the tables can do for us is to show us that $\log 3 \cdot 427 = 0 \cdot 5349$, that suits us nicely, for

$$3,427 = 1,000 \times 3 \cdot 427$$

and, therefore, $\log 3,427 = \log (10)^3 + \log 3 \cdot 427$.

The logarithm of 10 to the base 10 is the crux of the matter:

$$\log 10 = 1, \text{ because } 10 = 10^1.$$

So $\log (10)^3 = \log 10 + \log 10 + \log 10$
$$= 3 \log 10$$
$$= 3$$

If people understood that $10 = 10^1$ and therefore that the common logarithm of 10^n is n they would not get into a tangle in dealing with "characteristics" and "mantissae."

Returning to our example:

$$\log 3,427 = \log (10)^3 + \log 3 \cdot 427$$
$$= 3 + 0 \cdot 5349$$
$$= 3 \cdot 5349$$

The fractional part, $0 \cdot 5349$, given by the tables is called the "mantissa" of the logarithm, whilst the whole-number part, 3, which we must think out for ourselves, is called the "characteristic" of the logarithm.

In a similar manner we may find the logarithm of $0 \cdot 073$.
The tables give us $\log 7 \cdot 3 = 0 \cdot 8633$

Now $0 \cdot 073$ $\qquad = \dfrac{7 \cdot 3}{100}$

Therefore $\log 0 \cdot 073$ $\quad = \log 7 \cdot 3 - \log (10)^2$
$\qquad\qquad\qquad\quad = 0 \cdot 8633 - 2.$

Since the log tables contain only positive numbers we save ourselves a lot of work by expressing this result as

$$\log 0 \cdot 073 = \overline{2} \cdot 8633$$

in which we have a sort of half-breed number with a minus part (the characteristic) and an ordinary positive part (the mantissa).

156

	0	1	2	3	4	5	6	7	8	9	1	2	3	4	5	6	7	8	9
1	000	041	079	114	146	176	204	230	255	279	3	6	9	12	14	17	20	23	25
2	301	322	342	361	380	398	415	431	447	462	2	3	5	7	8	10	12	13	15
3	477	491	505	519	532	544	556	568	580	591	1	3	4	5	6	7	9	10	11
4	602	613	623	634	644	653	663	672	686	690	1	2	3	4	5	6	7	8	9
5	699	708	716	724	732	740	748	756	763	771	1	2	2	3	4	5	5	6	7
6	778	785	792	799	806	813	820	826	833	839	1	1	2	3	3	4	5	5	6
7	845	851	857	863	869	875	881	887	892	898	1	1	2	2	3	3	4	5	5
8	903	909	914	919	924	929	935	940	945	949	1	1	2	2	3	3	4	5	5
9	954	959	964	969	973	978	982	987	991	996	0	1	1	2	2	3	3	4	4

FIG. 4. *This is all there is to three-figure logarithm tables. So little!*

It may be helpful to use these two results to get the answer, using logarithms, to

$$\frac{3,427}{\sqrt[3]{0 \cdot 073}} \text{ or } 3,427 \div (0 \cdot 073)^{\frac{1}{3}}.$$

We have log 3,427 $- \frac{1}{3}$ log 0·073 = 3·5349 $- \frac{1}{3}$ ($\overline{2}$·8633).

The division by 3 looks nasty. Here a simple trick comes in useful. We make the $\overline{2}$ into a $\overline{3}$ and at the same time put a $+ 1$ with the mantissa: the $\overline{2}$·8633 is then unchanged but in a more convenient form for division by 3. $\frac{1}{3}(\overline{2}$·8633) = $\overline{1}$·6211.

Therefore log 3,427 $- \frac{1}{3}$ log (0·073) = 3·5349 $- \overline{1}$·6211.

We start subtraction from the right cheerfully enough and get the mantissa 0·9138 with a "borrowed" 1 to account for. "Paying back" the borrowed 1 to the $\overline{1}$ gives 0 for subtraction from 3. So the characteristic is 3, and the answer to the subtraction is 3·9138.

What number has a logarithm of 3·9138?

The tables show us that 8·200 has a logarithm of 0·9138.

The characteristic 3 indicates that we need a number 1,000 times as great, that is, 8,200.

Satisfy yourself that this is a reasonable answer by looking at the original $\frac{3,427}{\sqrt[3]{0 \cdot 073}}$. Is it?

If you wish to give yourself practice in the use of logarithms you can set yourself some or find questions in a text-book. We have devoted a little space to this explanation because negative characteristics are often misunderstood. If you think we have been too wordy, try working out the sum by ordinary arithmetic. It may have taken a few lines to explain, but the normal working would appear like this:

$\frac{3,427}{\sqrt[3]{0 \cdot 073}}$	3·5349
= 8,200 (to 3 significant figures)	$\overline{1}$·6211 $\quad \frac{1}{3}$ ($\overline{2}$·8633)
	3·9138

157

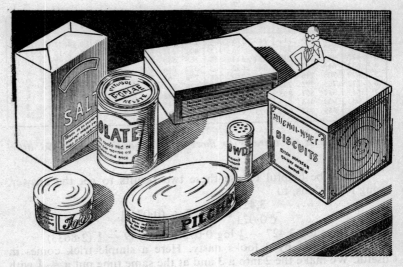

WHAT GOVERNS THE SHAPE OF A CONTAINER?

We shall now turn to some examples of the use of mathematics.

If you look along the shelves of a grocery shop, or of the pantry at home, you will find containers of various sizes and colours. You may notice that their shapes fall mainly into two classes: the brick-shaped and the cylindrical. Among the former there will be a pre-ponderance of boxes with square bases. Is this sheer chance or is there some economic explanation? It is reasonable to suppose that the manufacturer will want to make the best possible use of the material he has to buy for making the boxes. (Fig. 5.)

Mathematically, he can approach the box-making in this way. For a given area of cardboard, what height of box (square-based) produces the greatest capacity? We may disregard the overlaps at the joints because they will be required for any shape and will not seriously influence the shape.

$$S = 2b^2 + 4bh$$

is the formula relating S, the total area, to b, the length of edge of the base, and h, the height of the box.

$$V = b^2h$$

is the formula for its volume V (that is, capacity).

These two formulae may be regarded for our purpose as equations in which S is constant, while b, h and V are variables, or "unknowns."

There are two equations and three variables. It should be possible to reduce them to one equation with two variables.

We need an equation relating V to S. This can be obtained by expressing b in terms of S and h, or h in terms of b and S and then re-writing. Which is the more attractive method? Do you agree with the following?

$$V = b^2 \frac{(S - 2b^2)}{4b}.$$

We now want to know (Fig. 6) what value b has when V is at its greatest. There are two ways of proceeding. One would be to draw a graph showing V on one axis and b on the other end and pick out the point on the curve where V is greatest. This is a tedious job and, furthermore, is inaccurate because it depends on measurements and eye-judgments. The other method is to use the calculus; this method runs as follows:

$$V = b^2 \frac{(S - 2b^2)}{4b} = \frac{bS}{4} - \frac{b^3}{2}$$
$$\therefore \frac{dV}{db} = \frac{S}{4} - \frac{3b^2}{2}.$$

This expression shows the rate of increase of V with respect to b: when this rate of increase is zero, V has its greatest or least value, and we can find the value of b for that condition by solving the equation

$$\frac{S}{4} - \frac{3b^2}{2} = 0.$$

We have $b^2 = \frac{S}{6}$ $\quad \therefore b = \pm \sqrt{\frac{S}{6}}$ or $\pm \frac{1}{6} \sqrt{6S}$.

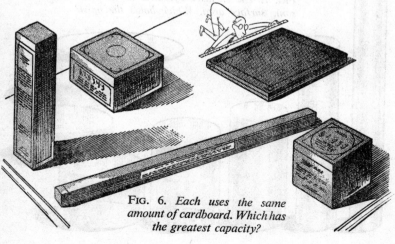

Fig. 6. *Each uses the same amount of cardboard. Which has the greatest capacity?*

Again, since $-b$ has no practical significance—for your manufacturer is not interested in negative measurements—we have the practical result:

The greatest volume is obtained when b is $\sqrt{\dfrac{S}{6}}$. At the same time

$$h = \frac{S - 2b^2}{4b} = \frac{S - \dfrac{S}{3}}{\dfrac{S}{4\sqrt{6}}} = \frac{2}{3} \times \frac{\sqrt{6S}}{\cancel{2}} = \sqrt{\frac{S}{6}}$$

In other words, the height and the side of the base are both the same length. And if S is one unit (say a square foot or 144 square inches)

$$h = b = \sqrt{\frac{1}{6}} \quad \text{(say } \sqrt{24} \text{ square inches, which is approximately 4·9 inches).}$$

A cube then is the most economical brick-shaped box.

By a similar approach we may find the most economical cylindrical-shaped closed box or tin (Fig. 7).

$$S = 2\pi r^2 + 2\pi rh$$
$$\text{and } V = \pi r^2 h$$

Which shall we eliminate, r or h? Do you agree with this equation:

$$V = \frac{Sr}{2} - \pi r^3.$$

From it you will find that when $\dfrac{dv}{dr} = 0$, the value of r is $\sqrt{\dfrac{S}{6\pi}}$.

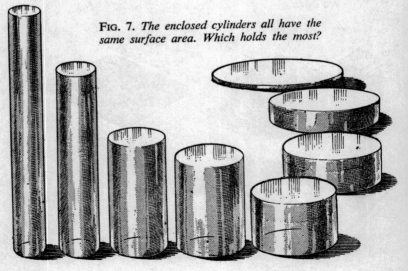

FIG. 7. *The enclosed cylinders all have the same surface area. Which holds the most?*

And if r has that value, then

$$h = \frac{1}{2\pi\sqrt{\dfrac{S}{6\pi}}} \cdot \left\{ S - 2\pi\frac{S}{\underset{3}{6\pi}} \right\} = \sqrt{\frac{2S}{3\pi}}$$

These two results are very awkward-looking quantities and it might be much simpler to compare them with each other like this:

$$\frac{r}{h} = \sqrt{\frac{S}{6\pi}} \times \sqrt{\frac{3\pi}{2S}} = \frac{1}{2}.$$

In other words, h must be twice as great as r to give a closed cylindrical box the greatest volume for a given area of material. It would be a good idea to see if any of the cylindrical tins on the grocery shelf bear out this conclusion. The height should be equal to the diameter.

You need not be surprised to find that some of the containers do not satisfy this condition. We have assumed that the materials are the same throughout, whereas in reality the sides may be of cardboard and the top and bottom of tinplate. Because cardboard is cheaper than tinplate the height is usually greater than the diameter when both materials are used.

These two results are not perhaps spectacular: one might have anticipated them. Do you think the same relation of length to diameter would be found for the open tube giving the greatest capacity for a given area of material? Find formulae for S and V as before and see what you get for $\dfrac{dV}{dr}$ or for $\dfrac{dV}{dl}$. Something inconclusive? Why?

You have the answer without considering $\dfrac{dV}{dr}$ or $\dfrac{dV}{dl}$; the equation $V = \dfrac{rS}{2}$ gives it to you.

While S is constant, V gets bigger as r gets bigger—indefinitely! And the alternative equation $V = \dfrac{S^2}{4\pi l}$ confirms it, for this says clearly that V gets bigger as l gets smaller.

There is no greatest possible value of V, because v can be as great as your tools will permit you to make it.

MAKING THE MOST OF A PERIMETER

What is the biggest area that can be enclosed by a given length of fencing and what shape has the enclosure? (Fig. 8).

The shapes from which we may choose are legion—triangles, rectangles, polyhedra, regular or irregular, and the circle. We may first find out whether the regular figure in each case—that is,

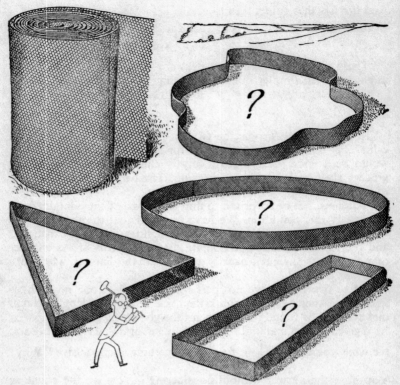

FIG. 8. *With a given length of wire netting, what is the greatest amount of land that can be enclosed? A piece that is circular, triangular—or what?*

equilateral triangle, square, regular pentagon, and so on—is the most economical shape of its own kind.

Take the triangle first. We will see if we can prove that with a given base and perimeter there is an ideal shape. Let the perimeter be $2p$ and the base be c, then the other two sides are x and $2p-c-x$ (Fig. 9).

The equation for the area is obtained from the general formula

$$A = \sqrt{p(p-a)(p-b)(p-c)}$$

and we have
$$A^2 = p(p-x)(p-\overline{2p-c-x})(p-c)$$
$$= p(p-c)(p-x)(c-\overline{p-x}).$$

Note that we are using A^2 instead of A for convenience—to avoid the use of $\sqrt{\ }$. It is quite proper to do so, because the biggest value of A^2 will belong to the biggest value of A. To make the expression easier to handle we may put K (a constant number) for $p(p - c)$.

Then $A^2 = Kc(p - x) - K(p - x)^2$

and we can find when this is at a maximum by differentiation.

$$\frac{d(A^2)}{dx} = - Kc + 2K(p - x).$$

What is the value of x when $\dfrac{d(A^2)}{dx} = 0$?

$$- Kc + 2K(p - x) = 0$$
$$\therefore 2(p - x) = c$$

$$\therefore x = p - \frac{c}{2}$$

x was one of the two remaining sides: the other is $2p - c - x$, which is, therefore, $2p - c - p + \dfrac{c}{2}$, that is, $p - \dfrac{c}{2}$ again. The triangle with a given base and a given perimeter which encloses the greatest area is therefore isosceles.

By a similar argument you may find out which triangle of given perimeter has the greatest area. Let the perimeter be $2p$, each of the equal sides a, and the base, therefore, $2(p - a)$. You will not be surprised perhaps to discover that the equilateral triangle gives the greatest area for a given perimeter.

The rectangle presents an easier argument. If its perimeter is $2p$ and one side is l, the other side is $p - l$. Then

$$A = l(p - l)$$
$$\text{and } \frac{dA}{dl} = p - 2l.$$

When $\dfrac{dA}{dl} = 0$, $p = 2l$, or $l = \dfrac{p}{2}$.

This shows what we might have expected, that the square is the greatest rectangle of given perimeter.

We may now compare the areas of the equilateral triangle and the square each of the same perimeter $12p$. (Can you guess why we prefer $12p$ to any other expression for the perimeter? If not, you will see as the argument proceeds.)

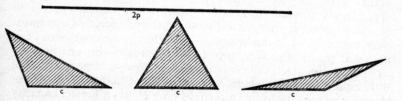

Fig. 9. *With a perimeter* 2p, *what triangle of base* c *has the largest area?*

163

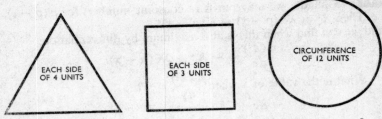

FIG. 10. *Each perfect of its kind, which contains the greatest area?*

Equilateral triangle of perimeter $12p$ has area A_T, where

$$A_T = \frac{1}{2} \cdot 4p \cdot \frac{4p\sqrt{3}}{2} = 4\sqrt{3} \cdot p^2$$

Square of perimeter $12p$ has area A_s, where
$$A_s = (3p)^2 = 9p^2$$

Which is the greater? And how does each compare with the circle of the same perimeter—that is, a circle with a circumference of $12p$ (Fig. 10).

If the area of the circle is A_c

$$A_c = \frac{(12p)^2}{4\pi} = \frac{\overset{36}{\cancel{144}}p^2}{\cancel{4}\pi} = \frac{36p^2}{\pi}$$

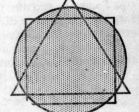

FIG. 11. *Superimposing the three figures, we see that the circle has the greatest area.*

How does this compare with the square and the triangle? If we may disregard all the other regular polygons (which are progressively closer approximations to the circle the more sides they have) it may be stated that the circle encloses the maximum area for a given perimeter (Fig. 11).

The conclusions we have reached in this chapter are all laws of nature which may be regarded as useful knowledge. Although the arguments which led to them are purely mathematical—that is to say, they proceeded theoretically, and bits and pieces of apparatus were not required in the business—nevertheless the conclusions can be tested practically. With pencil and squared paper, one may try to find a shape which will contain a greater area—a larger number of little squares—than a circle. Or, using boxes and tins of various shapes, one may try to find a container which has a greater capacity than a cube or a cylinder of height equal to its diameter.

4

The Mathematics of Travel

THE foundations of our civilization rest, as much as on anything else, on travel. The man who stays at home becomes narrow; he knows little of the world's resources or of other people; he may think that the earth is flat, or that the sun moves round the earth, for how else can he check his opinions except by travelling?

The food of the world depends on travel and transport; commerce would be nothing without it; warfare, which a few may still regard as a civilizing influence, has only achieved its present state by steady progress in the means of travel. There is hardly an action or an incident in the daily life of the individual which is not affected in some important way by movement and communication.

There may have been a time when this meant no more than getting up and walking, without any plan or certainty. Today this will not do. Even the shortest, most carefree, walk depends on much mathematical knowledge.

Let us consider two journeys, one short and the other longer, in order to see what is involved. First, the daily journey to work by a man who lives in the suburbs and works in the City. He must know the position of home and work, in relation to each other, the general direction, the distance between them, the speed of the train, his own speed, the time of the train and the cost of the journey.

Most of this information will already have been worked out and provided for him, in the form of maps, time-tables and fare tables. If there are alternative routes he may have to do a little calculation himself. Suppose, for example, that he lives midway between two stations. He will find out how long it takes him to walk to each station, and thereby make up a new time-table for himself.

If the time-table reads Northway 8.31 a.m., Southway 8.34 a.m., and it takes him 5 minutes to walk to Northway, but 10 minutes to Southway, then he will know that up to a certain time he may go to either station, but after that he has two minutes' grace, in which he can catch the train by going to Northway and paying the extra fare. His own time-table, therefore, reads Northway 8.26 a.m., Southway 8.24 a.m. Do you agree with these times?

Now let us consider a journey by air from London to Bombay. Although the details are quite different, and the scale of operations is much larger, the ingredients are the same; distance, direction, map-making and map-reading, measurement of time and speed, and cost, are all involved. These are the topics we shall deal with in this chapter; we shall try to show how much our travels, both short and long, depend on them.

POSITION FIXING

Before we can consider distance and direction, we must see how position is fixed, especially on a map. Standing on a particular spot, we wish to mark a sheet of paper (which is to become a map) in such a way that other people may find the same place.

This is frequently done when one person wishes to give directions to another for finding his destination. He may say, as he draws, "Here is the main road from X to Y and here are the traffic lights at A. If you go on for about half a mile, you will see a large new pub on the left, called *The Unicorn*. Take the next turning to the left, about here, and then the second on the right, here. That brings you to the front entrance of Z, here."

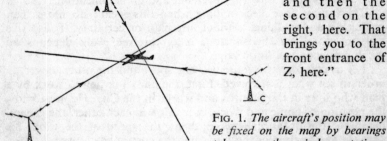

FIG. 1. *The aircraft's position may be fixed on the map by bearings taken on the wireless stations.*

If the map were already drawn, we should perhaps have some landmarks to help us. Fig. 1 shows how an airman has fixed his approximate position by finding the "bearings" of three wireless stations. If his measurements were exact and the aircraft perfectly still while he took his readings, the three straight lines would be concurrent (that is, they would pass through a point). It is sufficient for his purposes, however, to know that he was, at the time of sighting, within the triangle shown. He has other and better methods of fixing his position, but we will discuss those later.

Fig. 2 shows how a walker who is lost, and has no compass, has found his position on the map by identifying three or four landmarks and setting the map accordingly.

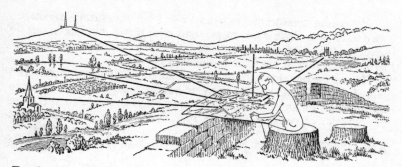

FIG. 2. *Where am I exactly? Setting his map by a few recognizable landmarks around him, the walker is able to determine his own position.*

Our problem, however, goes farther back than this, for the landmarks themselves must first have been fixed, some of them on a blank sheet. What information was needed to fix them? Two guiding lines, known as the axes of reference, and two measurements of distance are sufficient.

Fig. 3 shows how this might be done. The axes of reference are two straight lines, at right-angles to one another, drawn to pass through a point at Land's End. The lines need not be at right-angles, but are usually taken so for convenience.

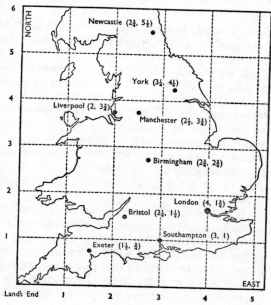

FIG. 3. *The positions of the towns have been marked on the blank map by using the co-ordinates shown, the first figure in each case being the easterly measurement. The axes point due east and north.*

167

By taking measurements from these axes, measuring parallel to each axis as in drawing a graph, and adopting a suitable scale, we may fix the relative positions of various towns on our sheet of paper according to the figures shown in brackets.

These measurements are all in units of half an inch (each representing 60 miles), but they might just as well have been in centimetres, or any other unit, without altering the general picture or the relative positions. Notice that the scales in both directions

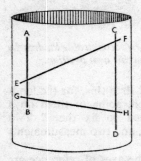 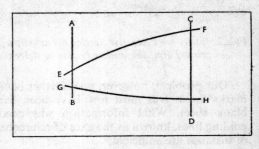

FIG. 4. *If you try to draw straight lines on the surface of a cylinder, you will find when you unroll it that only some of the lines are straight.*

are the same, as otherwise there would be distortion and distances measured in other directions than parallel to the axes would be incorrect.

If we wished to build up a relief map on our sheet of paper, we should, of course, need a third measurement, the height above sea-level, perpendicular to the face of the paper. For vertical measurements a different scale, much *larger* than the others, would be essential, if we wished to see anything, because the heights are so small in comparison with ground distances. We should need to remember that, whilst horizontal measurements on the paper would still be accurate in any direction, once off the paper they would only be so when taken vertically, because of the different scales employed.

In drawing this diagram we have made a serious assumption which may have an important effect on scale. Our paper is flat, but the earth is round. We live on a body which is almost a sphere, of radius a little less than 4,000 miles and circumference about 25,000 miles. We have assumed that this curvature makes no difference.

For maps of small areas the difference is trifling and may be disregarded. As our maps begin to take in larger areas, however, the importance of this difference increases. We shall see later, when we consider map-making, that the first problem is that of representing a curved surface on a flat paper. Our immediate problem, however, is that of the straight line. For there are no straight lines on a spherical surface, though there may be on other curved surfaces, as, for example, the cylinder shown in Fig. 4. This means that, in order to mark position on the earth's surface, we must use curved lines for our axes of reference.

If we make a clean, flat slice across a sphere, or, to express it mathematically, if we intersect a sphere by a plane surface, the section will always be a circle. You can see this if you make a sharp cut, in any direction, across an apple, which is nearly spherical. No matter what the direction of the cut, if it goes clean through you will see, when you take the two pieces apart, a complete circle. What is more important, as we are not concerned with the interior of the earth, if you put the apple together again, you will see that you have drawn a full circle on the outside of the apple.

The position of the cut, although it does not alter the shape, does affect the size of the circle; but the largest possible circle is always obtained by cutting clean through the centre.

This circle has exactly the same radius as the sphere itself, and is called a *great circle*. Through *any* two surface points we can always make a great circle. Every sphere has many great circles and all will have this in common: their radii will be the same as that of the sphere itself.

HOW LONGITUDE AND LATITUDE ARE FIXED

Two such circles on the surface of the earth are chosen to be our axes of reference. The first is fixed partly by the two points, known as the *poles*, about which the earth spins. As they are at opposite ends of the same diameter, all circles passing through them will be great circles, so that a third point is needed to fix the particular circle we are using. The particular point chosen lies in the Royal Observatory at Greenwich, a south-eastern suburb of London.

÷ × ÷ × ÷ × ÷ × ÷ × ÷ × ÷ × ÷ × ÷ × ÷ × ÷ × ÷ × ÷ × ÷ × ÷ × ÷ × ÷ × ÷ ×

Crossing the River

Two sportsmen and their two sons have to cross a river in their portable boat, which will carry only 200 pounds at a time. Each of the men weighs 200 pounds and each of the boys weighs half as much. How do they all manage to get across?

Solution on page 444

÷ × ÷ × ÷ × ÷ × ÷ × ÷ × ÷ × ÷ × ÷ × ÷ × ÷ × ÷ × ÷ × ÷ × ÷ × ÷ × ÷ × ÷ ×

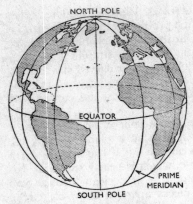

FIG. 5. *The prime meridian is the basis for measurements of longitude, the equator for those of latitude.*

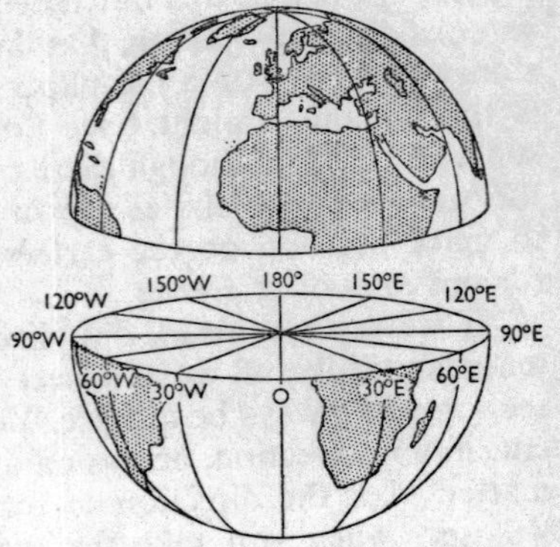

FIG. 6. *Measurements of longitude are expressed according to the angles they form with the earth's axis.*

The great circle on the earth's surface which passes through the two poles and Greenwich is our first axis of reference. The half of it between the poles which includes Greenwich is called the *prime meridian*. All measurements of *longitude* are taken from this circle, its own longitude, or rather, that of all points on it, being 0 degrees. The actual line at Greenwich, through which the prime meridian passes, is marked by a narrow strip of concrete in the grounds. More recently, the Royal Observatory has been moved to Herstmonceux, in Sussex, but the meridian marking is still to be seen at Greenwich.

The second axis of reference is another great circle, known as the equator. It is in a plane at right-angles to the diameter joining the two poles and exactly midway between them (Fig. 5). All measurements of *latitude* are taken from this line. Its own latitude, or that of all points on it, is 0 degrees. Of course, neither of these circles is marked on the earth; they exist only in the imagination and on maps. This accounts for the famous schoolboy howler, which described the equator as "a menagerie lion running round the middle of the earth."

Owing to the curvature of the earth, difficulties arise in measuring from these axes. Two different methods are used to overcome them, one for latitude and another for longitude. In both cases the basis of measurement is not a length, but an angle; but the sub-divisions are different, great circles being used for longitude and small circles for latitude.

170

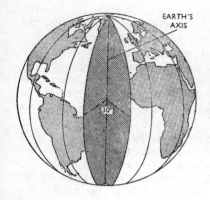

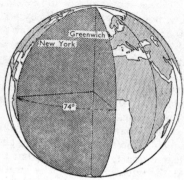

FIG. 7. A "slice" taken out of the
earth, as above, illustrates the meaning of 30 degrees of longitude.

FIG. 8. A larger "slice" like this
gives us the longitude of New York
in relation to the prime meridian.

Suppose we could cut the earth in halves at the equator and
look inside. Shutting our eyes to geological considerations (and the
extreme heat) we should see a large circle, whose centre was the
centre of the earth. If we could draw radii from this centre, they
would strike the surface at points on the equator. For example, if
the radii were drawn so as to make angles of 30 deg. with each other,
as in Fig. 6, they would end on the surface at points rather more
than 2,000 miles apart, since 30 deg. is one-twelfth of the whole
angle of 360 deg.

By joining these points to the poles we could make a set of
great circles, or meridians, just like the prime meridian described
above. If we arranged the radii so that one of them cut the prime
meridian, or 0° longitude, the others, going eastwards, would be
called 30° E., 60° E., 90° E., and so on to 180°. In the same way,
going westwards, we should have 30, 60, 90° W., and so on to 180°.
The 180 line would be neither E. nor W., for it would be the same
line for both.

Fig. 7 shows how the earth could be marked off by *meridians*, or
great circles between the poles. Each meridian is described by an
angle, the angle which its plane makes with that of the Greenwich
meridian, east or west, according to which side it lies. Thus, when
we say that New York has a longitude of 74° W., we mean that
the plane of the meridian through New York makes an angle of
74 deg. with the plane of the prime meridian, and lies to the west of it
(Fig. 8).

171

These meridians of longitude enable us to describe the position of a point east or west. They will have to be much closer than the 30 deg. apart which we used for the example above; for we saw that, on the equator, they were spaced out at intervals of over 2,000 miles, which would not be of very much help in locating a place or a ship. On our maps, and in our minds, we must have intervals of one degree; and for closer work we shall need smaller units, the *minute*, or sixtieth part of a degree, and the *second*, or sixtieth part of a minute.

How many miles apart are the meridians? If you look at Fig. 9, which represents, to an exaggerated scale, two meridians one degree apart, you will see that there is no answer to this question. At the equator, where it is largest, the distance represented by one degree of longitude is $\frac{1}{360}$ of the circumference of the earth, or a little less than 70 miles. At the poles the distance is nothing.

You will see that describing a position east or west is not enough

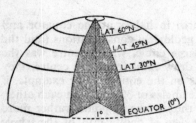 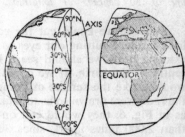

FIG. 9. *The meridians formed by one degree of longitude are farthest apart at the equator. They become closer as the latitude increases.*

FIG. 10. *Parallels of latitude as they would appear on the earth's surface. They, too, are expressed as angles formed with the axis.*

to fix it; we need another measure which fixes the position north or south. Between the two, if the unit is small enough, we shall have enough information to fix positions as closely as we may need. This second measure is called *latitude*. It is also expressed in terms of an angle, but not quite in the same way as for longitude.

As before, we imagine the earth to be sliced open, this time through a meridian, as in Fig. 10. Angles may again be marked on the exposed circle, reading from 0° at the equator, both upwards (north) and downwards (south) to 90° at either pole. Circles are drawn on the surface of the sphere through these points, but this time they are equally spaced and each parallel to the equator.

172

Except for the equator, they will thus no longer be great circles, but will decrease in size as the latitude increases, until at the poles, where the latitude becomes 90°, they will vanish entirely. You will see from Fig. 11 that the radius of the circle at latitude $L°$ is $R \cos L$. Thus one degree of arc (or "one degree of longitude") at latitude 30° N. is about 70 × 0·866, or 60 miles, whilst at latitude 60°N. it is about 35 miles.

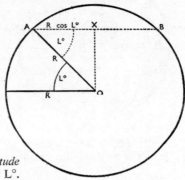

FIG. 11. *The radius of the circle of latitude* $L°$, *passing through* AB, *is* R cos $L°$.

The distance between two circles of latitude will, except for slight variations in the shape of the earth, be constant. One degree of latitude will represent $\frac{1}{360}$ of a great circle, and will represent an interval, north or south, of about 70 miles.

The latitude and longitude of some well-known places are given below. This information enables us to mark them on a model of the earth as shown in Figs. 12 and 13.

	Lat.	Long.		Lat.	Long.
London ..	.. 51°N.	0°	Sydney ..	.. 34°S.	151°E.
Paris ..	.. 49°N.	2°E.	Wellington (N.Z.)..	42°S.	175°E.
New York ..	.. 41°N.	74°W.	Hongkong ..	.. 22°N.	114°E.
Moscow ..	.. 56°N.	37°E.	Tokyo ..	.. 36°N.	139°E.
Cape Town ..	.. 34°S.	18°E.	San Francisco	.. 38°N.	123°W.
Lagos ..	.. 6°N.	4°E.	Panama ..	.. 9°N.	79°W.
Rio de Janeiro	.. 23°S.	43°W.	Honolulu ..	.. 21°N.	158°W.
Khartoum ..	.. 16°N.	33°E.	Fiji ..	.. 18°S.	178°E.

We have had to turn over the page, so to speak, to show the other side of the globe, for some of these places.

By giving the latitude and longitude of a ship in trouble, correct to the nearest second, we narrow the search down to a very small area. One second of latitude will represent $\frac{1}{3,600}$ of a degree, or, in distance, about 342 yards; one second of longitude will be no more than this, and may be much less, according to the latitude. The area, if we were able to locate it closely, would be the size of a big meadow.

In reading the foregoing account of how to describe the position of a point on the surface of a sphere you may have thought to yourself, "This is all very well, mathematically, but it is not of much use

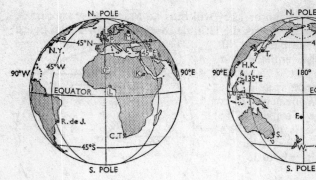

FIG. 12. *Fixing the positions of places in the foregoing table.*

FIG. 13. *Fixing the positions of the remaining places listed.*

to the traveller unless he can look about him in some special way in order to find out the longitude and latitude of the place where he is standing." True. As he cannot cut the earth into slices and put rulers or protractors over them, we should try to find some other method of observation instead.

Figs. 14 and 15 show how you may, by means of a simple reading from the Pole Star, determine the latitude for yourself. This is

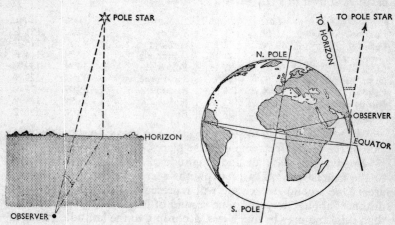

FIG. 14. *The angle between the Pole Star and the horizon is the angle of latitude of the observer. This fact can be proved by geometry.*

FIG. 15. *The angle marked is the same as that in Fig. 14. Prove that it is equal to L and you will see why Fig. 14 gives the latitude.*

174

because the Pole Star is almost constant in position, over the North Pole. Shakespeare says "constant as the Northern Star."

You may not get a result as accurate as those in the list above, but that will depend on the instrument with which you measure the angle. Aircraft navigators, by using an elaborate astro-compass, can get a very accurate reading. They do not depend on the Pole Star alone. Other stars, although their movement is much larger, have their positions accurately tabulated.

The position of a star in the sky is fixed by two angular measurements, similar to those of latitude and longitude, known as right ascension and declination. The day-to-day changes in position of a good many important stars have been calculated and tabulated, and the skilled navigator, by identifying one or more of these stars and taking his bearings from them, can determine his own position.

WHERE IS NORTH?

We are accustomed to thinking vaguely about direction; but although errors may not be serious for short journeys, where we are able to depend on landmarks for correction, for long journeys the position is different. An error of 10 degrees in a journey of a mile will bring us only about 300 yards away from our objective; but if we are going 100 miles, the same error in direction will take us 17 miles away from our destination.

Direction is measured as an angular displacement from a certain well known and easily identifiable line. "Left" and "right" will not do for this purpose, because they are personal, differing for different persons and changing for every change of course.

The basis of all geographical measurement of direction is north, that is, along the meridian towards the North Pole. We are accustomed, because of the small maps with which we usually deal, to thinking of all norths as parallel. If you asked three persons, in London, Bombay and New York, to point north, you might expect their hands to point along parallel lines.

They would not. The directions in which they would point are shown in Fig. 16, all to the North Pole, each along its own

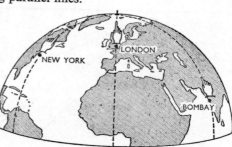

FIG. 16. *Pointing to the north from three places.*

meridian. If the pointers are within sight of each other their hands will be parallel; for the North Pole is so far away that it may then be looked on as the infinity at which parallel lines meet; but, if they are far enough apart, their hands may be at right-angles, or even pointing in opposite directions.

How is the north determined? By the Pole Star—when it is visible. Fortunately there is another method. There is a magnetic property of certain substances which causes them, when free to rotate, to turn so as to set in the same position of rest. From these substances magnets may be made which always come to rest pointing almost to the North Pole. This is because the earth is itself a sort of magnet, attracting the other magnet. The cause of the earth's magnetism is still not clear, although the Chinese knew of it and used the lodestone, which is magnetic, for navigation thousands of years ago. Dickens uses the phrase "drawn to the lodestone rock" to symbolize a powerful attractive force.

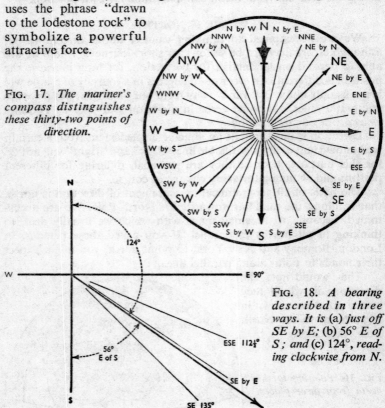

FIG. 17. *The mariner's compass distinguishes these thirty-two points of direction.*

FIG. 18. *A bearing described in three ways. It is* (a) *just off SE by E;* (b) *56° E of S; and* (c) *124°, reading clockwise from N.*

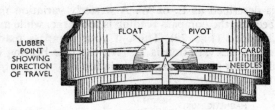

Fig. 19. *Parts of a magnetic compass. The float rotates, giving the needle freedom to turn.*

LUBBER POINT SHOWING DIRECTION OF TRAVEL

FLOAT   PIVOT

CARD

NEEDLES

Once we have fixed the north, we have the basis for other directions. We may use the older method, first marking an east to west line at right-angles to the north line; then subdividing the four right-angles further, until we have thirty-two subdivisions, each of $11\frac{1}{4}$ deg., named as in Fig. 17. These show the points of the mariner's compass. Or we may use the old surveyor's convention, which uses the north and south line only, reading in degrees, up to 90 deg., but indicating whether the reading is E. or W.; so that N.E. would be described as N. 45° E., and S.S.W. as S. $22\frac{1}{2}$° W.

The more modern method, as used in aircraft navigation, is to take all bearings from N., in a clockwise rotation; by this method N.E. is 045° (the 0 being put in to make all bearings of three figures), and S.S.W. is $202\frac{1}{2}$°. Fig. 18 shows a bearing of 124° by all three methods.

Modern travel, especially for long distances, requires great accuracy. Correction must be made for many possible sources of error. The most important of these is the presence of nearby masses of magnetic substances, which may turn the compass needle aside. An up-to-date compass is shown in Fig. 19.

A more recent improvement is the radio compass, or direction finder, which uses the directional properties of a looped aerial. You may have used your own wireless set in this way if you have had to turn it at a particular angle in order to get the best reception. This occurs when the plane of the aerial loop is in line with the transmitting station.

We have talked about "north," but unfortunately there are two norths; one the geographical, or "true," north, as shown in maps, the other the magnetic north, to which the magnet or compass needle points. The north magnetic pole is several hundred miles away from the geographical north pole and a correction, known as *magnetic variation*, must be made to compass readings to obtain the geographical direction for marking on a map.

This variation is different from place to place and is to be found marked on maps either as a marginal note or as isogonal lines, which are lines joining all points having the same variation. Variation

177

is described as E. or W. A westerly variation must be subtracted, because the compass reading is too large, while an easterly variation is added (Fig. 20). Thus, if your compass reads 142° at a place where the variation is 12° W., the true bearing is 130°; if it reads 065° at a place where the variation is 8° E., the true bearing is 073°.

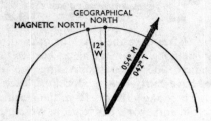

FIG. 20. *True and magnetic north. This bearing would be read as 054° from magnetic north. It is 042° from geographical north.*

There is a further complication, due to the fact that the magnetic field of the earth is subject to change. Apart from the occurrence of magnetic storms, which have a temporary effect on the compass needle, there is a small, steady change in variation, which soon puts maps out of date in this respect.

This annual variation is usually stated in the margin of a map, together with the date. Such a note, for example, found on a map of northern England, reads "Magnetic Variation 11° W., 1948; average annual decrease 11'." According to this, the variation in the latter half of 1953 had fallen to 10° W. By 2003, unless there are other, violent changes, it will be 0, or the compass will point to geographical north. After this, the variation will become easterly.

It will be seen that the variation, although small, will, in the course of time, become sufficient to cause errors of navigation if it is disregarded. There is an interesting story, of the "buried treasure" type, which makes use of this idea in its plot. After many exciting and hair-raising escapades, the hero and his party arrive at the lonely South Sea island, find the missing portion of the map, and locate the spot from a compass bearing, only to draw a blank. Alas, there is no treasure!

Suddenly the hero solves the mystery. The map is dated 1750. In 200 years, the variation has altered by some 37°. With this correction, the treasure is found, and all is well.

Here are two amusing problems to illustrate the special nature of the North Pole itself:

(1) A man, who is fond of a southerly aspect, wishes to build a house with windows on all sides, all facing south. Where must he build? The answer is, of course, at the North Pole.

(2) A man left his house, walked 5 miles south, then turned east and walked 3 miles. Here he paused to shoot a bear. Gathering up his spoils, he turned north, walked 5 miles and found himself at home again. What was the colour of the bear? The answer is white, because it is a polar bear, as the house must be the same all-southerly house as in the previous problem.

At the North Pole, then, compass readings and directions are peculiar because all roads point south, and all paths approaching it converge, so to speak, within sight, instead of appearing to be parallel as they do elsewhere.

MAPMAKERS' PROBLEMS

The first problem of the mapmaker is that of projection. He must represent the curved surface of the earth on the flat paper of the map. Some curved surfaces may be made to unroll, or develop, into flat surfaces; the curved surface of a cylinder will unroll into a flat rectangle. But no flat surface may be made to fit exactly to the surface of a sphere.

This is the big problem of the mapmaker. He could overcome it by using a curved surface, such as a globe, for his map, but this would not always be a practical solution, as maps need to be carried about, folded up and bound together in an atlas or in books. He must project, or throw the map on to a flat surface, or one which can afterwards be flattened out.

Something is bound to suffer. It may be shape, when individual countries, especially towards the edges of the projection, are not shown with their correct shapes. It may be distance, in which case it will not be possible to use the map to tell exactly how far it is from place to place. Or it may be area (most atlases contain such a map, in which Greenland appears many times larger than it really is).

What the mapmaker does is to offer alternative forms, in each of which one factor is preserved at the expense of the others. If you are interested in getting shape and direction right, you will use an "orthomorphic" map. If it is distance between places which is most important, you will use the "equidistant" type; otherwise you will use the "equal-area" type. Whichever you choose, the other factors will suffer, although for maps of small areas, such as those of single countries, the differences will not be serious.

These three types of map are produced by alteration of scale after projection. The actual projection itself may be one of three main types: conical, zenithal or cylindrical.

In the conical projection, a paper cone is imagined to be held over half the earth, as in Fig. 21, reaching down to the equator, with

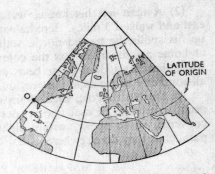

FIG. 21. *Conical projection, showing the latitude of origin.*

FIG. 22. *Part of the unfolded cone with the outlines of the resulting map.*

its vertex over the pole. It will touch the earth along a parallel of latitude. The projection is made with a point on this parallel, marked 0 in the diagram, as origin; that is, as though the earth were transparent and a strong light were placed in the centre of the sphere at 0, throwing a picture of the earth on the paper cone. If the cone is now opened out (Fig. 22), we see a map which is in conical projection. Another cone, correspondingly placed, will give the other half of the world.

Of course, the mapmaker cannot do anything like this. What he does is to draw, from calculations on this basis, a sufficient number of meridians and parallels for his purpose, as shown in Fig. 22, and to fit the rest of the map, the land masses, into the partitions which they make. It will be seen that, in this type of projection, the parallels of latitude are all circular, with the pole as their centre, whilst the meridians are straight lines radiating from the pole. If circles representing the parallels at regular intervals are spaced out equally, we get an "equidistant" map. By selecting a cone of the appropriate vertical angle we may get an "orthomorphic" map, or an "equal-area" map. The conical orthomorphic, or Lambert's projection, is best for maps in which most of the land area is to the east and west of the map.

In the zenithal projection, the origin, where the lamp is imagined to be placed, is at the centre of the earth, or some point directly below the centre of the area to be mapped; the projection surface, on which the map is to be thrown, is flat (Fig. 23). In this map, as in the conical projection, the parallels usually appear as circles (but this time complete circles) and the meridians as straight lines, radiating from the pole.

180

As before, if the radial distances between the circles are equal, the map will be equidistant; in an orthomorphic map, the radial distances increase as we go outwards from the centre, and decrease in an equal-area map. The map need not be centred round the pole; if it is not, the projection is described as oblique and the parallels will not appear as circles.

If a cylinder of paper is thought of as wrapped round the earth, touching it at the equator, as in Fig. 24, the projection is called cylindrical. The cylindrical orthomorphic map is Mercator's projection, first produced in 1568, the great ally of the Elizabethan seafarers. If the cylinder is inclined, so that the circle of contact is no longer at the equator, the projection becomes an Oblique Mercator, instead of a Transverse Mercator.

There are a number of other projections, but these are the most important. Which you will use will depend on what is of the greatest interest, correct shape and constant direction, accurate distance or accurate area representation. You cannot have them all at the same time on a flat map. A good atlas will show the same map under different projections, to suit each purpose.

Of the greatest interest, historically, is Mercator's projection. Until Mercator's map was produced, no serious attempt had been made to allow for the curvature of the earth. Mercator did this by increasing the distance between parallels in high latitudes, in proportion to the secant of the angle, although the actual mathematics of it was not worked out till later. At the same time, the meridians, instead of converging, were opened out, so that the distance which represented a degree of longitude was constant at all latitudes.

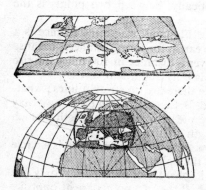

FIG. 23. *Map of Europe based on the zenithal type of projection.*

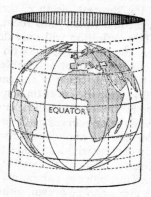

FIG. 24. *Cylindrical projection, the basis of Mercator's maps.*

181

× ÷ × ÷ × ÷ × ÷ × ÷ × ÷ × ÷ × ÷ × ÷ × ÷ × ÷ × ÷ × ÷ × ÷ × ÷
÷   ×
× ÷   ÷
× 　　　　　　　　*Choose Your Goblet*   × ÷
× 　 One of seven goblets, A to G, standing in a row is made of solid 　 ×
÷ 　 gold; the others are of base metal. The competitors are told that if 　 ÷
× 　 they count 1,000 starting at A (thus: A, B, C, D, E, F, G, F, E, D, and 　 ÷
÷ 　 so on) they will finish at the prize. The winner soon chose the right 　 ×
× 　 goblet without counting. What was his choice? 　 ×
÷ 　　　　　　　　　　　　　　　　　　　*Solution on page 444* 　 ÷
×   ×
÷   ÷
× ÷ × ÷ × ÷ × ÷ × ÷ × ÷ × ÷ × ÷ × ÷ × ÷ × ÷ × ÷ × ÷ × ÷ × ÷ ×

The effect of this was to distort shapes and alter distances as you moved farther away from the equator, until at the poles they were ridiculous. This was not then very important, because not much was known about those regions. In any case, if you were interested in regions further away from the equator, it was always possible to make an oblique projection, centred round these regions. Most maps, whatever the projection, are reliable within 10 degrees latitude or longitude from the centre.

What did make Mercator's projection so valuable was the constant direction of straight lines. A single setting of the compass would take you along a straight line drawn on his map.

This does not, at first glance, seem very far-reaching, especially if we have not considered the idea of distance very carefully before. We are accustomed to thinking of the distance between two points as the length of the straight line joining them, although there are many possible paths, straight and curved, between them. This is because we understand the term distance to mean shortest distance; and the shortest distance, theoretically, between two points is the straight line which joins them.

This definition will only do for Flatland, where the surface is a plane. We may make it do, on the earth, for short distances, because the curvature is not noticeable; over a distance of 100 miles the rise due to the curvature of the earth is only about 200 yards.

For large distances on a sphere there are no straight lines; whatever path we choose will be curved. Between any two points, we may draw as many curved paths as we please, of varying length. Which is the shortest and what is its length?

In dealing with longitude, we met the great circle, which is a circle whose centre is at the centre of the sphere. A great circle can be drawn through any two points on a sphere. For most points, only one such circle can be drawn, although, if the two points are at opposite ends of a diameter, every circle through them on the surface of the sphere is a great circle.

182

It may be shown that, when the great circle is drawn through any two points, the part of the circle which is between the points is the shortest distance, on the surface of the sphere, between the points. If the two points are on the same meridian, that is, have the same longitude, this distance is easily calculated and may be found from a table of meridional parts. Otherwise, a little knowledge of spherical trigonometry is needed for the calculation.

What is known as "great circle navigation" is based on this fact. In order to sail between two ports, the great circle joining them was found, and its path followed, as nearly as possible. There was, however, a serious difficulty. The great circle had no fixed direction. It turned away from or towards the North Pole all the way. This meant that compass bearing, except along a meridian or the equator, needed frequent change, making navigation difficult.

A better, though longer path for navigation is one which does not change its direction. This is the curve of constant direction, known as the *rhumb line* or *loxodrome*. One setting of the compass, pointing in the direction of the objective, will, if followed, continue to point there throughout the journey.

Mercator's map made this easy to find. On his map the rhumb line was a straight line. The direction could easily be found, and much calculation avoided. A good deal of navigation is by rhumb line, especially in aircraft, whose great speed makes the shortest distance less important.

How much longer is the rhumb line than the corresponding great circle? This will depend on the places. Along a meridian or the equator there will be no difference; between the two, it will vary. For example, from Oporto to New York, by great circle, is 3,000 miles; the rhumb line for the same journey is 3,120 miles. At a cruising speed, by air, of 200 miles per hour, this makes a difference of 36 minutes. At 20 knots it would mean about $4\frac{1}{2}$ hours longer.

THE QUESTION OF SCALE

Now that we have seen how the grid, or framework of the map, is drawn, we must decide how this is to be filled in. We shall need to locate places by finding their latitude and longitude, and find their distance and bearing from each other, by surveying. Before we do this, it is best to decide on a suitable scale.

Most maps are accurately reduced pictures of the countryside. A photograph is, in a sense, a map; aerial photography now plays a very important part in large-scale surveys. Distortion sometimes occurs in a photograph, but so it does, as we have seen, in large maps.

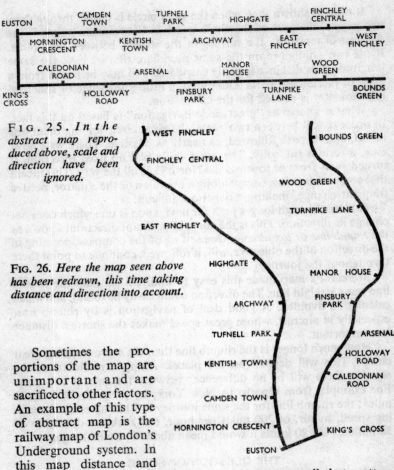

FIG. 25. *In the abstract map reproduced above, scale and direction have been ignored.*

FIG. 26. *Here the map seen above has been redrawn, this time taking distance and direction into account.*

Sometimes the proportions of the map are unimportant and are sacrificed to other factors. An example of this type of abstract map is the railway map of London's Underground system. In this map distance and direction, other than to and fro, are unimportant; all that matters is "in-betweenness." So long as stations are all shown in their true order, nothing else matters. Consequently, this map shows parallel lines, going due east and west, or north and south, with equidistant stations, when the truth, as may be seen by comparing Figs. 25 and 26, is far from so. But the whole truth does not matter here, for the abstract map is a much better guide to the traveller.

On other maps, scale is important, and depends on the purpose of the map. The larger the scale, the greater the detail; the smaller the scale, the clearer the general picture.

Large scales are usually expressed in inches to the mile in England, or in centimetres or millimetres to the kilometre abroad. Most people have seen or used the "one-inch" map, in which an inch of the map represents a true distance of a mile. This is a very good map for walkers and cyclists, as it shows footpaths and landmarks clearly. It is too large for the motorist, who is soon off the page, as it takes more than two hundred large pages to cover England and Scotland.

Notice that the scale is linear; that is, it represents length, not area. On a three-inch map, for example, one mile is represented by three inches; what area on this map represents a square mile?

The Ordnance Survey has produced maps of the British Isles to a variety of scales. Some are not issued to the general public, but most are available. The largest is a 25-inch map, on which every house is shown clearly, as half an inch represents about a hundred feet; what area on the map represents an acre? This is very useful for such purposes as land registration. A motorist will normally use a five-mile map, which represents five miles by an inch, or a ten-mile map. What scale would you need for a map of the British Isles to take up a page of this book?

Smaller scales are needed for navigation maps, as they must cover much larger areas and longer distances. These scales are usually expressed as a ratio, known as the representative fraction (R.F.). R.F. $\frac{1}{1000000}$ means that the measured distance on the map is one millionth of the true distance; this is roughly equivalent to 16 miles to the inch, but exactly equal to a scale of one millimetre to the kilometre. The representative fraction for a one-inch map is $\frac{1}{63360}$, as there are 63,360 inches to the mile.

You may enlarge your own map, if you wish, by using a pantograph, as shown in Fig. 27. This uses the property of similar triangles, that shape is preserved if lengths are increased or decreased in proportion. You may care to consider exactly what lengths the various parts of a pantograph would be to produce enlargements of 5 to 1.

FIG. 27. *Enlarging by means of a pantograph. The instrument may be adjusted to produce enlargements of different sizes.*

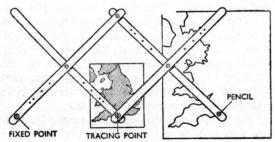

FIXED POINT   TRACING POINT   PENCIL

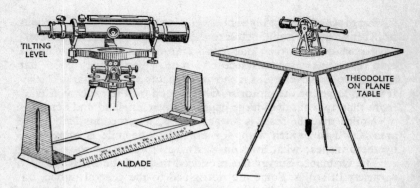

FIG. 28. *The tilting level measures differences in ground level, and is focused on a scaled rod held vertically at the point under observation. The alidade is sighted on a distant object to determine its direction. The theodolite measures angles both of inclination and of direction.*

WHERE THE SURVEYOR COMES IN

The work of filling in the map will be done by the surveyor. He will begin by locating his starting points, building up on them by triangulation. This consists in dividing the area into a large number of triangles, each of which is determined by trigonometry. Three measurements are needed to determine a triangle, although the surveyor will always take at least one more, as a check.

Bearings are taken from each of the two starting points, on a third point. These two angles, together with the distance between the starting points, determine the triangle, which can now be "solved" by trigonometry, the unknown sides and angles being calculated, or drawn to scale and measured. For checking purposes a back bearing may be taken, by reading from the third vertex to the two starting points. The back bearing should differ from the forward bearing by 180 deg., as this angle represents a complete right-about turn; if the difference is not 180 deg., there is some error.

The first triangle having been determined, its sides provide two new bases on which to build further triangles in the same way. Each in turn provides bases for more triangles, until eventually the whole country is covered by a network of triangles. These are the primary triangles. In a survey of Great Britain, two points on Salisbury Plain are taken as the starting points, from which the triangles spread outwards to the sea.

As the primary triangles are rather large, they must be broken up. This is done in the same way, by building up smaller triangles,

186

known as secondaries, within the first. Further triangulation is done within these triangles, until sufficient detail has been filled in. You will find these survey stations, or trig points as they are called, dotted about the countryside, especially on the tops of hills. It should be quite easy to locate one on a hilltop near your own home.

Some of the surveyor's instruments are shown in Fig. 28. Much depends on their accuracy, which is always being improved as precision engineering advances. A small error in one triangle multiplies itself rapidly as the triangles spread out. It is important to recognize that these errors are not mistakes, in the sense that the wrong answer has been obtained, but limits to the reliability of the instrument.

However accurate an instrument may be, we must eventually come down to a limit below which it cannot measure. It is fashionable to work out high speeds from the time taken over a measured mile, in miles per hour, giving the answer to three places of decimals; but only the first decimal place may be reliable, for an error of an inch in measuring the mile, and a hundredth of a second in timing, both more than likely, would affect the second decimal place. You will appreciate this point if you express one inch as a percentage of one mile and then find the effect of such a percentage increase or decrease on a speed such as 600 m.p.h.

PROGRESS IN NAVIGATION

Up to the fifteenth century, the needs of the navigator were limited, as, with only few exceptions, most sea voyages were made within sight of land. Only a little mathematics was called for. Rough methods of steering a course by the Pole Star at night, and by the sun during the day, were known to the Greeks. Latitude could be determined in the northern hemisphere by direct reading from the altitude of the Pole Star (Fig. 15). It is not difficult to draw up tables from which latitude may be calculated, for a known time and date, from a reading of the altitude of the sun. It is to be noted that the term altitude used here refers to an angle, the angle of elevation, not to a height. The mariner's compass, known by the Chinese long before, was in use in the Mediterranean by the thirteenth century. This knowledge was sufficient for the needs of the day.

With the advent of the well-rigged, ocean-going sailing ship, little more than four hundred years ago, this was no longer good enough. Maps like those based on Ptolemy were too inaccurate. We have seen how this need stimulated Mercator to improve the map; although even as late as in 1599, Edward Wright, to whom we owe the first calculations of the theory of Mercator's projection, bemoans the inaccuracy of the Elizabethan chart, in which an error of 200 leagues (or 600 miles) is by no means uncommon.

Better methods of determining latitude were needed, although the principles which were known to the Greeks were adequate. More accurate tables of the altitude of the sun were needed, necessitating improved instruments which were soon produced. Some of these instruments are shown in Fig. 29. Of special interest is the astrolabe, an instrument used for measuring the altitude of the sun and other heavenly bodies. It is not generally realized that Chaucer, the father of English poetry, wrote in 1391 a Treatise on the Astrolabe, addressed in simple language to "little Lewis, my son."

Other tables were needed to allow for small changes in the position of the Pole Star; and altitude tables for other stars, for use in the southern hemisphere, or elsewhere when the Pole Star was not visible. These again, for the most part, depended on more accurate

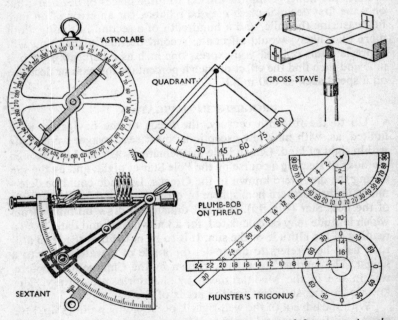

FIG. 29. *Some navigational aids. The astrolabe is used for measuring the altitude of heavenly bodies; the quadrant for measuring angles of inclination; the cross-stave for surveying by means of a base-line with offsets at right-angles; the sextant for finding the altitude of the sun; and Münster's trigonus for solving triangles of which the data are incomplete.*

observation, rather than on more intricate calculation, and were soon forthcoming; some such tables are still in use today.

The problem of longitude was more difficult and was not satisfactorily dealt with for the navigator until 1760, when the chronometer, making time measurement more accurate, was invented. We shall see later that longitude and time are very closely connected. Longitude may be conveniently determined on land by timing the same event, such as the occultation or eclipse of a star by the moon, in two different places; but on sea, in one place, it is a much more difficult matter. New and more difficult mathematics are needed to produce such tables as one predicting the movement of the moon.

The pioneer of the improved theory of navigation made necessary by the ocean-going ship was Prince Henry the Navigator, of Portugal, in about 1438. Realizing the need, he collected together all available knowledge of geography and astronomy, and laid the foundations of the modern science of navigation.

Modern navigation, especially since the development of aircraft and wireless, has gone a long way from this. In Elizabethan days, the seaman navigated largely by easting and northing. He ran east or west as far as he could, checking his latitude as he went along. When he turned north or south, as he had no reliable means of checking longitude, he estimated the distance by calculation known as dead reckoning, depending on landmarks to keep him right. These calculations were only estimates, as the readings were still rough, and it was quite common to be a hundred miles or more out. Sometimes new land was discovered in this accidental way.

Modern speeds have made this sort of situation intolerable, because errors are magnified by the speeds. Especially so is this in the case of aircraft; large errors still occur, but they are due to inexperience and incompetence rather than to defects of method.

The modern navigator has a choice of methods at his disposal. He will plan his course on an accurate map and take periodical readings to determine his position, as currents or winds may have taken him off his course. He may use a sextant, or a carefully calibrated astro-compass, to find the altitude of a star, from which he will determine, with the aid of tables, his latitude.

He may, by studying the map, find landmarks or seamarks from which to judge his position. He may calculate, from his position, the strength of the wind, using this in his subsequent calculations to find the new direction to his objective; or he may use instruments, constantly improving, which will do the calculation for him.

He will have a very accurate watch to check times and will receive very good forecasts of the weather, corrected from time to time as new conditions emerge. This is something new, but vital in flying, where conditions at different heights, as well as on the ground, must be known.

The most modern methods of all are due to advances in wireless telegraphy. A wireless station will, on request, give a bearing. This enables the navigator to plot, on a map, the line joining his position at that moment to the sending station. A second bearing from some other station will give him a second line; at the intersection of these two lines, or near it, allowing for his own movement since, is his position. A third bearing will make sure.

A wireless station may help the navigator by sending out a beam, which he can pick up and follow.

Which of these is the best method depends on circumstances, such as weather conditions, which affect the visibility of the stars, so that an altitude may not be available; and on the taste and experience of the navigator. Many navigators vary their method, or use one method to supplement or check another.

Whichever method he chooses, the navigator will have accurate instruments at his disposal. One such instrument, not required by a ship, is shown in Fig. 30. This is the altimeter, an instrument for recording height. Height is linked up with atmospheric pressure; the higher you go, the lower the pressure, because there is less air above you. The altimeter reads the pressure, but is marked off to show the corresponding height.

Other methods of measuring the height of an aircraft are being experimented with but have not yet come into general use. One such is called the sonic altimeter, because it makes use of the speed of sound, which is about 1,100 feet per second in air. A sound is sent out towards the earth, which reflects it back again. The double journey is timed and the distance deduced, or read directly, from a stopwatch which has been calibrated in feet instead of in seconds. The reflection altimeter does the same with wireless waves.

THE MEASUREMENT OF TIME

Time and travel are inevitably linked in our minds, as they must always have been. It is a far cry from the elaborate railway time-table or work schedule of today to the days when journey time, "two moons away" or "from sunrise to sunset," was a measure of distance. We still use similar time phrases for referring to distance in such expressions as half an hour away, five minutes' walk, or a day's march.

The first measurement of time depended on the recognition of what the mathematician would describe as periodic functions, or

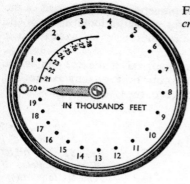

FIG. 30. *The altimeter, with which aircraft are equipped, measures air pressure and converts it into altitude.*

events which recur at regular intervals. At first these intervals would be only roughly equal, such as darkness and light, or the seasons. Better units would follow, but they would all be based on the relative movement of earth, sun and moon.

The earth has two different movements. It moves round the sun in an elliptical path, or orbit. The period of one full journey is what we call a year. The earlier theories, those of Aristotle and that of Ptolemy, which were accepted up to the sixteenth century, were geocentric, or held that the earth was stationary at the centre of the universe, the other bodies revolving round it. The heliocentric system, which regards the sun as centre, was first published by Copernicus in 1543, but was slow of acceptance.

The invention of the astronomical telescope by Galileo in 1610 allowed observations which supported the theory. The burden of proof, however, rested on Kepler, who produced in 1609 and 1619 three laws which were supported by observation and by mathematics. It was left to Newton, in 1687, to verify according to this system that the laws of motion of the heavenly bodies were the same as those on earth.

Kepler's laws were: (1) The planets describe ellipses about the sun, which is at one focus. (An ellipse may be regarded as a flattened circle. It has two foci, as shown in Fig. 31; every point on the ellipse is at the same total distance from the two foci.)
(2) The planets move

FIG. 31. F_1 and F_2 are the focal points of the ellipse. For all positions of P, the sum of the focal distances is constant.

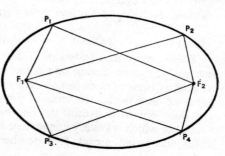

191

so that the line joining the sun to the planet covers equal areas of the ellipse in equal times. (3) The squares of the periodic times of the planets are proportional to the cubes of the major axes of their orbits.

This is illustrated in Fig. 32. The major axis is the line joining the two foci. If one orbit has a major axis four times as long as another, then the period, or time for a complete journey, for the first is $\sqrt{(4)^3}$ = 8 times that of the other.

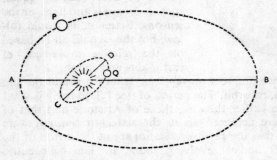

Fig. 32. *The orbits of two planets. If* AB *is four times* CD, *the planet* P *takes* $\sqrt{(4)^3}$ *or* 8 *times as long to go round the sun as does the planet* Q.

Nowadays we accept the idea that the sun is one of a number of fixed bodies called stars, around which revolve secondary bodies, of which the earth is one, called planets; around these in turn revolve satellites, or moons.

The earth has also a secondary motion. At the same time as it moves round the sun it is spinning around its own axis. The period of this revolution is called a day. If we stay at one place for a day and watch the sun, we shall see it rising, then setting; then it will disappear, because the earth, in revolving, has taken us round to the other side. This causes day and night; the side of the earth which is away from the sun is in darkness. The length of the period of daylight varies with the place and time of the year. Because the axis of the earth is tilted some places, very near the poles, will have long periods of constant daylight, and others long periods of night.

SOLAR AND SIDEREAL TIME

There are approximately $365\frac{1}{4}$ days in a year; that is, the earth rotates $365\frac{1}{4}$ times during one complete revolution around the sun. As each of these periods can be determined by astronomical observations, we have in this the basis of a system of measurement of time. The Babylonians first took the number of days in the year as 360, a number which was very convenient in their system of numeration, which was based on 60. It is to them that we attribute the sub-

192

division of units of time and angle into sixtieths, as 60 minutes to the hour and 60 minutes to the degree.

It is noon at any place when the sun crosses the meridian. The interval between two successive noons, which may be measured by astronomical observation, at Greenwich, for example, is called a solar day. Unfortunately, the solar day is not constant. We have seen, from Kepler's second law, that equal areas, not equal distances, are swept out in equal intervals of time. If the orbit were a circle this would make no difference; but as it is an ellipse the speed is altering, so that there is a variation in the length of the solar day. The difference is small, but accurate measurement must take it into account.

We get over this difficulty by averaging out the solar days in a year, to make a mean solar day of constant length. This is the day which our clocks, when they keep good time, will show. This is the time, called Greenwich Mean Time, which is given by the time signals which we hear on the radio. The other is the time which a sundial would show. Both times agree four times a year, on 16 April, 15 June, 1 September and 25 December. The difference at other times, known as the Equation of Time, may be found from tables.

This creates another difficulty, for it means that, whilst solar time could be checked by astronomical observations once a day, mean time could only be checked four times a year, which would not be good enough for checking clocks and chronometers. Another day, capable of frequent check, must be used.

This is called sidereal time, or star time. The rotation of the earth may be observed by timing a fixed star across the meridian. This is better than timing the sun, because it is regular. It gives a third day, called the sidereal day.

The sidereal day can be checked by daily observation on a star; it is about four minutes shorter than the mean solar day. This is because the earth, in a year, turns completely round the sun, making one more revolution than we are aware of, i.e. $365\frac{1}{4} + 1 = 366\frac{1}{4}$. As the earth is not revolving round the star under observation, there are thus $366\frac{1}{4}$ sidereal days. One sidereal day is approximately equal to 24 hours $\times \dfrac{365\frac{1}{4}}{366\frac{1}{4}}$.

To allow for this difference, sidereal clocks divide the day into 86,164 seconds, instead of 86,400. Each of these parts is a second of mean time; it is checked by daily astronomical observation and may be used for testing and regulating everyday clocks which show mean time.

The length of the solar year is not an exact number of days or even a convenient fraction. Correct to the nearest second, a year is

365·2422 mean solar days, or 365 days, 5 hours, 48 minutes, 46 seconds on our clocks. This is an impossible figure for a calendar; but if the dates of the seasons, and especially of the equinoxes, are to be about the same from year to year we must keep as near as possible to this figure. If we called a year 365 days exactly, in 800 years we should have midsummer in December and midwinter in July.

The leap year was introduced to avoid this variation. The legal year is kept at 365 days, but an additional day, called leap-year day, 29 February in our calendar, is introduced periodically to put things approximately right. Leap years were first introduced by Sosigenes, a Greek astronomer, in the Julian calendar, which began in 46 B.C. during the time of Julius Caesar.

Although the Julian calendar corrected most of the error, by adding one leap-year day every fourth year, this made the average year still 11 minutes 14 seconds too much. By 325 A.D., this had accumulated to nearly $69\frac{1}{2}$ hours. To make up for this, three days were missed out of the calendar for that year.

THE GREGORIAN CALENDAR

This was only a temporary measure, as the errors continued. In 1582 Pope Gregory XIII introduced the Gregorian calendar, which we now use. Ten more days had to be dropped, to deal with past errors. In the new calendar there were only 97 leap years in 400, as exact centuries, except when divisible by 400, were not to count as leap years. This reduced the error to 25·9 seconds, which will take over 300 years to accumulate to a day.

It was not till 1752 that the Gregorian calendar was adopted in England, by which time eleven days had to be omitted. This was not well received, the cry of "give us back our eleven days" being raised. There are still several marks of the old-style calendar. The end of the government financial year, for tax purposes, was on Lady Day, 25 March. The lost eleven days brought it to 5 April, where it still remains. Lammas Day, 1 August, was the day on which common

"I'll Put a Girdle Round the Earth"

Assume that the earth is a perfect sphere with a smooth surface and that a wire is stretched round it at the equator. If the wire were cut and two yards added to its length, so that it formed a ring equidistant from the equator at all parts, what would be the distance between the wire and the earth?   *Solution on page 444*

194

land was opened for grazing; it became 12 August, which still holds as the beginning of grouse shooting. We still hear of 5 January described as Old Christmas Day.

The influence of the moon on tides has always made it important to the traveller. As a unit of time, the lunar month was too difficult to fit into a year, and was replaced by the more adaptable calendar month. The seven-day week, with its days dedicated to deities, was an arbitrary unit which has remained.

SPLITTING UP THE DAY

The division of the day into smaller units, hours, minutes and seconds, did not bring with it the accurate clock until medieval times, in spite of the clock which is heard to strike three in Shakespeare's *Julius Caesar*. Until then water clocks, sand glasses (still in use for egg-timing), and hour candles, like those attributed to King Alfred, were sufficient.

The first attempt to use the earth to measure time was the sundial, which may have originated as a shadow stick in Babylonian times. Rapid strides were made when, early in the seventeenth century, Galileo found that the time of swing of a pendulum was proportional to its length. The formula for a simple pendulum is $t = 2\pi\sqrt{\dfrac{l}{g}}$, where $\pi = 3\cdot1416$, or about $3\frac{1}{7}$, and g, the acceleration due to gravity, is $32\cdot2$ feet per second per second, or 981 centimetres per second per second. Thus, a seconds pendulum, which makes a complete swing there and back in a second, should be about $9\cdot8$ inches or 25 centimetres long (from the point of suspension of the thread to the centre of gravity of the bob).

This gave the seaman a clock, so that he no longer had to depend on such instruments as the nocturnal to tell him the time. But the pendulum clock did not give accurate readings of longitude, for, although changes in length at different temperatures, owing to expansion, were compensated for, the force of gravity varies from place to place. Although the variation was small, it was common to use clocks which were twenty minutes out daily.

This is reminiscent of the two clocks, one of which was right twice a day, the other right once in a hundred years. Which would you rather have? When you have decided, remember that every clock which has stopped shows the right time twice a day; whilst a clock which loses a second a day will, if not adjusted, take more than a hundred years before it is right again.

The replacement of the pendulum by a coiled spring, together with improved methods of compensation, produced by the end of the eighteenth-century clocks and chronometers which lost or gained no more than a minute a month. These, with continued improvement, have sufficed the traveller till now.

Today the requirements of science, especially in the fields of wireless and radar, demand much more accurate instruments which will record thousandth or even millionth parts of a second. One method, in use in the everyday electric clock, uses the frequency of change of voltage in an alternating current. Even this small quantity is not exact enough, but the minute oscillations of quartz crystals under electrical pressure have given such great accuracy that in 1945 they exposed a slowing down of the rotation of the earth by about $4\frac{1}{2}$ milliseconds (thousandths of a second) a day. Under older methods this would have passed unnoticed until it had accumulated over a long period.

The chief impetus to the early clockmakers was the need for a means of measuring longitude. In 1714 the British Board of Longitude offered a prize of £20,000 for a means of measuring longitude accurate enough to enable the navigator to come within thirty miles of his destination on a voyage to the West Indies.

TIME AND LONGITUDE

Longitude is closely connected with time, because east and west movement is along the apparent route of the sun. Since the complete rotation of 360 degrees takes 24 hours, every 15 degrees of longitude will represent one hour. Since the sun is overhead at noon, by mean time, wherever you are, the time shown on your chronometer at noon will enable you to calculate the longitude.

If your chronometer, set right at Greenwich, reads seven minutes past two when the sun is directly overhead, your longitude must be $2\frac{7}{60}$ times 15 degrees, or 31° 45′ W. It is west because the apparent motion of the sun is east to west; the more easterly a place, the earlier it will receive the sun, and the later its local time. Places to the east are fast on our time, and to the west slow on our time. If the chronometer shows 9.40 a.m. at noon what is your longitude?

To avoid the confusion which would result from this gradual change of time, the world is divided into time zones. There is a sudden change of official time as you enter each zone, lasting till the next zone is reached.

There must also be a sharp division between days, as is illustrated by this well-known problem. Suppose it were possible to travel with the sun, at the same rate as the sun (that is, as the rotation of the earth). If you started out at 6 a.m., as the sun rose, on a Tuesday morning, wherever you looked out, on the way, it would be 6 a.m.

on Tuesday morning and the sun would be rising. But by the time you were back again where you started, the sun would have completed another apparent revolution, so that it would be another day, or 6 a.m. Wednesday morning. Where did it stop being Tuesday and start being Wednesday?

It is clear that some such arbitrary division is necessary. It is chosen where the minimum of difficulty would arise, and passes through the Pacific Ocean. It is called the Date Line. On one side it is Tuesday, but Wednesday on the other. A story, quite unfounded, is told of two islands, on either side of the line, where the sale of intoxicating liquors was prohibited on Sunday. Early every Sunday morning the boats would assemble, to take the entire population across the Date Line, where it was Monday, bringing them back again in time for their own Monday.

FASTER AND FASTER!

The scope and extent of travel have always been linked up with speed. Walking at three or four miles an hour, or even running at ten miles an hour, are very limiting. Horse and boat made longer distances possible. Cars and trains altered our notions of speed, although it is not long since medical opinion pronounced a speed of sixty miles an hour as an impossible strain on the human heart. *Round the World in Eighty Days* was the title of an exciting but incredible tale written fifty years ago.

The advent of the aeroplane opened up new and unbelievable vistas. Two hundred miles an hour is a commonplace cruising speed, almost a walking pace for an aircraft. The journey from London to Bombay, taking some three weeks by boat, may be flown in nineteen hours. The two-thousand-odd-mile crossing of the Atlantic is a matter of $4\frac{1}{2}$ hours. Faster! Faster! is the cry.

The speed at which sound travels through the air is about 1,100 feet per second, or 750 miles per hour. (A quick way to convert feet per second into miles per hour is to remember that 60 m.p.h. = 88 ft. per sec.) This was previously regarded as a limiting speed, but now we have "supersonic" flight, faster than sound. Journeys to other planets, born in the minds of imaginative authors like Verne and Wells, may not be as fantastic as they were once thought.

The speed of sound depends on temperature (increasing by about 2 feet per second for every degree centigrade) and on the medium through which it is transmitted (being about 4,800 feet per second in water). These speeds are mere trifles compared with that of light, which is 186,326 miles per second.

197

This speed, an important factor in the theory of relativity, is regarded as a limiting speed, the fastest possible. Suppose we can see an illuminated clock which reads twelve o'clock. If it were possible to travel faster than light away from it, then at each backward glance we would see the clock registering a time earlier than twelve o'clock because we would be overtaking light waves which were radiated by the clock-face before we began to move.

We do, in fact, regard light as instantaneous when estimating the distance of a thunderstorm. Sound travels about a mile in five seconds, so that one-fifth of the interval between flash and sound is a good estimate of the distance of the storm.

The great speed of light gives us a convenient unit for expressing very large distances. This is the "light-year," which is the distance travelled by light in a year. It is about six million million miles. The distance of the nearest star from the earth is four light-years. Some stars are so far away that the light we now receive from them set out on its journey during the reign of Queen Elizabeth I.

PROBLEMS OF TIME AND TRAVEL

To return to more mundane topics, here is a problem which shows up the reliability of speed measurements. Two policemen mark out a distance of a quarter of a mile along a straight piece of road, using a measuring tape. They stand at each end and time a car along this road, one signalling to the other when to start his stopwatch. According to the watch, the car takes 29 seconds for the quarter mile, which works out at 31·0 m.p.h. To what extent is this answer reliable?

This depends on the accuracy of the measurements, for every instrument has a limit below which it cannot measure. A fly cannot appreciate speeds of less than an inch a second. It is doubtful whether many human eyes can see differences as small as a twentieth of an inch. Let us suppose that the stopwatch reads correct to a fifth of a second. The personal equation—that is, the time between receipt of the message through the eye and its delivery at the muscles which cause the finger to move and stop the watch—may be as much as a fifth of a second each time. It will be fair to say that the real time might be anything between 28·6 and 29·4 seconds.

The stretching of the tape, the joins, and the difficulty of keeping a straight line in putting the tape down twenty times to make a quarter of a mile, may make the measurement at least a yard out. The true answer, on this supposition, may be anywhere between 28·6 seconds for 441 yards, which gives the highest value, and 29·4 seconds for 439 yards. The speeds, calculated from these figures, are

31·5 m.p.h. and 30·6 m.p.h. The original answer may easily be as much as half a mile an hour out. In practice, the margin of error is usually much greater than this.

Another problem on speed: You wish to make an average speed of 60 m.p.h. on a certain journey. When you have gone halfway you check up and find that you have only done 30 m.p.h. At what speed must you travel for the remainder of the journey to obtain the desired average?

You will find that this is impossible. Try it with a convenient distance, such as 240 miles. You will find that, even if you could go at 1,200 m.p.h. for the second half of the journey, it would only bring your average up to $58\frac{1}{2}$ m.p.h. You have used up all the time needed in the first half.

At the back of the official booklet on the Highway Code is a table showing the distance in which you can stop, according to the speed at which you are travelling. The basis of this calculation is not clear, because the reaction of the driver, differing from person to person, must come into it. Assuming that this were constant, it will be interesting to examine the figures, to see if we can deduce the rule which has been used, and extend the table to cover other speeds.

Here are the figures:

Speed	Thinking distance	Braking distance	Total stopping distance
10 m.p.h.	10 ft.	5 ft.	15 ft.
20 m.p.h.	20 ft.	20 ft.	40 ft.
30 m.p.h.	30 ft.	45 ft.	75 ft.
40 m.p.h.	40 ft.	80 ft.	120 ft.
50 m.p.h.	50 ft.	125 ft.	175 ft.
60 m.p.h.	60 ft.	180 ft.	240 ft.

It is obvious that the thinking distance is the same number of feet as there are miles per hour in the speed. This means that the thinking time, or rather the action time from message to foot move-

---

A Tale of Two Motor-cars

Speedwell always reckoned to average 40 m.p.h. on long journeys; his friend Potter could average only 20 m.p.h. in his old crock. They set out together with their wives along the same road and Speedwell said he would turn back after 45 miles and then they would picnic together when they met. How long did the run take?

Solution on page 444

199

ment, has been taken as $\frac{60}{88}$, or nearly 0·7 seconds. It shows that our assumption of an error of 0·4 seconds in two actions, in the police trap example given above, was quite modest.

The figures in the braking column increase with the speed, but not in accordance with an obvious rule. By subtracting each line from the next, we may see that the differences, 15, 25, 35, 45, 55, go up in tens, but this is not much help. It would mean extending the table only a step at a time; and it gives no help about inter-mediate speeds.

The simplest way of finding these is from a graph (Fig. 33). Closer inspection of the figures shows that, if the number of miles per hour is squared, then divided by twenty, the answer is the number of feet in the braking column. We may make a formula of this, if we call the speed s and the total stopping distance d; then

$$d = s + \frac{s^2}{20}.$$

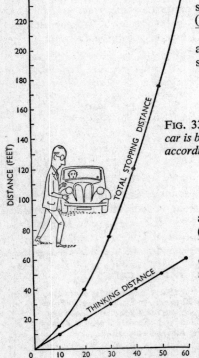

From this formula, if the speed is 25 m.p.h., then $d = 25 + \frac{(25)^2}{20} = 25 + \frac{625}{20} = 56\frac{1}{4}$; that is, at a speed of 25 m.p.h. the total stopping distance is $56\frac{1}{4}$ ft. At

Fig. 33. *Graph of the distances at which a car is brought to a halt from different speeds, according to the data tabulated on the preceding page.*

a speed of 36 m.p.h., $d = 36 + \frac{(36)^2}{20} = 100\cdot8$, or a total stopping distance of 100·8 ft. Check these answers from the graph.

We must understand that these speeds are all averages. When we say that a train travels at 60 m.p.h., we do not mean that it does exactly a mile every minute. We know that a train has to "get

200

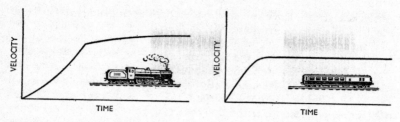

FIG. 34. *Characteristic velocity/time graphs for steam and electric trains. In one case slow acceleration goes with a high average speed; in the other a quicker start goes with a lower average speed.*

steam up," which means that for the first part of its journey its speed is much less than this. This accelerating process may take longer in some vehicles than in others. Fig. 34 shows the kind of velocity/time graphs you would expect for a steam train and an electric train. The steam train is slower in accelerating, as is shown by the steeper beginning to the graph for the electric train. It makes up for this by reaching a higher steady speed.

Any vehicle, from a standing start, must accelerate. To reach its average of 60 m.p.h. this train must at some time do more than 60, possibly 70 or 80 m.p.h. This makes calculation difficult because, if we wish to know the exact speed at any instant, we must find the distance it travels in a very small interval of time. This problem, the comparison of quantities which are too small to measure, led to the invention of the infinitesimal calculus, the most powerful tool in the mathematician's chest.

We have used the term velocity, which means the same as speed, the rate of movement—found by dividing the distance travelled by the time taken. Some books use velocity instead of speed when account is being taken of the direction of motion; we shall see later how important this is.

We have also used the term acceleration; this is the rate of increase of velocity. If at one moment your speed is 20 m.p.h. and a minute later you are doing 30 m.p.h., then your acceleration was 10 miles per hour per minute. It is more usual to have both units of time the same; from 50 feet per second to 60 feet per second in two seconds is an acceleration of 5 feet per second per second.

Like velocity, this acceleration is only an average, but we know that, if the force which causes it is unchanged, acceleration remains uniform or steady. The problem of uniform acceleration has received considerable attention, partly because gravity, the attraction of the earth, is a steady force; so that bodies falling under gravity follow the laws of uniform acceleration.

The acceleration due to gravity, called g, has been mentioned on p. 195. We may calculate the distance fallen by a body under gravity from a formula for uniformly accelerated motion, $s = ut + \frac{1}{2}ft^2$, where t is the time, f the acceleration, u the initial or starting velocity, and s the distance. Here the acceleration is g, which is about 32 feet per second per second. If the body is dropped (that is, not thrown), $u = 0$. When $t = 10$, $s = 0 + \frac{1}{2} \times 32 \times 100 = 1,600$; that is, a body falling for 10 seconds under gravity will fall 1,600 feet.

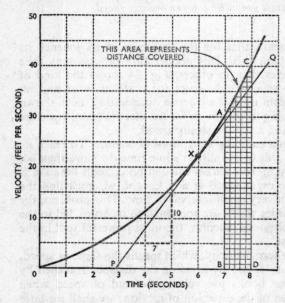

THIS AREA REPRESENTS DISTANCE COVERED

FIG. 35. *Another velocity/time graph. The slope of the tangent PQ at X gives the acceleration at that moment:* $\frac{10}{7}$ *ft. per sec. per sec. The area bounded by AB, CD, time-base and curve gives the distance travelled in the eighth second:* $175 \times \frac{1}{5} = 35$ *ft. (One small square represents* 1 *ft. per sec. per sec.* $\times \frac{1}{5}$ *sec. or* $\frac{1}{5}$ *ft. per sec.)*

Fig. 35 shows how a velocity/time graph may be used to find the acceleration at any instant. This is given by the slope of the tangent which just touches the curve at that point. The distance travelled in a given time may also be found from the graph; two ordinates—that is, perpendiculars—are drawn to the time axis. The area cut off by these ordinates, between the curve and the time axis, gives the distance. Care must be taken to see that units are right; if time is in seconds and velocity in feet/seconds, the distance will be in feet. For a curve such as this, the area may be found by counting squares.

Direction must be taken into consideration in combining velocities or accelerations. If you walk forward at 3 m.p.h. in a train going at 30 m.p.h., along the line of motion of the train, your combined speed, relative to the ground, is 33 m.p.h. If you walk back, still along the same line, your combined speed is 27 m.p.h. But if you walk across the train, at an angle, your combined speed is somewhere between the two, and must be found by some other method.

This is a common problem of the navigator, who sets a course, only to be driven off it by wind or current. He must be able to work

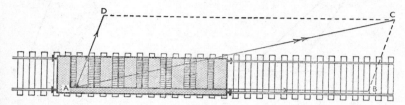

FIG. 36. *If a train is moving along* AB *and a passenger walks from one side of his compartment to the other, in the direction* AD, *he is actually moving —relatively to the earth—in a direction* AC *between the two.*

out the resulting course, to know where he is; and to find the speed and direction of the wind, to put his subsequent calculations right. The air navigator has two speeds to deal with: the air speed, as read by his indicator, and the ground speed at which, as the result of drift due to the wind, he is actually moving, relative to the earth.

It may be seen from Fig. 36 that, if a body has two velocities, it actually moves along a direction between the two. This may be found by drawing a parallelogram the sides of which represent, in magnitude to a suitable scale, the two velocities and also their directions. The diagonal between them will represent the resultant, or combined velocity, both in magnitude and direction.

The full parallelogram need not be drawn, as either triangle, *ABC* or *ACD*, contains all the information, both being identical, except in position. This is the triangle of velocities. In drawing this triangle, the second velocity must be drawn at the end of the first, not the beginning; as though the movement were in two stages, first one velocity applied, then the other.

The sides and angles of this triangle may be calculated by trigonometry, but it may be simpler and accurate enough to draw it to scale and measure. Fig. 37 shows the triangle for the following problem: A pilot sets a course of 135 degrees (that is, S.E.) along which he travels at an air speed of 200 m.p.h. An east wind (that is, coming from the east) blows him off this course at 30 m.p.h. What is his

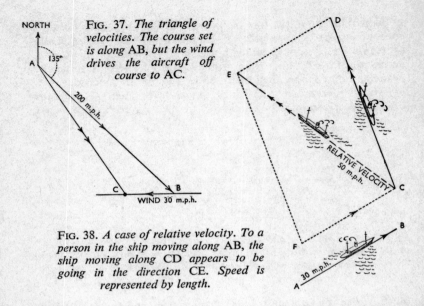

FIG. 37. *The triangle of velocities. The course set is along* AB, *but the wind drives the aircraft off course to* AC.

135°

200 m.p.h.

WIND 30 m.p.h.

RELATIVE VELOCITY 50 m.p.h.

30 m.p.h.

FIG. 38. *A case of relative velocity. To a person in the ship moving along* AB, *the ship moving along* CD *appears to be going in the direction* CE. *Speed is represented by length.*

ground speed and track? By measurement from the diagram we find that the ground speed is 180 m.p.h. and the track 142 degrees; that is, the wind blows him 7 degrees off course and reduces his speed by 20 m.p.h.

At one time this sort of drawing formed an important part of the work of the navigator; nowadays he can depend on instruments or wireless signals to do most of the work for him.

If this had been a nautical problem we might have given the speeds in knots instead of in miles per hour. A knot is a speed of one sea mile per hour. The sea mile is 6,080 ft.; it represents the average length of a minute of longitude at the equator.

Another use of the triangle of velocities is in connexion with relative velocity. If you look out from one ship towards another, the second ship will appear to be going faster than it really is if it is coming towards you, and slower if in the same direction. If it is on lines which are at an angle to your own, it will seem to go in quite another direction (Fig. 38).

This apparent velocity is called its relative velocity. It may be found by cancelling out your own velocity; that is, drawing an equal and opposite velocity and combining it with that of the other ship. This is important in calculating a course to intercept, say, another ship, whose own movement must be allowed for.

5

Number and Form in Nature

Now let us turn to biology and see how mathematics is of use in this science. Even if you have done very little biology you will find that you already know something about it, for surely you have heard at least one talk on diet on the radio, or read at least one article on this topic in your morning newspaper? If you have you will realize that although quality is important so is the quantity of the food; this is a homely example of arithmetic entering into biology. Turn to another page of your newspaper and you come across an article dealing with world population problems, the growth of population being illustrated perhaps by another mathematical device—the graph.

Look around the room and out into the garden; on a dish are some oranges—spheres; look at that tree beyond the piece of lawn—the trunk is essentially in the form of a cylinder. These two common examples illustrate geometry entering into biology. Then stroll down the garden and have a look at that row of broad beans. Are they all exactly the same height? They will vary about some average height; here we are meeting variation, the mathematical treatment of which involves statistics and biometry.

These few examples show that the association of mathematical ideas with biology is not really new. The reader will take heart from this and realize that the first steps have been taken even before he picks up the book to read this chapter. We can now build up steadily and surely from everyday experiences and ordinary common sense.

MEASUREMENT STAKES ITS CLAIM

In the early days biologists were content with the description and classification of the various plants and animals. Measurement did not enter seriously into this early work and, since it was lacking, any mathematical treatment was automatically excluded. The name of Galileo Galilei (1564–1642) is usually associated with the study of the physical sciences, but his attitude to science in general had an important influence on scientific workers in other fields, including biology. He emphasized, among other things, the importance of measurement.

The first man to apply the principles of Galileo in the field of biology was Sanctorius (1561–1636), who was a professor at the University of Padua, in Italy. If your doctor wants to check your pulse rate he feels the wrist in the appropriate spot and times the rate by using his watch. Sanctorius was the first to consider checking pulse rates and comparing them in different persons. For this he needed a measuring instrument. This instrument, called a pulsimeter, consisted of a small pendulum bulb suspended on a string. In use the string was shortened or lengthened until the swinging bulb just kept time with the pulse of the patient, the length of the string being taken as a measure of the pulse rate. Mathematically the idea was very simple, as you may see from Fig. 1.

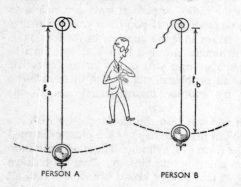

FIG. 1. *Comparative use of the pulsimeter. The time from the commencement of one pulse beat to the commencement of the next is proportional to the square root of the length of the string in use.*

PERSON A   PERSON B

The greatest innovation made by Sanctorius was the weighing of the human body in a specially constructed balance; illustrations of the latter remind one of those large scales often found on the promenade at the seaside. Sanctorius was able to eat and sleep in this oversize balance and record his changes in weight with the passage of time. As a result he was the first to show that the body loses weight by mere exposure to the air; this loss he ascribed to an "insensible perspiration." Nowadays we should say that there is a loss of weight due partly to a loss of water vapour from the skin and lungs and partly to the loss of carbon in the form of carbon dioxide given off by the lungs. Thus Sanctorius began the quantitative study of the body chemistry, now known as metabolism: a study which was to lead up to our present knowledge of foods and nutrition.

The next man worthy of note in the application of measurement in biology is William Harvey (1578–1657), who was educated at Cambridge and Padua and became a physician in London about 1600. He made a number of important discoveries but his name is

206

usually associated with his discovery of the circulation of the blood. One of his pieces of evidence for the latter was a calculation. He found that the left ventricle of the heart could hold two ounces of blood when full and that it pumped 72 times per minute.

Measurement enters into physiology at every turn, but the most familiar example is probably that of the oxygen requirements of the human being. It is of interest to note that the requirement for an adult human being is about 250 cubic centimetres of oxygen per minute; this is something more than the volume of a half-pint tumbler. Under conditions of very hard work the oxygen requirement may rise as high as 4,000 cubic centimetres per minute; this is the equivalent of about eight-ninths of a gallon. The intake of such a large amount obviously means deep and rapid breathing, but what is perhaps not quite so obvious is that the blood must flow through the capillaries of the lungs much faster to carry the required oxygen to the body tissues. Now 100 cubic centimetres of blood can take up and carry 18·5 cubic centimetres of oxygen as it passes through the capillaries of the lungs, and about 70 per cent of the oxygen is removed when the blood passes through capillaries in the muscles.

From the above information it is possible to calculate the rate of blood flow through the lungs when hard work is carried out. Calculate this rate of flow in cubic centimetres per minute for yourself. The rate is quite startling at first sight. Now the total amount of blood in the body is only about 5,000 cubic centimetres; you will soon come to your own conclusions as to what happens. You could obtain some practical idea of the rate of flow of blood to the lungs by comparison with the rate at which the tap over the kitchen sink can discharge water. Use a gallon can as your measure and remember that one gallon is the equivalent of 4,546 cubic centimetres.

GRAPHS AND ALGEBRA IN BIOLOGY

Very often in biology we make two series of measurements at the same time; for example we measure the growth rate of an organism at different temperatures. One way of presenting the information is to make two parallel columns as follows:

Temperature	Rate of growth (per 48 hr.)
16°C.	10 mm.
18°C.	12 mm.
20°C.	17 mm.
22°C.	24 mm.
24°C.	39 mm.
26°C.	56 mm.
28°C.	53 mm.
30°C.	43 mm.

This is all very well but it strikes the eye much more forcibly and aids the memory if the information is presented in a pictorial form, known as the graph. The above measurements may be presented graphically as in Fig. 2.

Graphs show how one factor varies as some second factor varies. Time is very often one of the variables, the other being some dimension or rate. Graphs appear in most types of biology book and tell a tale at a first glance. You will see in Fig. 2 that small changes of temperature have a more marked effect

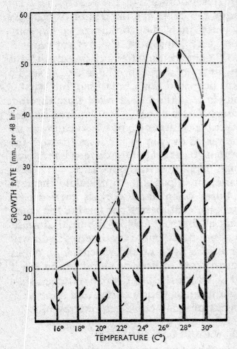

FIG. 2. *The figures tabulated on the preceding page come vividly to life when they are presented in the form of a graph.*

on growth in the region of 24 deg. C. than at lower temperatures and that a steady temperature of 26 deg. C. causes the most rapid growth. Have a look at Fig. 3. You will be able to tell at a glance what these graphs are intended to convey; it will be interesting to see how many inferences you can write down as you study them.

Graphs of population growth always excite interest when seen in the newspaper, particularly if those of different countries are shown together. Numerical ideas on population growth matured much later than numerical ideas in physiology, although there are many references in history to the taking of a census. More deliberate thinking about these matters is usually associated with the name of Thomas Robert Malthus (1766–1834), a clergyman and political economist, who wrote a book in 1798 called *Essay on the Principle of Population*. How do you think a human population would tend

208

to increase? You will probably have more than one answer to this question, depending on the assumptions you make initially. Malthus thought that a human population tends to increase by what is mathematically known as a geometrical progression; this means that the rate of increase at any time is proportional to the size of the population at that time and not its size at some earlier initial date. This geometrical progression is very simple to grasp if an actual case is represented in pictorial form as in Fig. 4. The initial female gives rise to four daughters in her lifetime; they in turn do the same. The successive generations of females are represented by the

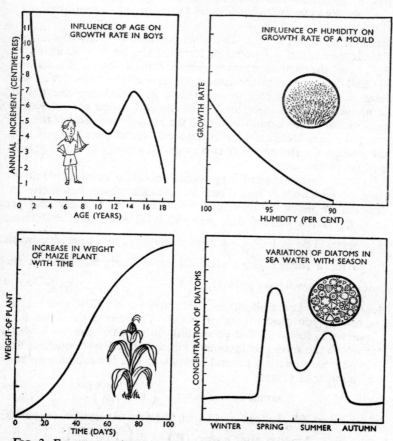

FIG. 3. *Four contrasting examples of graphs, each telling its own story.*

209

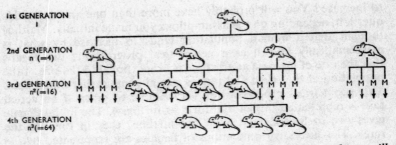

1st GENERATION
1

2nd GENERATION
n (=4)

3rd GENERATION
n^2(=16)   M M M M   M M M M   M M M M

4th GENERATION
n^3(=64)

FIG. 4. *Study these four generations of a mouse population and you will readily understand what is meant by a geometrical progression.*

terms *1, n, n^2, n^3, n^4*, etc. The total population of females at any time is the sum of a number of terms of the series *1, n, n^2, n^3, n^4, n^5, ... n^r*, the particular terms depending on the length of individual life and the time from the commencement of the "line." You will have met the basic idea involved here in considering the law of compound interest. Here interest at the end of the second year is paid on the initial capital sum plus the accrued interest for the first year; the initial capital here corresponds to an initial population, the interest for the first year corresponds to the population growth during the first year.

Let us consider the ordinary investment case of compound interest for a moment and see how it parallels the case of population growth. Assume we invest the sum of £1 for one year at *r* per cent per annum; at the end of one year the total amount after interest payment will be $£\left(1 + \dfrac{r}{100}\right)$. Now suppose we allow the investment to go for a further year; after the second interest payment the principal sum will have grown to $£\left(1 + \dfrac{2r}{100} + \dfrac{r^2}{100 \times 100}\right)$. Do you see how this last amount has been arrived at? Can you see the expression you must expand to get it? To what power must it be expanded? How does this power link up with the number of years for which the money is invested? No doubt you will conclude that it is possible to write a general formula to give the capital sum after any number of years:

$$\text{Amount after } t \text{ years} = \left(1 + \frac{r}{100}\right)^t.$$

If we invest $£P_o$ instead of £1 then the formula can be written as:

$$\text{Amount after } t \text{ years } (P_t) = P_o\left(1 + \frac{r}{100}\right)^t.$$

210

No doubt you will see that the expression $\left(1 + \dfrac{r}{100}\right)$ is a constant, which can be denoted by R, the formula then taking the form:

$$P_t = P_o R^t.$$

The growth of a population of organisms will follow the same formula, the rate of interest in this case being represented by the birth rate in a young population where death has not begun to take its toll. In an older population the rate of interest will be represented by the birth rate minus the death rate. If by any chance the death rate equals the birth rate the population will remain at a stationary level, this corresponding to the lending of a sum of money free of interest. If a graph of population growth is

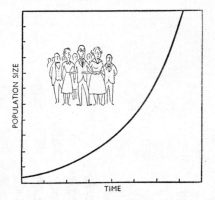

FIG. 5. *Characteristic shape of a population curve which follows the logistic law.*

drawn following the compound interest or, as it is sometimes called, the logistic law, it will have the form of the curve shown in Fig. 5. For any given scale of the graph the higher the net birth rate the steeper the curve.

Malthus realized that the food supply of a human population probably would not rise according to the compound interest law (that is, in geometrical progression) and that this would act as a curb to the rate of population growth. He was rather dogmatic and stated that whereas the population went up in geometrical progression, the available food supply went up only in arithmetical progression.

The contrast between these progressions is diagrammatically represented in Fig. 6. There are disputes still going on as to the rate at which food supplies can be increased. Some experts are pessimistic; others are optimistic and feel that the application of science can do much more than it has done.

Two men closely connected with the early study of human population growth were Quetelet and Verhulst. It is very interesting to note that about 1847 Verhulst demonstrated that the population

211

of the United States was going up in something closely akin to a geometrical progression, but that in older countries like France and Belgium the population-growth curve was already flattening out. It is most interesting to note that in recent years there have been strong indications that the population curve for the United States is beginning to flatten and that the curve is eventually going to look like those of the older countries. It appears that when a country is first colonized the factors impeding expansion are negligible but that as the country is exploited they become more significant and in various ways affect the rate of growth of the population. You might like to think over the factors which affect the age at which people

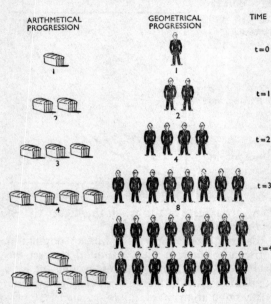

FIG. 6. *The food supplies available to a population can only be increased by arithmetical progression, asserted Malthus, while the population itself multiplies by geometrical progression. The effect of the two rates of increase is illustrated here.*

marry and the number of children they have. Try to visualize how these factors would vary in different types of community. Comparable population-growth curves for the United States and England and Wales are given in Fig. 7. The scales are different but the difference in shape shows up unmistakably.

Like Malthus, Verhulst considered that food supply was a very important factor. He thought that the retarding forces already mentioned above could be expressed as some function of the population size; the higher the population, the greater the factors making for a lowered birth rate. If we had a population increasing by a

212

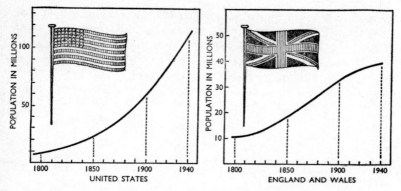

FIG. 7. *Contrasting population curves of "new" and "old" countries.*

pure geometrical progression we could write the following expression:
  Rate of Population Growth $= mP$.
Here m is a constant representing the birth rate, or net birth rate, and P is the population at the time in question. If, however, there is a retarding force coming into play which is related to the size of the population then our expression becomes a little more complicated:
  Rate of Population Growth $= mP - nP^x$.
Here n is another constant, probably representing the effects of food supply, incidence of disease, and so on, and x is the power to which P is to be raised. Examine the above expression and see if you can decide the minimum value of x if a retarding action is to be operative. The expression is probably too simple and more complex ones have been devised to express population growth, but the idea behind them all is the same. The idea is to give mathematical expression to the several factors at work and to be able to predict what is likely to happen to the size of the population in the future.

From expressions for rate of population growth it is possible to derive by means of the integral calculus expressions giving the size of the population after a given time. We have already met in our discussion of compound interest the formula for population assuming no retarding factors are at work. It was $P_t = P_o R^t$. Assuming this type of growth, the population growth of the United States was calculated and compared with the actual records. The tally between the two is very striking but, as has already been mentioned, there are very recent indications that the growth is ceasing to follow a simple geometrical progression. The actual and calculated populations are given in the table overleaf, and it is remarkable that they should

213

be so closely in agreement in spite of the many upheavals in that country, including a civil war, several external wars, and great influxes of immigrants from Europe.

POPULATION OF THE UNITED STATES

Year	Calculated	Observed	Year	Calculated	Observed
1790	3.9×10^6	3.9×10^6	1870	39.4×10^6	38.7×10^6
1800	5·3	5·3	1880	50·2	50·3
1810	7·2	7·2	1890	62·8	63·1
1820	9·8	9·6	1900	76·9	76·1
1830	13·1	12·9	1910	92·0	92·3
1840	17·5	17·1	1920	109·4	106·5
1850	23·2	23·2	1930	123·9	123·2
1860	30·4	31·5			

The type of curve we have been discussing applies not only to human populations but to the populations of other living organisms, such as bacteria, yeast cells and flies. The commonest garden example is probably green fly on the rose bushes, or black fly on the broad-bean plants; you will perhaps be only too familiar with these prolific pests. Here is material for an original investigation. Transfer a known number of black fly on to a clean plant, and then make a number of counts at equal intervals of time. You will be able to find out from the figures if a geometrical progression is being followed. An investigation of this kind would bring home the meaning of geometrical progression more forcibly than any amount of reading. If you attempt this small piece of research, remember to shield the plant to prevent the arrival of immigrants from other surrounding plants, otherwise your counts will be invalidated.

Interest in the mathematics of bacterial population growth began in 1911 and it was found that as long as plenty of food material is available for the bacteria the population rises in geometrical progression—that is, according to the compound interest law. However, as the food supply falls and poisonous materials accumulate in the

×÷×÷×÷×÷×÷×÷×÷×÷×÷×÷×÷×÷×÷×÷×÷×÷×÷×÷
÷ × ×
× ÷
÷ ×
× **Grandsons Galore** ÷
÷ ×
× Grandpa Gubbins, whose age was somewhere between fifty and ÷
÷ seventy, was fond of telling his friends: "Each of my sons has as many ×
× sons as brothers, and the combined number of my sons and grand- ÷
÷ sons is precisely the same as the number of my years." How old was ×
× Gubbins and how many grandsons had he? *Solution on page 444* ÷
÷ ×
×÷×÷×÷×÷×÷×÷×÷×÷×÷×÷×÷×÷×÷×÷×÷×÷×÷×÷

bacterial culture, retarding factors become more and more significant and the population ceases to increase according to the geometrical progression. Accordingly a more complex mathematical expression has to be devised for the growth rate, just as in the study of human populations. A point can be reached where the bacteria are dying off more quickly than new ones are being produced by fission. What will be the natural result of this state of affairs?

Calculated and observed populations have been recorded for several bacteria, including *Bacillus coli*, and there is close correspondence, just as there was between the calculated and observed populations of the United States. In such bacterial cultures there is a very rapid rise in population for a number of hours, the rise being essentially a geometrical progression; then a slowing down makes itself felt, and after about two days a fall in population starts, this fall continuing until relatively few bacteria are left in the culture.

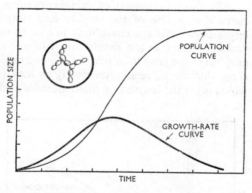

FIG. 8. *The top curve has the characteristic S shape that we get when plotting the growth of a yeast population. The lower curve represents the* rate *at which the population increases.*

POPULATION CURVE

POPULATION SIZE

GROWTH-RATE CURVE

TIME

Similar investigations with yeast cultures have demonstrated the presence of retarding factors, although there is not quite the same tendency for the population to fall as in the bacteria. The S-shaped curve obtained for a yeast population is given in Fig. 8.

In all S-shaped curves the point on the curve where the *rate* of population growth ceases to increase is called the point of inflection. It is possible to plot another curve on the same piece of graph paper showing how the rate of increase of population varies with time, and the result is shown in the lower curve of Fig. 8. It is interesting to note that this lower curve approximates to the normal-error curve which we shall be discussing a little later in this chapter.

Whilst, no doubt, you can readily see that any method of predicting changes in human populations can be of use, you may wonder why we worry about the application of these methods to other animals or to plants. In connexion with pest control, knowledge of likely increases in population would be very useful in organizing preventive measures; it would be particularly useful in locust control to protect important crops for human consumption. Only a beginning has been made in this direction. In nature animal populations often vary in an erratic fashion, this being due apparently to disease and weather conditions.

GROWTH RATE IN THE INDIVIDUAL ORGANISM

Here again the graph is a most useful pictorial device for showing up the variation of two variables. One variable is usually time, the other a length or a weight. Open up any book on the management of children and you will find graphs from which you can read off what young Billy should weigh or how tall he should be at a certain age, assuming he is average.

The graph for growth of a single organism may be a simple smooth curve if it is one of the smaller and simpler organisms, but with larger organisms the curve may not be so simple and may show up various phases in the development of the organism. However, the graphs for the growth of parts of a living organism may be of a simple type; this will be seen quite clearly by looking at the graph in Fig. 9, which is for the length of a plant stem formed during a single growing

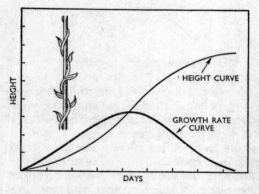

FIG. 9. *Normal growth of a bean plant. These smooth curves are obtained if we plot the data relating to a single bean plant during the course of one growing season.*

season. The rate-of-growth curve is the lower of the two shown. Can you think of any other parts of animals or plants which display steady growth?

In many animals, for example a caterpillar, the graph of weight against time is far from smooth. It shows quite clearly the times

216

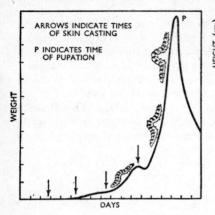

FIG. 10. *Below we have the type of irregular curve corresponding to the growth of a caterpillar.*

ARROWS INDICATE TIMES
OF SKIN CASTING

P INDICATES TIME
OF PUPATION

WEIGHT

DAYS

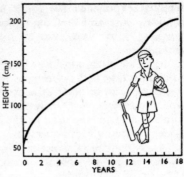

FIG. 11. *The graph above, representing the growth of a boy from birth to the age of eighteen, displays another type of irregular curve.*

when the coats are cast and the change from the larval stage to the pupal stage. This is shown in Fig. 10. The growth curve of a human being, again, is not a regular one. The curve in Fig. 11 is based on the records of measurements taken on a male human being over a period of eighteen years. Note that this is for a particular person, not something compiled from a series of averages obtained from hundreds of individuals. Have a look at the curve; it is not a simple smooth curve. Can you suggest why?

VARIATION AND THE NORMAL-ERROR CURVE

Variation is found in all living organisms. It is due to inheritance or environment, or both. Variation in human height is obvious in any crowd, such as at a football match. If you have had any connexion with farming you will have noticed the variation in size in a litter of young pigs or in a flock of poultry. Again, variation is obvious among plants, witness the variation in size of pea pods on a plant and in the number of peas they contain.

Granted that variations seem to be universal in living things, the question arises whether there is any hope of getting them into some order and understanding them. Consider the football crowd again for a few moments. What would you notice about them? Would all sizes be equally represented? If not, which heights would be rarest? No doubt you already have some ideas, even if you are a little hazy about putting them into words. You know, for instance, from

217

personal experience that very tall men and very short men are relatively rare and that the majority of men seem to be of roughly average height. Now let us try to put a little more precision into our thought.

First we must consider the idea of an average. The best-known type of average is the *arithmetic mean*: this is the average of everyday life. If we wish to obtain the arithmetic mean of a number of individual measurements of height we simply add together the measurements and divide the total by the number of measurements. Averages worked out in various sports like cricket are of this type.

Another type of average is known as *the median*. This literally means the middle observation of a series of observations arranged in order of magnitude. To take a common example, say we have a group of men with the following heights:

70, 67, 68, 74, 70, 73, 72, 68, 70, 69, 71, 71 and 69 inches.

We first arrange these in order of magnitude as follows:

67, 68, 68, 69, 69, 70, 70, 70, 71, 71, 72, 73, 74.

Which is the middle observation or measurement of the series? This figure is the median of the series. Is it the same as the arithmetic mean? Check this for yourself.

One last type of average needs to be mentioned. This is the one known as *the mode* and is very much used in all statistical work. It is taken as the most commonly occurring observation in a series. In the series of human heights we have been considering above it would be 70 inches. However, the mode of a series only shows up unmistakably when a large number of observations is made; putting it another way, a very small group of men may not be representative of the population of which they form a part and to talk of their mode might be misleading.

To recapitulate, there are three kinds of average: the *arithmetic mean, the median* and *the mode*.

Having obtained some clear idea of an "average," we now want to know more about how the individual measurements are scattered about the average value; in other words, we want to give precision to the idea of variation and express it in mathematical terms. There are several ways of measuring the scatter about the average. One way is to measure the *range* of a series of measurements. If in a group of men the tallest is 74 inches and the shortest is 67 inches, the range is 74-67 = 7 inches. Do you think the range is a good measure of variation about the average? What are your reasons?

A second way, having somewhat greater precision, is to give the *inter-quartile range*. This is carried out as follows. Obtain the median in the way already mentioned; this will divide the series

× ÷ × ÷ × ÷ × ÷ × ÷ × ÷ × ÷ × ÷ × ÷ × ÷ × ÷ × ÷ × ÷ × ÷ × ÷ × ÷ × ÷
÷   ×
×   ÷
÷   *Well Played, Sir !*   ×
×   The Vicar saved the game for his side and scored forty runs,   ÷
÷   thereby raising his batting average for the season from twenty-   ×
×   seven to twenty-eight. How many runs would he have required to   ÷
÷   bring his average up to thirty?   Solution on page 444   ×
×   ÷
÷ × ÷ × ÷ × ÷ × ÷ × ÷ × ÷ × ÷ × ÷ × ÷ × ÷ × ÷ × ÷ × ÷ × ÷ × ÷ × ÷ × ÷ ×

into halves. Then find the median of each half in turn. The median of the lower half series is the *lower quartile*, that of the upper half is the *upper quartile*. The difference between the upper and lower quartiles is the *inter-quartile range*.

Say, for example, we measured some bean plants at maturity and obtained the following series of measurements: 27, 24, 20, 21, 23, 24, 25, 22, 26, 23 and 21 inches. We first arrange them in order of magnitude as follows: 20, 21, 21, 22, 23, 23, 24, 24, 25, 26, 27.

The middle term of the series is 23. This divides the series into two halves: a lower half (20, 21, 21, 22, 23) with its own median of 21, and an upper half with its own median of 25. The difference between 25 and 21, namely 4, is the inter-quartile range. This means of measuring scatter or variation has the merit of very largely excluding the influence of extreme measurements on the result. It is greatly superior to the earlier range measurement, which is obviously very prone to sampling errors.

A third method of measuring variation is to calculate the *mean deviation*. This consists in adding together the differences between the several measurements and the median, irrespective of sign, and dividing this sum by the number of measurements. Try and work out the mean deviation of the following series of height measurements, taking 70 inches as the median:

67, 68, 68, 69, 69, 70, 70, 70, 71, 71, 71, 72, 72, 73 and 74.

The last method of measuring variation involves calculating the *standard deviation* and it is the most important method in use. There is nothing difficult about it provided the steps in the process are mastered. It is arrived at as follows:

(1) Calculate the arithmetic mean of the series of measurements.
(2) Find the difference between the arithmetic mean and each individual measurement in turn.
(3) Square each difference.
(4) Add together the squares so calculated.
(5) Divide their sum by the number of measurements involved.
(6) Finally, find the square root of the result calculated in (5).

This may seem all very involved but an actual example worked out should make it quite clear. It may be mentioned right away that the calculation is greatly facilitated by arranging it in tabular form. Let us suppose that we measure twenty men for height; we would arrange our data as follows:

Man Number	Height (inches)	Deviations from Mean minus	plus	Square of Deviation
1	69	1	–	1
2	70	–	–	0
3	72	–	2	4
4	71	–	1	1
5	69	1	–	1
6	68	2	–	4
7	66	4	–	16
8	70	–	–	0
9	71	–	1	1
10	72	–	2	4
11	69	1	–	1
12	73	–	3	9
13	71	–	1	1
14	69	1	–	1
15	68	2	–	4
16	70	–	–	0
17	73	–	3	9
18	67	3	–	9
19	72	–	2	4
20	70	–	–	0
Total 1,400		15	15	Total 70

Divide by 20
Arithmetic Mean = 70

The sum of the squares, 70, has to be divided by 20, the number of measurements made. This gives 3·5, and the square root of this (1·87) is the standard deviation.

The idea of standard deviation is so important that the reader should test his grasp of the method at this point by working out with pencil and paper the standard deviation for the series 1, 2, 3, 4, 5, 6, 7, 8, 9, 10, 11. Before you calculate it do you think it will come out greater or less than the 1·87 in the above example? And why?

In mathematical terms the standard deviation is usually expressed as follows:

$$\sigma = \sqrt{\frac{\Sigma (X - \bar{X})^2}{N}}.$$

In this expression σ is the Greek letter sigma and is the symbol for the standard deviation, X represents any particular single measurement, whereas $\bar{X}$ is the arithmetic mean of the series of measurements; so $(X - \bar{X})$ is a deviation and $(X - \bar{X})^2$ is that deviation squared. The symbol Σ means *sum of*; hence $\Sigma(X - \bar{X})^2$ is the sum of all the squared deviations. The number of measurements in the series is of course represented by N.

Whether we are dealing with the weight of bean seeds, the height of human beings or their intelligence quotients, the same technique can be used. It crops up in every mathematical approach to variation in plants and animals.

So far we have got two measures in connexion with variability: an average value and a measure of variation (called the standard deviation) about that average. For comparative purposes it is sometimes useful to have a figure which in itself compares the arithmetic mean with the standard deviation. This is called *the coefficient of variation*. It is calculated as follows:

$$\text{Coefficient of variation } (C) = \frac{\text{Standard deviation} \times 100\%}{\text{Arithmetic mean}}.$$

Look back and calculate the coefficient of variation in the case of human heights used to illustrate the method of calculation of standard deviation. In comparing variability in different human races this coefficient is important, as not only will the standard deviation differ from race to race but so also will the arithmetic mean. Mere comparison of the standard deviations would not be a fair comparison.

Having now obtained an idea of the terms in which variation in living organisms can be expressed we can go on to consider the normal-error curve. For purposes of illustration let us pick out at random a hundred men from a crowd and measure their heights. The results would appear somewhat as follows:

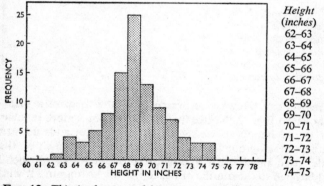

Height (inches)	Number of men
62–63	1
63–64	4
64–65	3
65–66	5
66–67	8
67–68	15
68–69	25
69–70	13
70–71	9
71–72	7
72–73	4
73–74	3
74–75	3
	100

FIG. 12. *This is the sort of histogram we get from the adjoining table of heights of a hundred men.*

221

These results can be shown in a graphical form usually known as a histogram. The histogram will appear as shown in Fig. 12. Let us go on measuring men until we have measured a thousand; our table would now look something as follows:

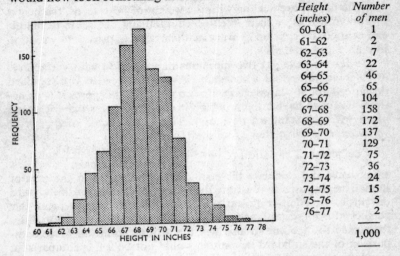

Height (inches)	Number of men
60–61	1
61–62	2
62–63	7
63–64	22
64–65	46
65–66	65
66–67	104
67–68	158
68–69	172
69–70	137
70–71	129
71–72	75
72–73	36
73–74	24
74–75	15
75–76	5
76–77	2
	1,000

FIG. 13. *From the measurements of a thousand men we obtain a more symmetrical histogram, as above.*

FIG. 14. *The smooth, bell-shaped curve which results when the steps in the height scale are much reduced and the number of people measured is greatly increased.*

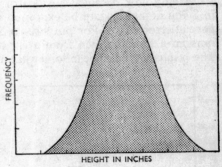

These results can likewise be presented in the form of a histogram, as shown in Fig. 13. Notice that the histogram is more regular. Now what would happen if we measured many thousands of men and, instead of making our histogram with steps of one inch on the height scale, used much smaller steps, say one-tenth of an inch? What must happen to the outline of the top of the histogram? It will, of course, eventually become a smooth bell-shaped curve as shown in Fig. 14.

222

The bell-shaped curve so obtained is usually a normal-error curve in the mathematical sense or a very close approximation thereto. Countless characters in living organisms display variation of this type and clearly it would be worth while to know more about it; so let us leave the biological facts for a few moments and see if we can find out what the normal-error curve represents mathematically. This understanding is quite straightforward provided we proceed step by step. If we can find out something mathematically about the normal-error curve then we shall have another tool for use when considering the fact of variation. We shall find the normal-error curve is the master link between statistics on the one hand and the theory of probability on the other. Here we will make what seems like a digression and consider probability.

WHAT WE MEAN BY PROBABILITY

Say we have a bag containing a very large number of balls, half of them black, the other half white. Now we draw one ball out. What is the probability that it will be black? Or white? Very easy, you will say, there is a fifty-fifty chance in each case. This may be expressed as probability of black $= \frac{1}{2}$ and probability of white $= \frac{1}{2}$, the probability of a ball of some sort coming out of the bag being 1. Instead of writing fractions in each case we could let W represent the probability of white coming out and B represent the probability of black coming out. A comparable problem in probability is presented by spinning a coin. Perhaps you would like to spin a coin a large number of times, record the results, and notice the ratio of heads to tails? What do you find?

Now let us take the matter a stage further. Suppose we take one ball out, note its colour and return it; shake the bag and draw out a second ball, again noting colour and replacing. What possible results are there? What are the probabilities of each possible result? Halt at this point and before proceeding come to your own conclusions; it requires no mathematical knowledge—just the application of common sense. If you have had difficulty, let us see if the matter can be explained. First, how many possibilities are there? The first ball may be black—assume it is for a moment. The second ball may be white or black. Thus there are two possibilities: black-black and black-white. If the first ball was white, not black, then again there are two possibilities: white-black and white-white. To summarize, the possible combinations are: black-black, black-white, white-black, white-white.

Now we have to consider the probabilities of the several combinations. The probability of black coming up on the first draw is

$B = \frac{1}{2}$; the probability of its coming up on the second draw is the same; the probability of black-black is obtained by multiplying the separate probabilities, namely $B \times B$, or $\frac{1}{2} \times \frac{1}{2} = \frac{1}{4}$. Note particularly here that the separate probabilities are not added but multiplied. Can you see why? In a similar way the probability of two whites is $W \times W = \frac{1}{2} \times \frac{1}{2} = \frac{1}{4}$; the probability of black-white is $B \times W = \frac{1}{2} \times \frac{1}{2} = \frac{1}{4}$; and the probability of white-black is $W \times B = \frac{1}{2} \times \frac{1}{2} = \frac{1}{4}$.

Recapitulating in tabular form, we have:

$$\text{Probability of black-black} = B^2 = (\tfrac{1}{2})^2 = \tfrac{1}{4}$$
$$\text{white-white} = W^2 = (\tfrac{1}{2})^2 = \tfrac{1}{4}$$
$$\text{black-white} = BW = (\tfrac{1}{2})^2 = \tfrac{1}{4}$$
$$\text{white-black} = WB = (\tfrac{1}{2})^2 = \tfrac{1}{4}$$

Now, looking at this summary, what is the probability of obtaining a black and a white, irrespective of order? Do you see that it is $2BW$ or $2WB$, namely $2(\frac{1}{4}) = \frac{1}{2}$? Summing up, then, we could say that the probability of two black balls is $B \times B$, or B^2, the probability of two white balls is $W \times W$, or W^2, and the probability of mixed colours is $2B \times W$, or $2BW$. It is now important to notice that these probabilities may be represented by the terms of the expansion of the expression $(W + B)^2$. Check for yourself that this conclusion is correct.

One final stage and we shall begin to see definite order entering into this business of probability. Suppose that we draw three balls in turn from the bag, replacing each after noting whether it is black or white. What are the combinations which are possible? Get out pencil and paper and see how many you can find. Also, what are the probabilities of the several combinations? Did you find it difficult? If so, let us look at the method of working it out. Assuming the first ball is white, what could it be followed by? Obviously white-white, black-black, black-white or white-black. Thus, with a white ball leading off on the first draw there are only four possible combinations. In the same way there are four combinations when a black ball starts off. The grand total of combinations is therefore eight. What now is the probability of any particular combination coming up? The product of the individual probabilities, namely $\frac{1}{2} \times \frac{1}{2} \times \frac{1}{2} = \frac{1}{8}$. From this work out on paper the probabilities of the following sets of three balls, irrespective of the order in which they appear:

> Three whites
> Two whites and one black
> One white and two blacks
> Three blacks.

Enough has been said above to make this possible. Compare your results with the expansion of the expression $(W + B)^3$, remembering that $W = \frac{1}{2}$ and $B = \frac{1}{2}$.

At this point you will see daylight beginning to appear. It is becoming apparent that hit or miss methods for ascertaining probabilities can be scrapped and a mathematical expression employed instead. What we have come across here, without the name being used so far, is the Binomial Expansion. Instead of learning it as a matter of duty we have arrived at it in a natural way, and we have seen in the process that it has great usefulness.

USING THE BINOMIAL THEOREM

Expressed in its general form the binomial theorem looks quite formidable, but in essence it is nothing more than we have been dealing with over the last page or two. Here it is in the form in which we have met it:

$$(W + B)^n = W^n + nW^{(n-1)}B + \frac{n(n - 1)}{2!} W^{(n-2)}B^2$$
$$+ \frac{n(n - 1)(n - 2)}{3!} W^{(n-3)}B^3 + \ldots B^n$$

In this B represents the probability of black coming out of the bag, W represents the probability of a white ball coming out, and n represents the number of balls drawn at one time. Note also that 2! denotes *factorial* 2, namely 2×1; in the same way 3! represents factorial 3, namely $3 \times 2 \times 1$. Taking $n = 3$, and remembering $W = \frac{1}{2}$ and $B = \frac{1}{2}$, substitute these values in the above expression and see that you come to the same result as we reached earlier for the case where the balls were withdrawn in batches of three. It may seem difficult at first, so let us take it step by step as follows:

$$(W + B)^n = W^n + nW^{(n-1)}B + \frac{n(n - 1)}{2!} W^{(n-2)}B^2$$
$$+ \frac{n(n - 1)(n - 2)}{3!} W^{(n-3)}B^n$$

Taking n as 3 we have:

$$(W + B)^3 = W^3 + 3W^2B + \frac{3(2)}{2 \times 1} WB^2 + \frac{3(2)(1)}{3 \times 2 \times 1} B^3$$
$$= W^3 + 3W^2B + 3WB^2 + B^3$$

In other words, out of eight draws one in eight will give all three balls white, one in eight all balls black, three out of eight two white balls and one black ball, and three out of eight draws will give two black balls and one white ball.

You will now begin to realize that the binomial theorem, far from being a dry-as-dust expression, is a very useful mathematical tool for dealing with cases of probability where working out from first principles every time would prove very tedious and time-consuming.

Now let us use the binomial theorem to find out the probability of various combinations if we draw ten balls from a bag containing equal numbers of white and black balls. The possible combinations are obviously:

> Ten black
> Nine black and one white
> Eight black and two white
> Seven black and three white
> Six black and four white
> and so on, to
> Ten white.

By the binomial theorem the probability of ten black balls is given by $B^n = (\frac{1}{2})^{10} = \frac{1}{1,024}$.

Likewise, the probability of ten white balls is given by W^n; in other words, the probability is the same as for ten black balls. Just common sense you will say. Yes, it is just that.

The probability of nine black balls and one white (and nine white balls with one black) is given by the second term of the binomial expansion:

$$nW^{(n-1)}B = 10(\tfrac{1}{2})^9 \times \tfrac{1}{2} = \tfrac{10}{1,024}.$$

The probability of eight black balls and two white (and eight white and two black) is given by the third term of the binomial expansion:

$$\frac{n(n-1)}{2 \times 1} W^{(n-2)}B^2 = \frac{10(10-1)(\tfrac{1}{2})^8(\tfrac{1}{2})^2}{2 \times 1} = \tfrac{45}{1,024}.$$

The probability of seven black balls and three white balls (and seven white and three black) is given by the fourth term of the expansion:

$$\frac{n(n-1)(n-2)}{3 \times 2 \times 1} W^{(n-3)}B^3 = \tfrac{120}{1,024}.$$

The probability of six black balls and four white balls (and six white balls and four black) is given by the fifth term of the expansion:

$$\frac{n(n-1)(n-2)(n-3)}{4 \times 3 \times 2 \times 1} W^{(n-4)}B^4 = \tfrac{210}{1,024}.$$

The last probability to be worked out is for five black balls and five white balls. This will be given by the sixth term of the expansion, as follows:

$$\frac{n(n-1)(n-2)(n-3)(n-4)}{5 \times 4 \times 3 \times 2 \times 1} W^{(n-5)}B^5 = \tfrac{252}{1,024}.$$

226

Collecting together the several probabilities, we have the following summary:

Probability of		
ten blacks	=	$\frac{1}{1,024}$
nine blacks and one white	=	$\frac{10}{1,024}$
eight blacks and two whites	=	$\frac{45}{1,024}$
seven blacks and three whites	=	$\frac{120}{1,024}$
six blacks and four whites	=	$\frac{210}{1,024}$
five blacks and five whites	=	$\frac{252}{1,024}$
four blacks and six whites	=	$\frac{210}{1,024}$
three blacks and seven whites	=	$\frac{120}{1,024}$
two blacks and eight whites	=	$\frac{45}{1,024}$
one black and nine whites	=	$\frac{10}{1,024}$
ten whites	=	$\frac{1}{1,024}$

This means that if we take 1,024 batches of ten balls each then it is probable that we shall draw five black plus five white 252 times, and so on. These probabilities can be presented in the form of a graph as given in Fig. 15. Notice that the graph is a symmetrical

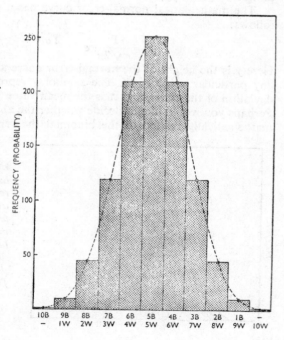

FIG. 15. *Frequency histograph which shows the probability of drawing particular combinations of black balls and white balls from a bag containing an equal number of each. The combinations possible are shown on the horizontal axis. The frequency with which each is likely to turn up, in the course of 1,024 repetitions of the process, is shown on the vertical scale.*

FREQUENCY (PROBABILITY)

227

one. No doubt you can see that we are arriving at a curve very like that showing distribution of height in men or of weight in bean seeds. What would happen if instead of dealing with batches of ten balls we dealt with batches of one hundred? It would mean a binomial expansion of many more terms and there would be 101 points to plot on our graph instead of only eleven. A much smoother curve would result, approximating still more closely to a height-distribution curve. As n is raised in value so the graph will approximate more and more closely to the smooth bell-shaped curve.

We see from all this that the normal-error curve is in reality a probability curve. This is an important conclusion with very important consequences. It was first used, not in biology, but in astronomy in connexion with the theory of errors of measurement. To take an exact measurement is impossible; error creeps in through the instrument used because of the inherent limitations of its construction, and also because of error in handling by the human observer. For example, if you measure the length of a strip of metal a very large number of times you will finish up with a series of readings which are not all the same but which will give a normal-error curve when plotted on graph paper.

The mathematical normal-error curve has a precise formula, as follows:

$$y = \frac{1}{\sigma\sqrt{2\pi}} \cdot e^{\dfrac{-(X - \bar{X})^2}{2\sigma^2}}$$

Here y is the height of the normal-error curve above the x axis for any particular value of X. The symbol σ represents the standard deviation of the curve, and $\bar{X}$ is the mean value for the distribution. Perhaps you would like to decide whether the above formula will be mathematically related to the binomial theorem? A normal-error

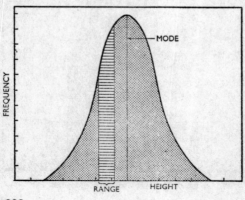

FIG. 16. *Height distribution curve. If we regard the whole area under the curve as unity, the ruled area is a measure of the probability that an individual chosen at random will have a height falling within the indicated range.*

curve strictly stretches away to infinity in both directions but for practical purposes only the main central portion is of interest. The mean of the observations is in the exact centre of the curve, and since the curve is symmetrical the mode and the median coincide.

Another important point to note is that the area contained between any two vertical lines drawn up from the x axis to meet the curve is a measure of the probability of an observation coming within that range (see Fig. 16). This is a most important fact. Can you see the possible uses to which this fact could be put? Expressing the above in terms of standard deviation, which we considered earlier on, the percentage area between verticals from points corresponding with σ and $-\sigma$ is 68 per cent of the total area; between 2σ and -2σ it is 95 per cent; and between 3σ and -3σ it is 99·7 per cent. Note that the vast pro-portion of cases comes with the

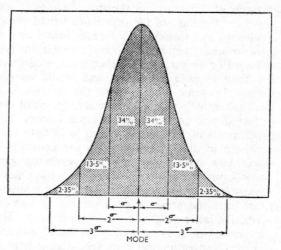

FIG. 17. *Diagram showing the area percentages which are enclosed by verticals variously displaced from the mode.*

range 3σ to -3σ; in other words, a range equal to six times the standard deviation. The above point will be made clear by reference to Fig. 17.

You have probably already realized that the properties of the normal-error curve are of the greatest importance in estimating probable error and in connexion with the theory of sampling. They also crop up in connexion with the concept of *significance* in the interpretation of experimental results. Just a word of warning about bell-shaped curves. In practice it is unwise to regard any bell-shaped curve resulting from the graphical representation of practical measurements in biology as being a perfect normal-error curve in the mathematical sense. So much statistical treatment of results assumes normal distribution that we need to know that in fact we have a

229

normal distribution or something closely approximating to it. If the distribution is well away from a normal one then subsequent calculations are invalidated at the outset. Tests can be made for normality of a distribution; this involves quite an amount of mathematical work, yet in a new investigation it would have to be carried out.

We have seen that the normal-error curve is, mathematically speaking, a probability curve, yet it crops up in practice directly we become interested in the distribution of height or weight in living organisms. Can you see any connexion between probability on the one hand and the fact of variation in living organisms on the other? Putting it another way, what is the possible mechanism behind variation?

One possible explanation would be to account for all the variations in terms of differences in the surroundings in which the organisms grow up; the bulk of the organisms would grow up under average conditions and would reach average height or weight; others would grow up under better than average conditions and would be greater in height or weight; on the other hand, others would grow up under less than average conditions and would be smaller in height or weight. In some cases, where the organisms are all genetically identical (exactly alike from the standpoint of heredity), variation is in fact due to purely environmental factors. This is shown by the experiments of Johannsen, begun in 1900 to test the inheritance of variation in dwarf beans, which are normally self-pollinated. No doubt you are familiar with this common garden vegetable and know from personal experience that the seeds are not all of the same weight. Johannsen started off with a single mother bean seed (pure line) and grew a plant from it which in due course produced seeds, the latter ranging from small to large. These in turn became mother beans. A large seed was planted and in due course it gave the next generation of bean seeds, also displaying variation, and having a certain mean weight; likewise a small bean was planted and eventually gave a new generation of bean seeds, showing variation.

But what of the mean weight and standard deviation of the progeny of the small seed? Within the limits of sampling error it was the same as that for the progeny of the large seed. In other words, variations were due to environmental influences and not to any intrinsic difference between the beans. This was a startling discovery in its day. It will be appreciated by reference to Fig. 18. We can say, then, that where we are dealing with organisms which are all intrinsically or genetically alike variations are due to environmental factors which will vary in the incidence on the individual organisms so as to result in a normal-distribution curve for weight, height, and so on.

But environmental influences are not the only ones which can result in something approaching the normal distribution. Some plants when grown under remarkably even conditions can display significant variations right through from small to large, and the distribution approaches the normal. Here one comes to the conclusion that the differences are due to internal differences; the

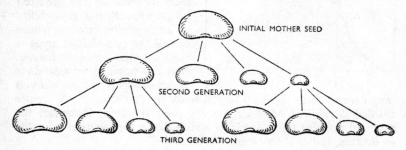

FIG. 18. *The result of Johannsen's interesting bean experiment. The progeny of the smallest bean in the second generation showed the same range of variation as the progeny of the largest bean.*

individual plants are not similar in their internal make-up; their inheritance from their parents has not been the same. In cases of this kind a large number of internal factors or *genes* are involved with the development of the height of the plant. As we shall see later, the factors which any plant inherits from the previous generation are the result of chance, and it is because of this fact that the height distribution follows the normal curve, which as we have seen already is a probability curve.

THE USE OF PROBABILITY INTEGRALS

A problem which often arises in connexion with any normal distribution is that of calculating the proportion of the population of organisms which will fall within a particular range of size. Look at Fig. 19 and imagine we want to know the proportion of organisms which would fall in the shaded area. It has been proved that for all normal curves the ratio x/σ (where x is the deviation from the mean and σ the standard deviation) bears a definite relation to the proportion into which the normal curve is divided by an ordinate raised at any deviation from the mean. Tables have been prepared, called probability integrals, which, given the value of x/σ, can be

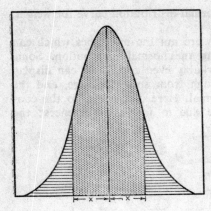

FIG. 19. *The use of probability integrals. What proportion of organisms will fall within the area under the curve covered by the stippled shading?*

used to read off the required proportion. If the probability of an organism coming within one of the two shaded areas is required, the value is halved. It is not possible to reproduce tables of this type here, but you may care to look them up in the book by Professor R. A. Fisher entitled *Statistical Methods for Research Workers*. However, the essential point at this stage is to realize that a technique is available to do this, rather than to go into details.

THE USE OF THE STANDARD ERROR

If you were investigating the variation of height in some particular organism, which would give you the most reliable information, the measurement of ten individuals or the measurement of a thousand? Obviously, the greater the number that can be measured the more accurate will be the picture obtained. Yet in many cases time or circumstances preclude the measurement of very large numbers. Is there any way of gauging the reliability of the sample from the population? Fortunately there is and it involves the idea of a standard error. It can be defined as follows:

$$\text{Standard error of sample} = \frac{\text{Standard deviation of sample}}{\sqrt{\text{Number of individuals in sample}}}$$

$$= \frac{\sigma}{\sqrt{n}}$$

From the figure so calculated, and using the probability integral tables referred to above, it is possible to calculate the probability of the true mean of the population being within a given range on either side of the mean of the sample. In other words, a measure of the reliability of the information obtained from the sample can be obtained. This technique applies not only in biological matters but also in other spheres of activity where sampling is involved.

Imagine that we have two breeds of cattle and we wish to know if one breed is larger than the other at maturity. Life is too short

232

to measure thousands of each breed; we have usually to be content with measuring a relative few, say about fifty of each. But an apparent snag creeps in. Are the samples really representative? All that we can find out is the probability of their being representative, but this is something well worth knowing if we cannot examine the whole population of each breed. The calculation involves a knowledge of the standard errors of the two samples, a knowledge of the difference between their means, and again the use of the probability integral tables. If the probability so calculated comes out at odds of 19:1 or higher then the difference between the two samples is regarded as significant. This is sometimes referred to as the 5 per cent level of significance.

The idea of significance is always cropping up in the discussion of the results of biological experiments. It is such an important subject that Professor R. A. Fisher has written a book on it entitled *The Design of Experiments*.

THE IDEA OF CORRELATION

Correlation is a measure of the association between two factors. A simple example of correlation would be that between weight and pulling power in cart-horses; this would be called a positive correlation. What other cases of positive correlation can you think of? The living world is full of interesting examples. See how many you can collect. A correlation may, on the other hand, be negative; an example would be the volume of milk produced by cows and the fat content of the milk. Usually, as the volume produced goes up the percentage of fat declines.

Complete positive correlation is denoted by a correlation coefficient of 1, complete negative correlation by a correlation coefficient of -1. Complete lack of correlation is denoted by a correlation coefficient of 0. How is this correlation coefficient arrived at? It is usually denoted by r and is given by the following formula:

$$r = \frac{\Sigma(X - \bar{X})(Y - \bar{Y})}{N \, \sigma_x \, \sigma_y}$$

The use of the formula is best illustrated by taking a possible case. Say, for example, we are interested in working out the correlation coefficient between height and weight for a group of people. In the formula N represents the total number of people σ_x represents the standard deviation for height, and σ_y the standard deviation for weight. $\bar{X}$ is the mean value for height and $\bar{Y}$ the mean value for weight. What we have to do is to take an individual and measure the height (X) and the weight (Y); we can then work out ($X - \bar{X}$) and ($Y - \bar{Y}$) and multiply the two values together. This is repeated for each individual and the several products are added together; the addition is denoted by the symbol Σ in the formula.

The same technique is used in finding the coefficient of correlation between different types of mental activity; for example, between two subjects studied by schoolchildren. You can check your grasp of the technique by trying out the following problem.

Ten children were given tests in algebra and arithmetic, the maximum score in each subject being 10. The results were as follows:

Child:	A	B	C	D	E	F	G	H	I	J
Algebra Score:	4	6	8	8	10	5	4	5	1	9
Arithmetic Score:	7	4	8	10	8	7	3	9	6	8

From the above figures calculate the coefficient of correlation between the two sets of marks.

Since only a small number of pairs of marks is involved you will find the following derived formula for the coefficient most useful. It is:

$$\text{Coefficient of correlation} = \frac{\dfrac{\Sigma(XY)}{N} - \overline{X}\,\overline{Y}}{\sigma_x\,\sigma_y}$$

Here σ_x may be calulated from the derived formula—

$$= \sqrt{\frac{\Sigma(X^2)}{N} - \overline{X}^2}$$

Likewise σ_y may be calculated from the formula—

$$= \sqrt{\frac{\Sigma(Y^2)}{N} - \overline{Y}^2}$$

You will find it best to set out your figures in columns systematically as follows:

Algebra Mark (X)	Arithmetic Mark (Y)	X^2	Y^2	XY
4	7	16	49	28

etc., etc.

You will find that the correlation coefficient is a positive number and in value is nearly ·5. What significance can be attached to the result? We conclude that there is a definite connexion between the performances in algebra and arithmetic—not a complete correlation, which would be indicated by a correlation coefficient of $+ 1$, but nevertheless something worthy of note. It can be taken to indicate that from a mental point of view algebra and arithmetic have certain elements in common and that one who performs well in one will tend, on average, to perform at least fairly well in the other.

How accurate is the value for the coefficient likely to be when only ten children have been investigated? Here we are up against the old problem of sampling. Study of several more samples would soon

234

give us an idea of the reliability of our initial figure; they would not lead to a change of sign in the coefficient but they might cause us to raise or lower the value slightly. If our coefficient had come out at $-\cdot5$ instead of $+\cdot5$ it would have indicated a negative or inverse correlation; that is, the better at arithmetic a child is, the worse he tends to be at algebra. Correlation coefficients generally can come anywhere between -1 and $+1$.

There are other allied techniques for calculating the degree of correlation but the foregoing example is sufficient to show how the problem is tackled on statistical lines. The calculation is important in the study of growth processes. In some of these, growth rates of different parts keep in step and a correlation coefficient approaching 1 may be calculated; in other cases a lower figure is obtained.

Now we must leave the normal-error curve and all that centres round it and proceed to deal with another biological topic where again probability forms the centre of the subject—namely, heredity.

HEREDITY AND ITS MATHEMATICS

Heredity as a subject concerns itself with the inheritance of characters by young animals or plants from their parents. Alternative names for the subject are genetics and Mendelism; how these names have risen will become obvious later on. You will know something of the subject already from everyday observation: one cannot go more than a day without thinking of it. Popular conversation is always commenting on the likeness of so-and-so to his father, uncle or grandfather. Poultry breeders breeding from pure White Leghorn poultry expect to obtain more White Leghorns in the next generation. Breed from what are known as mongrels and no one is surprised at the motley collection which appears in the next generation.

The idea of inheritance is as old as Man, and unconscious experiments and attempts at selection have been going on from time immemorial. Over the centuries selective breeding of animals and plants gave important results from a practical point of view but no real advance was made in understanding the factors which are at work or the mathematics of inheritance. A number of biologists, including the celebrated Charles Darwin, came near to a solution of the problem, but lost their way because instead of considering the inheritance of a single character at a time they tried to consider all the characters displayed by an animal or plant at once. Again, none of them seems to have realized that the laws of inheritance would prove to be statistical laws.

Several of these pioneers used the garden pea, a plant which yielded far-reaching results in the hands of Gregor Mendel. The latter was born in 1822 and carried out his experiments, in what is now Czechoslovakia, during the middle of the last century. Many heard of his work at the time but no one appreciated what was taking place under their very noses; still, this was excusable since no one in the scientific world could see any more clearly. We will have a look at what Mendel did before we come to consider the mathematical explanation of the results obtained.

The key to Mendel's success was partly due to his choice of the garden pea as the experimental material, but was also due to the following vital points:

(1) He chose strongly contrasted characters for investigation (for example, tallness and dwarfness).

(2) He dealt with only one (or only a few) pairs of contrasted characters in any one experiment.

(3) He kept very precise pedigree records of each plant studied.

(4) He treated his results on *statistical* lines. This is the most vital point and the most interesting from our present point of view.

(5) He was prepared to construct an hypothesis based on *probability* to account for his numerical results.

Long before Mendel began his experiments he knew that the garden pea had a number of clearly marked varieties which bred true from generation to generation because of the self-pollinating properties of the pea flower. Many of these varieties will be familiar to you; have a look at any seed catalogue and refresh your memory of some of the kinds seedsmen supply these days. Mendel looked for varieties which had sharply contrasting characters to use in his crossing experiments, and after a number of preliminary tests he chose the following seven pairs of characters for investigation:

(1) A pair differing in the shape of the ripe seed, the contrasting characters being *round* and *wrinkled*.

(2) A pair differing in the colour of the seed-leaves within the seed-coat; that is, *yellow* and *green*.

(3) A pair differing in the tint of the seed-coat; that is, *white* and *coloured*.

(4) A pair differing in the shape of the ripe pods; that is, *inflated pod* and *constricted pod*.

(5) A pair differing in the colour of the unripe pods; that is, *green* and *yellow*.

(6) A pair differing in flower position; that is, *axial flower* and *terminal flower*.

(7) A pair differing in the height of the plant; that is, *tall* and *dwarf*.

If you have peas growing in the garden at this moment why not go out and have a look at them to see what their real characters are in terms of pod shape, position of flower on the plant, and so on. Before going on to describe a typical Mendelian experiment and its explanation in terms of probability, it must be mentioned that in the time of Mendel sexuality in flowering plants was basically understood, although other important details became known somewhat later. It was realized that the counterpart of the animal egg-cell is contained in the young seed (ovule) and that the counterpart of the animal sperm is to be found in the germinating pollen grain. Mendel knew nothing of the chromosomes and genes we hear so much about today.

In his first experiments Mendel carried out the crossing of forms of garden pea differing in only one pair of contrasted characters. Although seven pairs were so investigated it is necessary to describe only one of them to bring out the principle involved. In one experiment he crossed a pure-breeding, round-seeded pea with a pure-breeding, wrinkled-seeded pea. He found that the seeds produced as a result of the crossing were all round; he sowed these seeds and allowed the plants so produced to self-pollinate. He found, when large numbers were concerned, that the seeds in the pods of the self-pollinated plants were not all alike; they were in the ratio of three round seeds to every one wrinkled seed.

Mendel did not stop at this point but sowed this latest crop of seeds and allowed the resulting plants to self-pollinate. He obtained most interesting results. Wrinkled seeds gave plants which produced only wrinkled seeds in turn; in other words, they seemed just like the original wrinkled peas he started with. One-third of the round peas gave plants which produced round seeds only, just like the original round peas he started with. The remaining two-thirds of round seeds gave plants which produced round and wrinkled in the ratio of 3:1; in other words, they seemed to be like the second generation. The results are portrayed in Fig. 20a.

The Gambler Who Lost

The gambler had lost all his money. He had a gold chain of seven links which his opponent agreed to value at £1 per link. The play proceeded at £1 per game and the debts were settled after each. The gambler lost each time, as his opponent expected. What was the least number of links that had to be cut? *Solution on page 444*

It should be noted here that Mendel carried out the first generation crossing in both directions and obtained the same numerical results. That is, in one experiment he pollinated the pure round-type pea flower with pollen from the pure wrinkled-type pea flower, while in the other pollen went from the pure round to the pure wrinkled. From what has been said the reader will have noticed that roundness can mask wrinkledness; that is to say, the wrinkled character can appear in a later generation. The masking character Mendel called the *dominant* character, the one which was masked he called the *recessive* character.

Presented by his careful recording with the above numerical data, Mendel then had the brilliance to see that a hypothesis based on probability, given certain conditions, could provide an explanation of the experimental results. The necessary conditions were:

(1) That when the second generation produces its sex cells any individual sex cells shall carry either a factor for roundness *or* a factor for wrinkledness, but not both.

(2) That sex cells, or gametes, of the two types shall be formed in equal numbers.

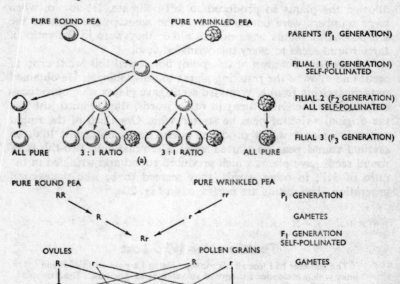

FIG. 20. *The inheritance of seed-coat surfaces in peas.* (a) *Result of crossing round and wrinkled peas.* (b) *The same result set out symbolically.*

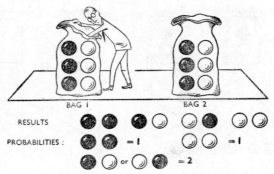

FIG. 21. *Four combinations are possible if we draw one ball from the first bag and one from the second. The probability of each is as indicated.*

RESULTS

PROBABILITIES :

Before we set out Mendel's explanation let us digress to consider another simple case of probability. Imagine two bags, each containing white and black balls in a 50:50 ratio. We draw a ball from bag 1 and one from bag 2; what are the possibilities? Obviously black-black, black-white, white-black, white-white. Forgetting about *order* of appearance, we find that the probabilities of complete black:mixed:complete white are 1:2:1. Or, looking at it in another way, out of every four withdrawals three withdrawals will contain at least one black ball. Remember, as always, that the ratios will be as indicated only when a very large number of withdrawals is carried out. Fig. 21 should make the above points clear.

Returning to the Mendelian experiment, let us set out the explanation of the results in symbolic form as shown in Fig. 20*b*. Do you see that a flower carrying factors for round (R) and wrinkled (r) is the counterpart of our bag with even numbers of black and white balls? If it is acting in a maternal manner it will produce ovules (young seeds), half carrying the factor R, the other half carrying the factor r. Likewise, if a flower carrying the factors R and r is a pollen provider it will produce pollen grains, half of which will carry the R factor and the other half the r factor. When pollen grains and ovules meet they will thus pair up just like the balls referred to above. R meeting R corresponds to two blacks turning up, r meeting r corresponds to two white balls, and R meeting r corresponds to a white and a black coming up. Just as the probability of a black and a white is twice the probability of two blacks or two whites, so the probability of an Rr combination is twice that of either RR or rr. Now if R always masks the r factor we can see that there must be three round seeds to every wrinkled seed in the third generation (F_2). Thus, probability provides an explanation of the experimental results.

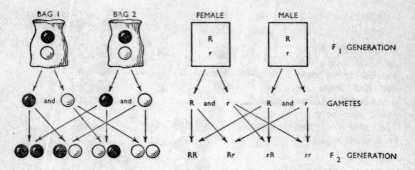

FIG. 22. *It can be seen that there is an exact parallel between the probability example, where we were concerned with black and white balls, and the inheritance of round and wrinkled characters in peas.*

Just in case you are not quite sure of the parallel between the breeding experiment and the probability case it may be helpful to set out the possible ball and sex-cell combinations in the manner of Fig. 22.

Mendel employed large numbers in this particular experiment. The total number of dominant forms showing up in the third (F_2) generation was 5,474, and the total number of recessives was 1,850, the ratio of dominants to recessives being 2·96:1. Mendel gave great stress to the idea of gametic purity; that is, that the sex-cell can carry only one factor, and also that when sex-cells merge the factors are not fused together but can part company later when the next set of sex-cells is formed. This is sometimes called the First Law of Mendel and may be expressed as follows: that of a pair of contrasted factors (for example, round and wrinkled) only one can be represented in a single gamete.

Mendel then put his probability hypothesis to the test to see if it would actually forecast the result of a crossing experiment even before the experiment was carried out. The question he put to himself was essentially the following. If we back-cross the hybrid second (F_1) generation with one of the pure parents, what will appear in the next generation? Can you see what the result should be? Get out pencil and paper and see what you can make of it; enough has been said to enable you to see through the problem on your own. It will suffice at this point to add that the predicted result and the actual breeding results tallied completely, thus giving a very strong indication of the correctness of the probability hypothesis.

Mendel was not content with one monohybrid crossing but carried out seven in all; all results tallied with his probability hypothesis.

Before we pass on to a consideration of the dihybrid experiments of Mendel, it is worth stressing that he did not know what really represented his factors in the sex-cells. The clearing up of this point came very much later.

EXPERIMENTS IN DIHYBRID INHERITANCE

Having obtained a clear idea of monohybrid inheritance Mendel went on and carried out cross-pollination between two pure-breeding forms of garden pea which differed in two pairs of contrasted characters. Actually Mendel carried out a number of such crosses but one of them is ample to illustrate the principles involved. The case we will consider here will be the one where a pure-breeding pea having yellow, round seeds was crossed with a pure-breeding pea having green, wrinkled seeds. The experimental results are best represented pictorially as in Fig. 23. Note that out of every sixteen seeds in the F_2 generation, nine are yellow and round, three are green and round, three are yellow and wrinkled, and one is green

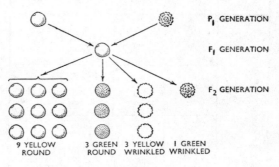

FIG. 23. *Results of an experiment to show the inheritance of two pairs of characters in garden peas: round and wrinkled, yellow and green.*

and wrinkled. This ratio applies only when large numbers are considered. Look at these numbers. What do you notice about them? What is the ratio of all-yellow seeds to all-green seeds? And all-round seeds to all-wrinkled seeds? What is the meaning of this (because there *is* one)? Yes, Mendel spotted what you have just spotted, namely, that we are really faced here with two 3:1 ratios. This could only mean that there was no interference between the inheritance of the two pairs of characters, and since a probability hypothesis explained the monohybrid inheritance it must necessarily provide an explanation of dihybrid inheritance.

241

Let us set out the factorial scheme for the experiment as follows:

Pure, Yellow, Round Pea	*Pure, Green, Wrinkled Pea*	
YYRR	yyrr	1st generation
YR	yr	Gametes
	YyRr (then self-pollinated)	2nd generation
Male—YR Yr yR yr	YR Yr yR yr—Female	Gametes

The combinations which come up in the next generation are difficult to follow unless they are worked out systematically on what is usually called a checkerboard. Let it be noted that there are four possible combinations of a colour factor with a seed-surface factor, also that it is assumed that gametes of the four types are produced in equal numbers. This is an essential point, but one which is commonly forgotten by biologists in thinking about this matter. Now refer to Fig. 24, which shows both symbolically and pictorially the theoretical result, a result which coincides with the actual breeding results. In drawing in the pictures of the seeds in Fig. 24 it had to be borne in mind which were dominant factors and which were reces-

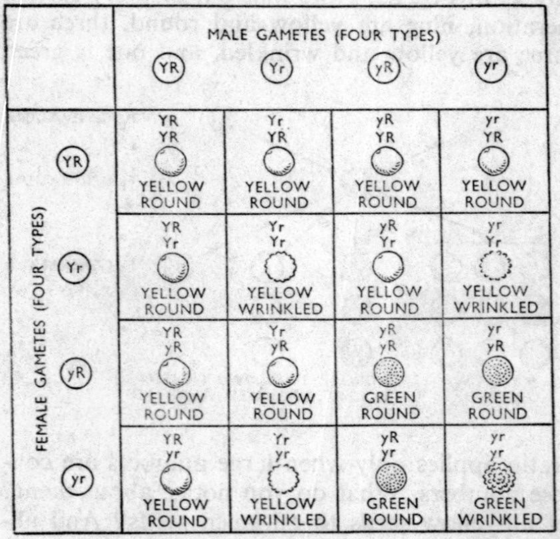

FIG. 24. *Checkerboard method of showing on a probability basis the results of dihybrid inheritance in the F_2 generation.*

sive. For example, if Y appears anywhere the pea must show the yellow character; if Y is totally lacking it must be green, and so on.

It may be interesting to note here that from a probability point of view the dihybrid (F_1 generation) is comparable to a bag containing an equal number of balls and cubes, half of each being white, the other half black. Gamete formation and sorting of the factors is comparable with drawing a ball and a cube from the bag, returning them after noting their colours. There are four combinations possible, as follows: black cube-black ball, black cube-white ball, white cube-black ball, and white cube-white ball; the probabilities are also obviously equal for the four combinations. They are the counter-parts of the germ-cells YR, Yr, yR and yr in the crossing experiment.

Reverting to Fig. 24, note carefully that not all the seeds which look the same externally are the same from a factorial point of view, nor will they behave the same when self-pollinated. Here a series of questions arise by which you can test your understanding of the matter:

(1) How would the yellow, round form $YyRR$ behave if self-pollinated?

(2) How would the green, round form $yyRr$ behave if crossed with a $YyRR$ type?

(3) How would the green, wrinkled form $yyrr$ behave if self-pollinated?

(4) How would the green, round form $yyRR$ behave if crossed with a $yyrr$ type?

(5) How would the yellow, wrinkled form $YYrr$ behave if self-pollinated?

Doubtless you have found the answer to the last question at least. It is a pure-breeding form; moreover it is not the same as the original pure-breeding parents—it has yellow associated with wrinkled factors. This is the first hint we have had of the possibility of obtaining new pure-breeding forms by combining characters not previously associated. It provides a technique for the development of new forms of animals and plants.

The independent assortment of the various factors when the second generation (F_1) produces gametes is often expressed as the Second Law of Mendel, which runs as follows: Each one of a pair of contrasted factors may be combined with either of another pair. In actual fact, cases are known where free assortment does not take place; this is the phenomenon known as linkage, of which further mention will be made later on.

TRIHYBRID INHERITANCE

The principle involved here is exactly the same as in mono-hybrid and dihybrid inheritance, and again experimental results and theoretical forecasts tally. As an example of this we can quote the crossing of two pure-breeding peas, one having round yellow seeds and coloured flowers, the other pea having wrinkled green seeds and white flowers. In the second (F_1) generation the peas will all have round yellow seeds and coloured flowers, as these are the dominant characters. Now what will happen when these plants are self-pollinated? In symbols we can set it out as follows:

Round, Yellow, Coloured Pea	*Wrinkled, Green, White Pea*	
RR YY CC	rr yy cc	P_1 generation
RYC	ryc	Gametes
Rr Yy Cc (self-pollinated)		F_1 generation
RYC RYc Ryc ryc rYC ryC rYc RyC		Gametes

(Types in equal numbers, both male and female)

It is now suggested that you take out pencil and paper and construct a checkerboard with $8 \times 8 = 64$ squares and work out the various new resulting combinations. Refer back to the checkerboard for the dihybrid inheritance and it will refresh your memory of the method. When you have put the letters in the several squares you can write in how the various peas will appear. Remember, if *R* appears at all in a square the form must appear round; if not, it will be a wrinkled form. If *Y* appears in a square at all it must be a yellow form; if not, it will be a green form; if *C* appears at all it will be a coloured form; if not, a white form. When you have completed your checkerboard write in your results below:

	Yellow, Round and Coloured	. . . .
	Yellow, Round and White	. . . .
	Yellow, Wrinkled and Coloured	. . . .
Number of	Green, Round and Coloured	. . . .
forms showing	Green, Wrinkled and Coloured	. . . .
	Yellow, Wrinkled and White	. . . .
	Green, Round and White	. . . .
	Green, Wrinkled and White	. . . .
	Total	. . .64. . .

As in the cases of monohybrid and dihybrid inheritance it will be noted that not all those which appear the same externally or phenotypically are the same in internal factors. This point arises throughout heredity; only by breeding on into a further generation can we be sure of the internal factors present. Only a homozygous form (for example, *YYRRcc*) can breed true. In conclusion, it will be interesting

× ÷ × ÷ × ÷ × ÷ × ÷ × ÷ × ÷ × ÷ × ÷ × ÷ × ÷ × ÷ × ÷ × ÷ × ÷ × ÷
Can You Help?

My friend Skwareham, who sold carpets, said that if he had to multiply two numbers together he usually squared their average instead. The answer was always too big but was near enough, he said. I told him that if he was all that keen on squaring instead of multiplying, he might as well do a little bit more and get the answer right. What else ought he to do? Solution on page 444

÷ × ÷ × ÷ × ÷ × ÷ × ÷ × ÷ × ÷ × ÷ × ÷ × ÷ × ÷ × ÷ × ÷ × ÷ × ÷ ×

to put in tabular form the relationship between the numbers of pairs of contrasted characters in an experiment and the variety of forms which come up in the succeeding generation:

Number of Pairs of contrasted characters	Number of different gametes formed by F_1 generation	Number of classes in F_2 generation	Number of combinations in F_2 generation
1	2	2	3
2	4	4	9
3	8	8	27
4	16	16	81
n	2^n	2^n	3^n

REDISCOVERY AND ECLIPSE OF MENDEL'S WORK

You may know already that the discoveries of Mendel were not received with open arms. Mendel gave two lectures to the local scientific society about 1865 and an account was printed in the publication of this society, copies of the account reaching the scientific libraries of Europe's capitals. No one appreciated his work, and Mendel died in 1884 with his advances unrecognized; probably his mathematical approach was too much for the botanists of the day. Whatever the reason, the fact remains that there was a great deal of ineffective groping around until 1900, when three separate biologists rediscovered Mendel and his work. Initially, each thought he had discovered something new on his own account, but looking back into the literature found out that Mendel had anticipated him by about half a century. Almost immediately numerous repeats of Mendel's experiments were carried out and they demonstrated the correctness of his ideas in general. Since 1900 the science of heredity has never looked back.

So far we have not mentioned the physical basis of the Mendelian factors. Only a few months elapsed after the rediscovery of Mendel's work before it was suggested by Boveri and Sutton that it is the chromosomes within the nucleus of the cell which represent or bear the Mendelian factors. If we count the number of chromosomes in the nuclei of the cells of a particular animal we find the same number each time. Moreover, we find that there are always two of any one kind in a nucleus; that is, instead of saying there are twelve chromosomes in a particular nucleus we could say there are six pairs. The behaviour of the chromosomes at the time germ-cells or gametes are being formed converts a suspicion of their role in heredity into a certainty. During one of the cell divisions, when germ-cells are being produced, the chromosome number is halved, and halved in a very definite way. The two chromosomes making up a particular pair part company, one going into one daughter cell, the other into the other daughter cell formed at the same time; this remark also applies to all the other pairs. Except for this the sorting out of the chromosomes into half-sets is quite random. Do you see the importance of this? It represents the probability basis of heredity.

When fertilization takes place and a male germ-cell fuses with a female germ-cell, two half-sets of chromosomes combine to form a single nucleus. In this way the full number is reconstituted. The full chromosome number is called the diploid number, the half number the haploid number. The above processes can be best appreciated by reference to Fig. 25, where they are diagrammatically represented.

These chromosomes provide us with just the probability mechanism to explain the experimental breeding results. At first sight one might think that one chromosome represented one factor, but experience soon showed that the number of factors exceeds the number of chromosomes. The conclusion is that each chromosome is responsible for bearing several factors, these factors now being called genes.

Assuming the chromosome hypothesis of heredity to be correct, we can now represent the case of crossing a pure round pea with a pure wrinkled pea in a pictorial manner, as shown in Fig. 26. It is possible, of course, to do the same for a dihybrid crossing experiment and it is suggested that you take pencil and paper and work

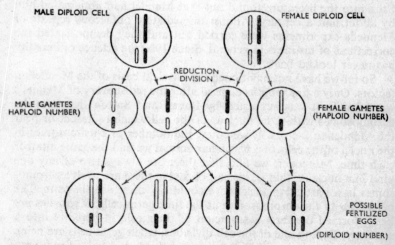

FIG. 25. *The halving of the chromosome number before gametes (sex-cells) are formed, and the reconstitution of the diploid number by fertilization.*

246

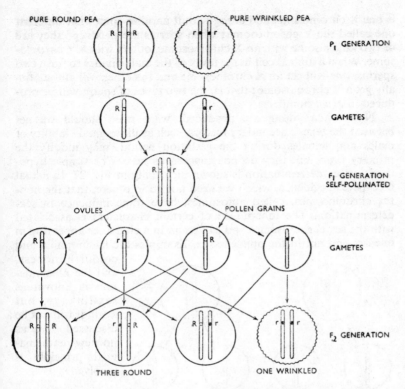

PURE ROUND PEA   PURE WRINKLED PEA

P₁ GENERATION

GAMETES

F₁ GENERATION
SELF-POLLINATED

OVULES   POLLEN GRAINS

GAMETES

F₂ GENERATION

THREE ROUND   ONE WRINKLED

FIG. 26. *Diagram illustrating in terms of chromosomes the results of crossing a pure round pea with a pure wrinkled pea.*

one out for yourself; this will test your understanding of what has been discussed above. Pictorial representations of this type are generally used only for teaching purposes. For normal working it is quicker to keep to the letters such as we have been using earlier on; even so, it is advisable to think sometimes of what the letters represent in physical terms.

SEX DETERMINATION

In animals, at least, the diploid chromosome sets differ in the character of one pair of chromosomes, the latter being usually called the sex chromosomes. In mammals, for example, there is in the female a pair of so-called X chromosomes, and when eggs are produced each of them carries a single X chromosome. In the male there

247

is one X chromosome and along with it another somewhat different one called the Y chromosome; when sperms are produced they are of two kinds, some with an X chromosome, others with a Y chromosome. When a diploid cell in the testis of the male divides to form two sperms, one will get an X chromosome and the other will automatically get a Y chromosome; that is, the two types of sperm will be produced in *equal* numbers.

Now when young are produced, what ratio should we get between the sexes? Secondary factors, such as differential viability of males and females during the gestation period, may modify the primary ratio, but they do not concern us here. The simple hypothesis of sex determination is shown pictorially in Fig. 27. In actual fact there is evidence, which we need not go into here, that the non-sex chromosomes, called autosomes, have some influence in sex-determination. The inheritance of certain characters is associated with the sex chromosomes and can result in a character appearing in one sex and not in the opposite sex. Examples are haemophilia and colour-blindness, and the phenomenon is known as sex-linkage, but again it will not be discussed here as no new mathematical principle is involved.

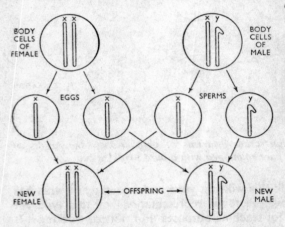

Fig. 27. *This shows the simple chromosome hypothesis of sex determination.*

LINKAGE, CROSSING-OVER AND CHROMOSOME MAPS

The first case of what is now called linkage was discovered by Bateson and Punnett in 1906 during their work on inheritance in the sweet pea. Two pure-breeding races of sweet pea were crossed, one having purple flowers and long pollen grains, the other red flowers and round pollen grains. In the next generation (F_1) they found the plants all had purple flowers and long pollen grains, these being the dominant characters. They then self-pollinated these plants and expected to obtain a F_2 ratio of $\frac{9}{16}$ long-pollened, purple; $\frac{3}{16}$ long-

248

pollened, red; $\frac{3}{16}$ round-pollened, purple; and $\frac{1}{16}$ round-pollened, red. They obtained, however, the following results:

F_2 generation	Purple long	Purple round	Red long	Red round
Actual numbers	4,831	390	393	1,338
Expected numbers	3,910·5	1,303·5	1,303·5	434·5

Inspection of the figures will show that forms like the original parents crop up more often than they should if random assortment has taken place; new combinations crop up less often than they should. At the time, the investigators realized that the factors tended to hang together, and they called it "coupling of the factors." Other like cases cropped up and in 1910 Morgan gave the present name of *linkage* to the phenomenon, pointing out that one could explain it by supposing that factors or genes which show linkage are located on *the same chromosome*. This suggestion is generally regarded as the correct one.

If two genes are located in the same chromosome and the chromosome remains intact in inheritance, the factors should remain together in all cases; that is, the linkage should be complete. This is not what happens, for the linked genes sometimes separate. They may be held together in about 95 per cent of the cases and separated in 5 per cent of the cases. The physical basis of this separation is what is known as crossing-over, a process which occurs during the formation of the germ-cells. In essence what happens is that corresponding or homologous chromosomes exchange material and separation of previously associated factors can occur. The new combinations resulting in the next generation are known as cross-overs.

This will be appreciated most easily by taking an actual case and representing it pictorially as in Fig. 28. A pure-breeding maize with coloured, full grain was crossed with a pure-breeding maize having colourless, shrunken grain; since coloured and full are dominant characters the next generation (F_1) were all with coloured, full grain. Actually this generation was back-crossed with a pure, colourless, shrunken plant like one of the original parents. If there was complete linkage only two forms would be expected, those in the left-hand bottom corner of the figure, but in fact two other forms appeared, namely, coloured, shrunken and colourless, full; this indicated cross-over. In this case the normal expected forms made up 96·4 per cent of the F_2 generation, the cross-overs only 3·6 per cent.

Over the last few paragraphs there has been little mention of mathematics, but we now arrive at a point where a mathematical approach appears again. In thinking about crossing-over the biologists saw that it provided a method of finding out the order

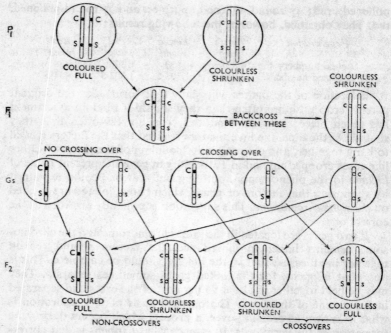

P₁ COLOURED FULL

COLOURLESS SHRUNKEN

F₁ — BACKCROSS BETWEEN THESE — COLOURLESS SHRUNKEN

Gs NO CROSSING OVER   CROSSING OVER

F₂ COLOURED FULL   COLOURLESS SHRUNKEN   COLOURED SHRUNKEN   COLOURLESS FULL

NON-CROSSOVERS   CROSSOVERS

FIG. 28. *An experiment in crossing different kinds of maize, showing the origin of cross-over forms on a back-cross with a pure form.*

of the genes in the chromosomes and probably a means of determining their relative distance apart. If two factors are distant from each other on the chromosome we should expect them to be separated very frequently, as there would be a high probability of a cross-over taking place between them. Conversely, two factors close together on the chromosome would be rarely parted from one another. Working on this assumption, biologists carried out various crossings to determine the percentage of cross-overs coming up when various pairs of factors were tested; these percentages were called *cross-over values*, and by using them it was possible to construct a *chromosome map* giving the factors in their correct order. Investigation from another direction (that of cytology) has confirmed that the order of factors obtained in this way is correct; the only modification it brought in was some alteration in the relative distances apart of the factors. An actual case of chromosome mapping will make the approach quite clear.

Bridges and Morgan in the United States carried out a great deal of work on the chromosomes and breeding of the fly *Drosophila melanogaster*. In the course of their investigations of the many genes of number II chromosome of the fly they obtained the following data for the cross-overs between the genes black, curved, purple, speck, star and vestigial. The genes are connected with colour, wing character, and so on.

Linked Genes	Total Flies	Cross-overs	Cross-over value
Black, curved	62,679	14,237	22·7
Black, purple	48,931	3,026	6·2
Black, speck	685	326	47·7
Black, star	16,507	6,250	37·9
Black, vestigial	20,153	3,578	17·8
Curved, purple	51,136	10,205	20·0
Curved, speck	10,042	3,037	30·3
Curved, star	19,870	9,123	45·9
Curved, vestigial	1,720	141	8·2
Purple, speck	11,985	5,474	45·7
Purple, star	8,155	3,561	43·7
Purple, vestigial	13,601	1,609	11·8
Speck, star	7,135	3,448	48·3
Speck, vestigial	2,054	738	36·0
Star, vestigial	450	195	43·3

It is possible to use the cross-over values in the last column to determine the order of the several genes on the chromosome. We can assume that the distance between any two genes is proportional to the cross-over value obtained in the crossing involving those two characters. For example, we can take the black gene and the curved gene as being 22·7 units apart, the black gene and the purple gene as 6·2 units apart, and so on. We can gradually work out the order of all the genes. If we plot the possible positions of the genes using the first five cross-over values only, we obtain the result shown in Fig. 29. There are several ambiguities here which can be resolved

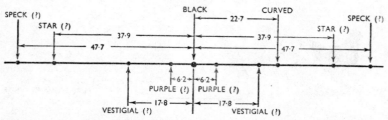

FIG. 29. *Initial stage in plotting the gene positions on the chromosome of the fly. Ambiguities are resolved by the remaining cross-over values.*

by the use of the remaining cross-over values. You should now use these and determine the correct alternatives. Do not expect an absolute fit in terms of units, but the cross-over values are quite good enough to give you the correct gene order.

We have assumed that the chance of a cross-over is strictly proportional to the distance between the genes on the chromosome. This assumption, however, is not quite correct, so that although this method of mapping the genes gives their correct order it may not necessarily give the correct relative distances between them. Anyhow, it does show an interesting example of the application of mathematics.

MULTI-FACTOR INHERITANCE

In some cases there is plenty of evidence that a single character may be controlled by several genes. In such cases it is difficult in the first place to establish purity for that character; and when relatively pure forms are crossed, clear-cut categories are lacking in the F_2 generation. We usually obtain a series, the majority displaying something about the average value of the character and smaller numbers displaying extreme values—in fact, we obtain something very like a normal-distribution curve. How does this link up with probability? The example usually quoted in this connexion is that of East, who crossed two *relatively* pure types of maize, one having long ears and the other short ears, although both displayed some variation about a mean. The F_1 generation had ears of intermediate

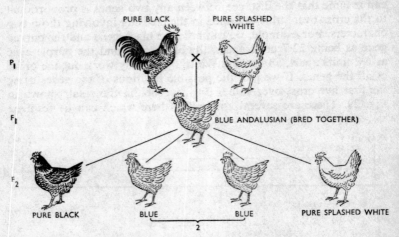

FIG. 30. *The origin of the Blue Andalusian—an interesting case of incomplete dominance in the breeding of poultry.*

mean and range. On self-pollination a F_2 generation was produced which did not fall into clear-cut groups but formed an intergrading series from short-eared to long-eared, with a mean not very different from that of the F_1 generation. This F_2 generation of maize plants is comparable with a collection of men varying in height from short to tall, in whom height is certainly controlled by a number of genes.

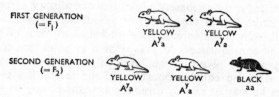

FIRST GENERATION
(= F_1)

YELLOW $A^y a$ × YELLOW $A^y a$

SECOND GENERATION
(= F_2)

YELLOW $A^y a$ YELLOW $A^y a$ BLACK aa

FIG. 31. *A case of lethal genes in mice. The 2:1 ratio displayed in the F_2 generation is explained by the fact that one-fourth of that generation die as embryos and have the constitution $A^y A^y$.*

At one time it was thought that this sort of intergrading inheritance was something fundamentally different from the simpler Mendelian inheritance, but now it is merely regarded as a more complicated manifestation of the latter. To describe mathematically the variability of the several generations of maize investigated by East, the ordinary statistical methods were employed; for example, the determination of the mean and the standard deviation.

In concluding this section of the chapter let us remind ourselves that the gene theory of inheritance is fundamentally a probability theory. All its rules or laws are statistical ones. It can often predict what will happen if a large number of cases is considered; it cannot predict what will happen in a single case, although it can give an idea of the probability of a particular result turning up. This statistical basis must be remembered, as it will for ever limit the use of the science in prediction. If you have followed the above you will have no difficulty in following inheritance in any plant or animal as presented in the usual books on genetics. Some more examples of interest are given in Figs. 30 and 31.

GEOMETRY IN THE BIOLOGICAL WORLD

It was pointed out earlier that the idea of geometry cropping up in biology is not really very strange. You have probably taken it all for granted for so long that conscious awareness of it has almost disappeared. Think of the living things which display a spherical form, a disk-like form or a cylindrical form.

Consideration of this topic falls into two main categories: firstly, the effects of change in size in a particular kind of body shape, and, secondly, the kinds of geometrical form which are to be found in the living world, some of which have already been briefly mentioned.

Have you ever read *Gulliver's Travels*? Do you remember the voyage to Lilliput? If you do, you may recall that the Lilliputians were described as being merely miniatures of ordinary human beings. Did this strike you as reasonable or as odd? Perhaps you are still undecided, so we will look a little into this problem of change in size and its consequences. At first sight it appears that to obtain a larger animal or plant all we have to do is to increase all the dimensions by an equal proportion. If the reader has thought on these lines he may be readily forgiven, as many biologists sometimes tend to fall into the same error.

Look at the two cubes shown in Fig. 32. The small one has an edge length of one foot, the larger one an edge length of two feet. We could say that one cube is twice the "size" of the other. Or do

FIG. 32. *In considering the two cubes, how are we to express the size of one in relation to the other without ambiguity?*

you disagree? If you disagree, can you say why you disagree? Work out, with pencil and paper if necessary, the surface area of the small cube and the large cube. Do we obtain a 1:2 ratio, such as we have for length of edge? Now work out the volume of each cube. What ratio between the two do you arrive at this time?

The fact will have been impressed upon you by now that there is more to this business of "size" than is obvious at first sight. Let us summarize the results at which you will have arrived:

	Small Cube	Large Cube	Ratio
Length of Edge	1 ft.	2 ft.	1 : 2
Surface Area	6 sq. ft.	24 sq. ft.	1 : 4
Volume	1 cu. ft.	8 cu. ft.	1 : 8

Looking at the ratios on the right-hand side, we see that they vary according to whether we are considering length, surface area or volume. Now which is the best indicator of size of the three? Since we usually weigh objects to determine differences, probably the best ratio to take is the one which is proportional to weight or most nearly so. This one is volume. In case you think the ratios given above are something peculiar to the cube it would be a good idea to consider the ratios for two spheres, one having twice the diameter of the other.

Now can you see any general way of expressing the relationships between length, surface area and volume? If we let L represent the length of the edge of a cube, how can we represent the surface area? And the volume? Look at the ratios for the cube again and see if you can see the relationships between the last figures in each case. These figures are 2, 4 and 8. Very easy, you will agree. If L is the edge length, L^2 will be proportional to the surface area and L^3 will be proportional to the volume—and also to the weight if the cube is of uniform material. Whatever form you may care to take, including the spherical form, these relationships will be found to hold good. The fact that the body of a living organism does not conform exactly to a simple geometrical form does not invalidate the general argument.

The elementary principles which we have established above, simple though they are to understand, have a large number of important consequences that are not generally appreciated. One of these consequences is seen in the study of the growth of young animals. What do we see here? In many cases the rate of increase in the length of the animal, say a fish, seems to be very rapid at first and then to slow down gradually, giving an impression of slower growth processes. This impression is usually a false one: if we look at length when we are interested in growth processes we are looking at the wrong dimension. If we are interested in growth we should not be interested in L but in L^3, the volume, or in the weight, which will be more or less proportional to the volume.

Think about the following problems. Say we have an aquarium fish which doubles its weight in a given time. What will have happened to its volume in the same period? Now a slightly more difficult problem. Say a fish has doubled in weight in a period of time. What increase in length would you expect to see in the same period of time? Don't try without pencil and paper if you are at all puzzled by the last problem; set it out and it will help you to see the problem more clearly and so lead you to the solution.

Many common effects of scale in living animals and plants are due to the fact that some physical forces act only on the surface area of the organism and are proportional to L^2, whereas others, chiefly the force of gravity, act on all the material of the body, irrespective of its position, and so are proportional to L^3. Some of the consequences of this are easy to see. For example, if the absolute size of a living organism is altered some form of disharmony must arise: the skeleton of an animal so altered may not be strong enough to support the total weight of the body. Now if change in size tends to bring disharmony, what must take place if harmony between the parts is to be maintained? There is only one way out. It is for the proportions of the living organism to be altered so that a workable relationship between length, area and volume is maintained.

Just the same problems arise in engineering; if the scale of a bridge is altered the bridge proportions also must be altered. If the proportions were kept the same the larger the bridge the weaker it would be, and finally a size would be reached where it would collapse under its own weight.

It is accepted as a commonplace that different sizes of mammal, such as elephants, deer, dogs and mice, do not have exactly the same body proportions. Not only that, but the legs seem to loom larger and larger in proportion as the size of the animal increases. In the light of what has been said already, is there any fundamental explanation for this tendency? Ask yourself the following questions and put the answers down on a scrap of paper. If the length of a mammal is doubled what will happen to the weight? What will support this weight anyway? The legs, but what will happen to them if their dimensions are doubled? Will they be carrying the same number of pounds per square inch of their cross-section as in the smaller edition of the mammal? What must happen to the proportions of the legs to correct matters? If you have difficulty just go back and think about the cubes again; imagine them to be resting on a table and exerting a pressure owing to their weight. The conditions would be as follows:

	Small Cube	Large Cube	Ratio
Area in contact with table	1 sq. ft.	4 sq. ft.	1 : 4
Volume	1 cu. ft.	8 cu. ft.	1 : 8

From this it follows that the pressure per square foot on the table is twice as much in the case of the large cube as in the case of the small one. The same argument applies even if we are dealing with a mammal standing on four legs: if the legs merely go up in proportion to the length then the thrust per square inch of their cross-section increases steadily. When the length has been doubled the thrust has also doubled. There is only one way to compensate; it is to make the legs relatively more robust, and in general that is what we find in Nature.

256

Although limbs have been especially mentioned in this connexion the same arguments apply to other parts. This principle is well seen in the evolutionary history of some animal groups. The modern horse is not just the early horse of the Eocene Period magnified up; many changes in proportion of parts have been incorporated, some of which are directly related to mechanical considerations. There is no doubt that dimensional factors have set a limit to the maximum size of land animals.

Whales have reached sizes greater than any of the land animals, even if the largest of the extinct reptiles are included. What possible reason is there for this fact? There must be some other factor coming into the picture. What is it?

Two groups of animals are warm-blooded, the mammals and the birds. Here volume/surface-area relationships play an important part. These animals have a control mechanism which keeps their temperature at a stable level, usually much higher than that of their surroundings; heat is always being lost in the process, however, and this loss has to be made good by burning up food in the body tissues. Let us consider a mammal of a certain size and then imagine we can decrease its linear dimensions by a half. Is it still a balanced organism from a heat production or heat loss point of view? Let us set it out as follows:

	Original Mammal	Mammal in 2nd Condition
Length	2 units	1 unit
Surface Area	4 ,,	1 ,,
Volume	8 ,,	1 ,,

Has the surface/volume ratio kept the same? What will tend to be the consequences of this? You can take heat production as being proportional to weight and so to volume. No doubt you see that as our mammal becomes smaller the ratio of external surface to weight becomes greater. To some extent this can be compensated by boosting

At the Inn

Three travellers arrived tired and hungry at a lonely inn. The innkeeper apologized and said he could only offer them a meal of potatoes. When he brought in the dish all the men were asleep. After a while one of the three woke up, ate a third of the potatoes, and went back to sleep. Soon afterwards another woke up, ate a third of the potatoes that remained, and promptly fell asleep again. Then the third man did likewise. When the innkeeper came back he found that eight potatoes were left. How many had he put on the dish?

Solution on page 444

the heat production in the body and adding a thick coat as an insulator, but there are limits and we never find mammals as small as a beetle or a cockroach. Some small birds cannot exist outside a very warm climate and even then have to spend most of their time gathering food.

Another common example where surface/volume relationships are of great importance is the digestion of foods within the body, particularly the digestion of fats. Emulsification of fats, that is, the breaking up of large droplets into small droplets, takes place and a great increase in the surface area of fat takes place, so increasing the rate at which enzymes can act. Assume we have a large spherical droplet of fat which is split up into a hundred very small droplets; the total volume of fat remains the same but what of the surface area? Get out pencil and paper and see what result you get; you will be surprised.

Another striking example of the effect of dimensions may be noticed in going round the bird houses in a zoo; namely, the difference in proportions of the birds of different sizes. One of the main factors at work in bringing about these differences is that the weight of the bird goes up as L^3 but the lifting power of the wing goes up only as L^2. This assumes that the proportions remain the same as the bird is increased in size. To see what happens, look at the following figures, complete the blank spaces and come to your own conclusions:

Species	Weight	$\sqrt[3]{Weight}$	Wing Length	$\dfrac{\sqrt[3]{Weight}}{Wing\ Length}$
Sparrow	30 grammes	3·11	0·11 metres	27·4
Pigeon	350 ,,		0·30 ,,	
Gull	1,000 ,,		0·60 ,,	

In the above table the cube root of the weight can be taken as an approximate measure of relative length. If the birds are all built on the same proportional plan then all three figures in the last column will be the same. Are they according to your calculations? The wing length of the largest bird is greater than one would suppose at first sight. It has to increase in relative length (and breadth) to give the requisite lift.

Although the lifting system is somewhat different in detail from the lift of the plane of an aeroplane, the same general principles will apply in the case of the latter. With an aeroplane the minimal speed (stalling speed) varies as the square root of the linear dimensions; if we quadruple the dimensions we double the stalling speed, and without doubt the same general principle applies with birds as well. Observation shows that the heavier birds must fly fast or not at all.

Let us finish this theme of dimensions and their consequences with three queries to think over and solve. Your solutions may not be new to science but, what is more important, they will be new to you.

(1) You probably decided earlier on that whales could be larger than land mammals because of the buoyancy effect of the water? But it appears that something else keeps their size within bounds. What is it? Think on physiological lines.

(2) In general you think of large mammals as having deep voices, whereas small ones have piping ones. Can you suggest a fundamental reason for this? Do not confuse pitch with volume in thinking about this problem.

(3) Insects do not reach such large sizes as most other animals. This is usually attributed to their method of breathing by tracheae. Try thinking about this problem on quantitative lines and see if you think the usual explanation is a valid one.

THE GEOMETRY OF BODY FORM

As we were reminded early in this chapter, there are many familiar geometrical forms in the living world around us. Usually any particular geometrical form is not perfectly represented but has a sufficient approximation to strike the imagination and excite interest. In living organisms there is nearly always some form of

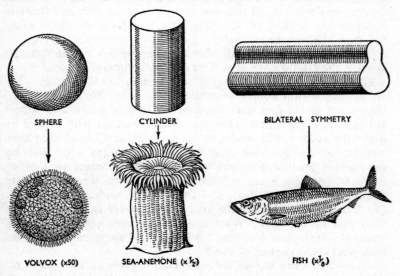

SPHERE   CYLINDER   BILATERAL SYMMETRY

VOLVOX (x50)   SEA-ANEMONE (x ½)   FISH (x⅙)

FIG. 33. *Common examples of marine life displaying geometrical symmetry.*

259

symmetry present. This symmetry may be about a point, when the resulting body form is a sphere; about a straight axis, when the body form will be a cylinder; or about a plane, when the body form will be bilaterally symmetrical. Look at Fig. 33 and this will be quite clear.

The spherical form often shows up quite clearly in cells, particularly female reproductive cells, of the multicellular organisms. This spherical shape reminded one of the soap bubble, the shape of which is due to the forces of surface tension. Among the forces which determine the forms of cells, the force of surface tension is considered to be of supreme importance, although there are often modifications of form due to other operating forces such as gravity, osmosis and mechanical pressure.

The spherical form is found in many adult organisms, but these are all small microscopic forms living in fresh or sea water. One beautiful spherical form, known as volvox, is multicellular and consists of a hollow spherical wall in which are located hundreds of small green cells. Each cell is connected with its neighbours by fine protoplasmic strands and has a pair of whip-like cilia which project into the external water and help row the organism along. The spherical form is a result of the effects of surface tension during the cell divisions and of the non-packing tendency of the daughter cells. Gravity and mechanical pressure play little or no part and there is no distortion of the pure spherical form. The form may have some functional significance as well.

Have you thought at all about the properties of the sphere? What is the relationship of surface area to volume if the sphere is a solid? What is the relationship of surface area to solid matter if we are dealing with a hollow structure like volvox? We may find out the answer to the first question with the help of pencil and paper. We can put the question in this way. Imagine a cube with edges 2 ft. long; the volume will obviously be 8 cu. ft. and the surface area will be 24 sq. ft. Now find out by calculation what will be the surface area of a sphere having a volume equal to that of the cube—namely 8 cu. ft. Remember that the formula for the volume of a sphere is $\frac{4}{3}\pi r^3$, and that for the surface area is $4\pi r^2$. Do you find that the surface area of the sphere is greater or less than that of the cube? What general statement could you make about the surface of a sphere? What will be some of the possible biological consequences of this?

Note that there are no spherical land organisms. Do you think this is just an accident or are there factors at work which make such a land form a physical impossibility?

Passing now to the cylindrical form, we find it is most prevalent in plants as represented by their stems and roots, although subsidiary parts such as leaves and flowers are attached to the stem system. This radial symmetry is almost certainly associated with their immobility, which in turn is linked up with their holophytic method of nutrition. Radial symmetry is rather exceptional in animals but is found in such types as the jellyfish and sea-anemones. These radial forms are either relatively fixed (as in the sea-anemone) or give only up and down movements (as in the jellyfish), lateral movements being due to water currents.

If we study the disposition of the material in a stem of a herbaceous land plant we find that it is not uniform; there is a marked tendency for the mechanical tissue to be placed toward the periphery.

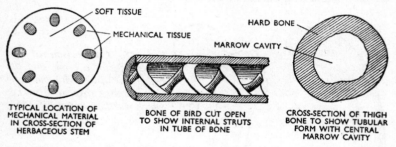

SOFT TISSUE
MECHANICAL TISSUE
HARD BONE
MARROW CAVITY

TYPICAL LOCATION OF MECHANICAL MATERIAL IN CROSS-SECTION OF HERBACEOUS STEM

BONE OF BIRD CUT OPEN TO SHOW INTERNAL STRUTS IN TUBE OF BONE

CROSS-SECTION OF THIGH BONE TO SHOW TUBULAR FORM WITH CENTRAL MARROW CAVITY

FIG. 34. *Examples from Nature of the disposition of mechanical material.*

This is strictly comparable with engineering practice, where tubes of material are used in constructional work rather than solid rods. Why is this outward positioning of mechanical material so effective in both cases? Why not discuss the engineering case with someone in that line?

The same principle is seen at work in the long bones of the skeleton of an animal such as the ox. The hard mechanical material forms the outer part of the bone and only a soft marrow occupies the centre of the bone. Get a leg bone of an ox, saw it across and have a look at the arrangement for yourself. Some long hollow bones in birds have well marked internal struts which add greatly to the strength but little to the weight; these internal struts have their engineering counterpart in what is known as Warren's truss. Fig. 34 shows diagrams of some of the structures referred to above.

Bilateral symmetry is found in most groups of animals and without doubt is primarily to be associated with their locomotor needs, which in turn are to be associated with their holozoic method of nutrition. Everyday examples illustrating this bilateral symmetry are a fish, frog, dog, earthworm, insect and lobster. In all these we have great powers of essentially horizontal motion, with a head leading the way. This balance between left and right sides has obvious advantages. Where the locomotion is not very swift or is through a medium which does not offer much resistance there is usually not much stress on streamlining, but where locomotion is swift through a resistant medium streamlining is very apparent.

Another example where we see a very strict parallel between a living structure and an engineering structure is afforded by the head of the thigh bone where it fits into the hip. If this is cut in halves it is seen that the internal bony material is disposed in the same way as the lines of stress in a loaded crane. Reference to Fig. 35 will reveal the amazing parallel we find here.

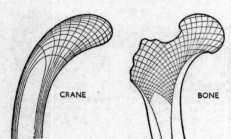

CRANE   BONE

Fig. 35. *Comparison of the stress lines of a crane and the trabeculae of a thigh bone show this remarkable similarity, which was first noticed in 1866.*

The same general phenomenon is seen in any bone which carries weight and is liable to flexure; it shows up particularly well in many bones of the hind limb. Note that here construction is tied up with the force of gravity. If the latter had had a different value in past ages when many of these structures were being evolved, they must have evolved somewhat differently. A lowered force of gravity would have resulted in a lighter type of skeleton, a higher force of gravity would have necessitated a greater development of internal reinforcement.

Returning to body form, it must be noted that the spiral form occurs in quite a number of living organisms, particularly in the snail group. In general a spiral is a curve which starts from a point of origin and continually diminishes in curvature as it recedes from this point. This definition excludes the cylindrical helix, of which the spiral staircase is an engineering example and the climbing stem of the convolvulus a botanical example.

Almost all spiral forms in Nature belong to the group known as equiangular or logarithmic spirals. This can be understood by

262

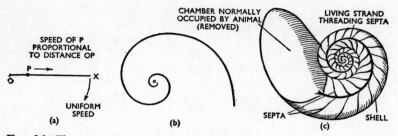

FIG. 36. *The equiangular spiral.* (a) *How the spiral is generated.* (b) *The spiral formed.* (c) *Section through the shell of a pearly nautilus.*

reference to Fig. 36a. The centre is at O and we visualize a line OX, called the radius vector, revolving about O. Then we visualize a point P on the radius vector, this point moving outwards from O at a speed always proportional to its distance from O. The path traced by P as OX rotates at constant speed is an equiangular spiral; perhaps you have already spotted that we are here dealing with a geometrical progression. The most beautiful natural example of an equiangular spiral is seen in the shell of a marine mollusc called the pearly nautilus. The shell is wound in a flat spiral and when this shell is cut into two equal parts the basic spiral design is quite obvious, as Fig. 36c will show. Can you think of the geometrical form one would have to coil to obtain the form of the nautilus shell?

Leaf arrangement affords examples of both the spiral and the helix. If we take a stem and note the positions in which the several leaves are attached we find that they are usually arranged in the form of a helix. The angle between one leaf base and the next above will vary from plant to plant. Where there is a taper on a stem, as we approach its tip the leaf bases are not strictly arranged in a helical form but in a spiral form. Another common plant structure in which a spiral arrangement is apparent is the pine cone, where the scales are arranged in a series of ascending spirals.

In leaving at this point the subject of geometry in biology, we may reflect that it has been a neglected aspect of biology in recent years but will loom larger and larger as we dig deeper in search of biological fundamentals. It is a side of biology full of challenges and questions awaiting answers.

⑥

Mathematics of the Builder and Handyman

To BUILD is one of the most deeply satisfying things a man can do. Even if you cannot make a new house you can get some of this satisfaction by keeping the old one in good trim: but to do good work you must plan with care and that means calculation. You want to avoid becoming a figure of fun like the man described in St. Luke who began and was not able to finish because he had not counted the cost. Concrete, brickwork, wood and paint are all materials the handyman can use and each has its own special brand of calculation.

There is much truth in Le Corbusier's definition of a house as "a machine for living in." The art of the architect is to make it that, and something more; but we who live in it need to know how the machine works if it is to give us maximum comfort.

It may help in some of your detailed constructional or maintenance problems if you have an overall picture of how a house is con-

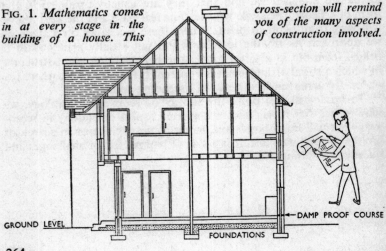

FIG. 1. *Mathematics comes in at every stage in the building of a house. This* cross-section will remind *you of the many aspects of construction involved.*

GROUND LEVEL

DAMP PROOF COURSE

FOUNDATIONS

structed. Fig. 1 gives a section through a small modern house. Here is a very brief summary of the stages in building it.

Foundations. Beneath where the walls of the house will come trenches are excavated and filled with concrete for foundations, according to certain rules based on calculations. The wall is then built up to ground level and the earth within the house is covered with hardcore (broken bricks and rubble) and concrete. During this stage the drainage is also laid in concreted trenches. These drains must slope at a minimum gradient of 1 in 40, so that in setting out the trenches, levels must be calculated to give the correct fall.

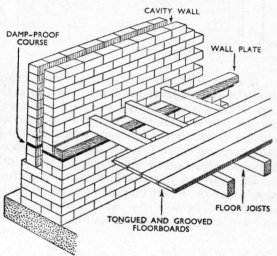

FIG. 2. *This is what the builder means by a suspended wood floor. The example shown is for a ground floor, but since 1945 the method has been confined to upper floors in order to conserve timber.*

CAVITY WALL

DAMP-PROOF COURSE

WALL PLATE

FLOOR JOISTS

TONGUED AND GROOVED FLOORBOARDS

Any building, large or small, must be thought of as a heavy object resting on earth. How much load this earth can bear is a matter of calculation and it must not be exceeded.

Floors. Being built since 1945, the house in Fig. 1 has a "solid" ground floor; that is, the floor you would tread on rests on 6 in. of concrete. Below that is 6 in. of hardcore, and below that is the earth. In a building of earlier date there will be a suspended wood floor at this level, best understood from Fig. 2. Upper floors will in any case be built like this.

Walls. If the house is of brick the walling is carried up to the eaves, the brickwork conforming to the rules of bonding—of which examples appear later in this chapter—and providing the openings for doors and windows and the bearings for the timbers called wall plates, on which rest the floors and roof.

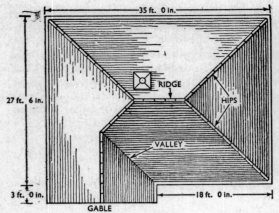

FIG. 3. *Advanced geometry and calculations of special kinds are needed for roof construction. Apart from the main job of forming the timber framework, there are various mathematical problems concerning the slate or tile covering.*

Roofing. The timbers forming the roof framework are "cut to length" and the sides and ends cut to correct angles so that there is everywhere a good bearing of one flat surface on another truly parallel. The determination of the lengths and angles, or "bevels," requires most complex geometry, which some builders master while others are content to follow rule-of-thumb procedures using a rigid L-shaped rule, marked with numerous scales, called a steel square.

Consider how you would cut such timbers for the roof of even a simple outhouse with only two sloping surfaces—that is, of gable construction, as in Fig. 6—and then consider the problems of lengths and bevels for a roof such as in Fig. 3. On the framework are laid

FIG. 4. *Typical drainage system for a small house.*

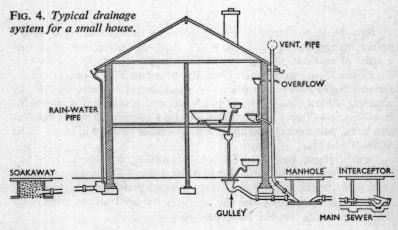

light horizontal timbers called battens, spaced according to exact calculations of the size and overlap of the slates or tiles they are to support.

Services. If you have to make alterations or additions to the supplies of gas, water or electricity to your house, much of your work may be of a destructive kind while you search for the pipes or wires. They are as far as possible placed during the previous stages and the flooring and decoration laid over them. They are a vital part of the

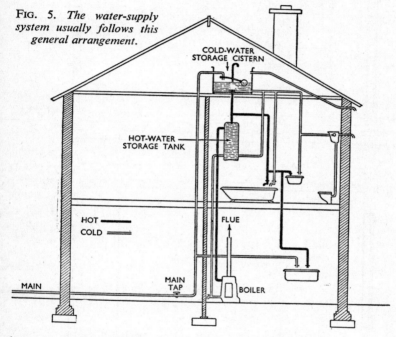

FIG. 5. *The water-supply system usually follows this general arrangement.*

COLD-WATER STORAGE CISTERN

HOT-WATER STORAGE TANK

HOT ━━━━
COLD ═══

FLUE

MAIN

MAIN TAP

BOILER

house machine, and if you have a maintenance job to do it is well worth while to record all that you can find out about the run of the services in the form of simple sketches on card, kept near the main valves or meters. This applies also to the drainage system running beneath your garden. Figs. 4 and 5 illustrate a typical drainage layout and water-supply system of a small house.

Finishing: Plastering and Decorating. The final stages are the plastering of all walls and ceilings to give a fair surface, and the covering of these surfaces and the woodwork with the finish selected. There are some very important technical matters concerning the

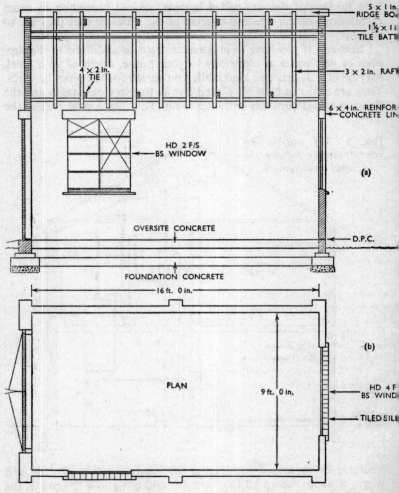

5 × 1 in.
RIDGE BO.

1½ × 1 i
TILE BATT

3 × 2 in. RAF

6 × 4 in. REINFOR
CONCRETE LIN

4 × 2 in.
TIE

HD 2 F/S
BS WINDOW

(a)

OVERSITE CONCRETE

D.P.C.

FOUNDATION CONCRETE

16 ft. 0 in.

(b)

PLAN

9 ft. 0 in.

HD 4 F
BS WIND

TILED SILL

effect of plastered surfaces on the paint you put on them, but apart from one point they do not concern us here. The one point worth emphasizing is that a cubic foot of walling may contain half a gallon or more or water, and this must be allowed to dry out before applying any but a temporary decorative finish. Always calculate your quantities: suppliers will always give the covering power of paints, and wall renderings can be worked out from figures given later in this chapter.

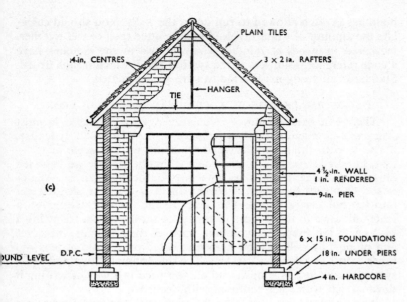

PLAIN TILES

4-in. CENTRES

3 × 2 in. RAFTERS

HANGER

TIE

4½-in. WALL
1 in. RENDERED

9-in. PIER

(c)

6 × 15 in. FOUNDATIONS

18 in. UNDER PIERS

4 in. HARDCORE

GROUND LEVEL   D.P.C.→

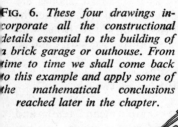

FIG. 6. *These four drawings incorporate all the constructional details essential to the building of a brick garage or outhouse. From time to time we shall come back to this example and apply some of the mathematical conclusions reached later in the chapter.*

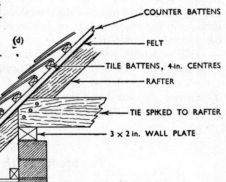

COUNTER BATTENS

FELT

TILE BATTENS, 4-in. CENTRES

RAFTER

TIE SPIKED TO RAFTER

3 × 2 in. WALL PLATE

(d)

To illustrate calculations on the various aspects of small-scale building, sketches of a small outhouse are given in Fig. 6. The methods of construction illustrated are traditional, and in an actual building there is scope for many modifications, particularly in respect of the plain-tiled roof with its large requirement of timber. Reference must be made to books on building construction to learn in detail how the work is carried out. Note also that though a gutter is shown no suggestion is made as to the disposal of rain water, which in such

269

buildings is often allowed to run down the walls. You should calculate the amount of water involved in a possible spell of wet weather, measured in inches of rainfall. The windows in the sketches have a code reference, followed by the symbol "BS," which means British Standard: all ready-made windows are so designated.

DUODECIMALS: THE BUILDER'S WAY OF CALCULATING

There is a special kind of calculation very widely used in most stages of constructional or maintenance work. You probably realize, if you stop to think about it, that we count up in a scale of ten— tens, hundreds, thousands, and so on—simply because we have ten fingers (counting thumbs as fingers). Unfortunately, in Anglo-Saxon countries the basis of measurement is the foot, divided not into ten but *twelve* inches. This leads to the use of fractions on a scale unknown in those more fortunate countries which, following a lead set in the French Revolution, have all their weights, measures and money, as well as their numbers, based on a scale of tens—in other words, a "decimal" system. The duodecimal ("two and ten") system works just as simply, and all you need is a way of writing it down which won't get confused with decimals.

The simplest way is to take the foot as a standard. Inches are twelfths and belong to the first place of duodecimals (just as tenths belong to the first place of decimals), called "primes"; twelfths of an inch go in the second place of duodecimals, called "seconds," and so on. Here is a comparison:

$$1 \cdot 25 = 1 \text{ unit} + 2 \text{ tenths} + 5 \text{ hundredths}$$
$$1 \text{ ft. } 2\tfrac{1}{2} \text{ in.} = 1 \text{ unit (foot)} + 2 \text{ twelfths} + \tfrac{1}{2} \text{ a twelfth}$$
$$= 1 \text{ unit} + \tfrac{2}{12} + \tfrac{6}{144}$$

You know that the 2 and the 5 in the first example mean 2 tenths and 5 hundredths by their position in first and second place. In duo-

Problems With Cubes

(1) What is the least number of cubical bricks that can be either spread out to form a square or stacked to form a cube?

(2) Hilary lost one of her cubical building bricks and then found she could make only one solid oblong, whereas previously she could make four different ones. How many bricks were there in the complete set?

(3) John had more building bricks than Hilary. He found he could pack them all together to make a big block in three different ways. How many more bricks did he need to make a solid cube? *Solutions on page 444*

decimals the "place" is indicated by dashes, so that

$$1 \text{ ft. } 2\tfrac{1}{2} \text{ in.} = 1 \text{ ft. } 2' \ 6''$$

It is unlucky that here a single dash stands for inches, because it could be confused with the ordinary shorthand for feet and inches: but this notation for duodecimals has been found to give the best results. To keep out of trouble when working in duodecimals *always* write "ft." or "sq. ft.," and so on as the case may be for the standard unit.

Now run through this calculation: Find the area of a window opening 3 ft. 3½ in. by 4 ft. 5 in.

```
Multiply   4 ft. 5′
      by   3 ft. 3′ 6″

      ─────────────────

     13 sq. ft. 3′
      1          1′  3″
                 2′  2″  6‴

      ─────────────────────

     14 sq. ft. 6′  5″  6‴
```

This is what you say to yourself, or out loud if you are alone (except the parts in brackets—they are explanatory). *First line:* 3 × 5′ = 15 (3 ft. has no dashes, 5 has one. Therefore it is 15′, for in this notation you simply add the dashes as if they were "indices"). 15 is 12 and 3. Put down 3′ in the one-dash column and carry 1. 3 ft. × 4 ft. = 12 sq. ft., and 1 is 13. (These are standard units, so you go no further.) Put down 13 in the units column. *Next line:* 3′ × 5′ = 15″. Put down 3″ under the two-dash column and carry 1′. 3′ × 4 ft. = 12′ and 1′ is 13. 13′ = 12′ and 1′. Put down 1′ and carry 1 to units column.

You should be able to say the third line for yourself. A useful trick is to remember that the commonest calculation when we cast out 12 is in putting pence into shillings and pence, so that in the examples above you can use this by saying "6 × 5 = 30 (2s. 6d., put down 6 and carry 2)." There is no need to keep a check on the number of dashes except at the start, to get the first one down in the correct column: after that it follows on automatically. Nothing above 11 may be written in with "dashes": not, that means, until you reach the standard unit column.

Before going on to other examples, the answer to this one is worth a second look. It says 14 sq. ft. 6′ 5″ 6‴. What do the "dashed" parts mean? 6′ means $\frac{6}{12}$ of the unit, which is the square foot. 5″ means $\dfrac{5}{12 \times 12}$ of the unit, and 6‴ means $\dfrac{6}{12 \times 12 \times 12}$ of the unit.

So the $6' = \frac{6}{12}$ sq. ft., or $\frac{1}{2}$ sq. ft., and the answer is a little more than $14\frac{1}{2}$ sq. ft.

$\dfrac{5}{12 \times 12}$ sq. ft. or $\frac{5}{144}$ sq. ft. is 5 sq. in., since there are 144 sq. in. in 1 sq. ft. If this occurs in the final figure in estimating, it will obviously be ignored as being too small to matter, and even more so with the 6‴. It is, however, most unwise to throw out these little parts till you are near enough to the end to see just how small they are compared with the whole.

An interesting stage in duodecimals occurs when finding costs; for the shilling is divided into 12 pence. Consider, for instance, how you would most easily calculate the cost of a new flooring to a room 12 ft. 4 in. × 11 ft. 8 in. with an additional bay 3 ft. 3 in. deep and 6 ft. 5 in. wide. The cost of the flooring is 19s. 3d. per sq. yd. and the calculation is much easier if you convert this to the cost per sq. ft. thus:

$$19\text{s. 3d. per sq. yd.} = \frac{19\text{s. 3d.}}{9} \text{ per sq. ft.}$$
$$= 2\text{s. } 1\tfrac{3}{4}\text{d.}$$
$$= 2\text{s. } 1'\ 8'' \text{ in duodecimals.}$$

Work out the area in two parts: the total should come to 164 sq. ft. 8′ 11″: so that the final calculation looks like this:

$$\underline{164 \text{ sq. ft. } 8'\ 11''}$$
$$\ 2\text{s.} \qquad 1'\ 8'' \text{ per sq. ft.}$$

The only "side work" needed is in handling the large number of 164 sq. ft.: for example, 164 sq. ft. × 8″ gives us 1,312″ = 109′ 4″ = 9 units 1′ 4″.

Are you clear as to what the units are in this answer? If you multiply a number of square feet by a price in shillings per square foot you get the cost in shillings.

The answer to the final multiplication looks like this: 352s. 4′ 4″ 10‴ 4⁗. What does it mean? 352s. is £17 12s. 4′ means 4/12 of a shilling, or 4d. 4″ means 4/12 of a penny; 10‴ and 4⁗ are clearly even smaller fractions of a penny, and all these can now be ignored. The final figure is thus *£17 12s. 4d.*

The cost per square foot was, in duodecimals, 2s. 1′ 8″. What is this in usual money notation? You may be tempted to ignore the $\frac{3}{12}$d. which is the value of 8″ here, or (even more tempting) propose to continue the sum on a basis of a cost of 2s. 2d. per sq. ft. Reworking the sum as 164 sq. ft. 8′ 11″ × 2s. 2′, the result, 356s. 11′ 3″ 10‴, is about 4s. 7d. too high. This will not matter in a rough estimate but is not good enough for presenting a bill. This illustrates the unwisdom of approximating too soon.

FIG. 7. *Here's a load of trouble. What has gone wrong and how do you think it happened?*

Duodecimals are in constant use for working builders' quantities. Comparison with other methods should soon convince anyone of their value. Try it for yourself.

Having now become familiar with this special method of calculating, let us turn to some of the more specific aspects of mathematics in connexion with building construction.

THE NEED FOR FOUNDATIONS

We have already described a house as a heavy object resting on the ground. Since the ground is more or less soft there is clearly a limit to the weight that can safely be rested on it. What decides that limit?

Clearly not the total weight: think of the great buildings in London, resting on clay—one of the most unsatisfactory soils to build on. By comparison, look at Fig. 7. You can probably see what has gone wrong, but can you say why? The garage was an addition after the house was built. The farther side wall has sunk, cracking the end wall across and allowing the garage to lean away from the house. The much heavier house wall has not sunk at all.

You are probably ready with the answer: the soil gives way because the *pressure* is too great. Pressure is $\frac{load}{area}$, and an enormous load results in as low a pressure as you wish if it is spread over a large enough area. This is one reason why a house has *foundations*—to spread the load on the earth, or to divide the load by a larger area and

273

so reduce the pressure. Here are some figures of the maximum safe pressure for various sub-soils:

Description of sub-soil	Maximum safe load in tons per sq. ft.
Made ground	up to $\frac{1}{2}$
Loamy soils	$\frac{1}{2}$ to 1
Soft chalk, soft clay or wet sand	1
Fairly dry clay or sand	2
Firm dry clay	3
London blue clay; compact gravel	4

What, for instance, is the pressure at the foot of a house wall 18 ft. high due only to the weight of wall? This is a simple question to which the answer, again, is $\frac{load}{area}$: an average figure for the weight of brickwork is 120 lb. per cubic foot, and you have to find the total weight of a certain amount of wall and divide by the area of its base.

You may think that there is not enough information here—you have the proposed height, 18 ft., and a general figure representing the density of the material, but nothing more—nothing to indicate what to take as the length or thickness of the wall. Far from leaving you handicapped, this leaves you free to make the problem as easy as you choose; for you select the area that suits you best, find the number of cubic feet and so the load, and then divide by your area to get the pressure. Check that the method is sound. If the area is, in fact, say, three times the one you chose for calculation, that will give (1) three times the load and (2) three times the area to divide by, so the pressure will work out the same.

The obvious choice for an area is a square foot. Think of a column of brickwork 18 ft. high and 1 ft. square. Applying the pressure formula and remembering that pressures are worked out usually as load per square inch, you will find the pressure is 15 lb. per sq. in.

Allowing for floors, roof and contents, the pressure is usually taken to be 20 lb. per sq. in. The figures in the above table converted to lb. per sq. in. show that this would be far too great a pressure for some soils. Since the house load is fixed, the pressure must be reduced by increasing the area, and that is the purpose of foundations. The garage in Fig. 7 was probably built without adequate load-spreading foundations.

PREPARING AND LAYING THE FOUNDATIONS

For such an addition as the outhouse in Fig. 6, or a small greenhouse, it is necessary to excavate and lay foundations. Top-soil is considered to have no bearing strength at all and must be removed— 6 in. is usual. In planning where to store the top-soil it is worth considering how much space it will take. Remember, then, that:

(1) Excavated soil is 25 per cent greater in volume than before it is dug out.

(2) If stacked in a wedge shape as in Fig. 8a the volume is only half length × breadth × height.

(3) If stacked in a pyramid or cone as in Fig. 8b the volume is only one-third area of base × height. In both cases the soil will stack only at a fairly definite surface angle called the "angle of repose."

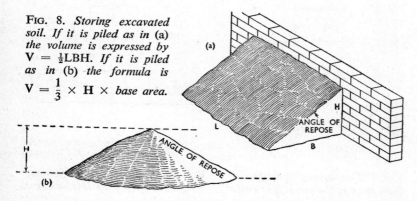

FIG. 8. *Storing excavated soil. If it is piled as in (a) the volume is expressed by* $V = \frac{1}{2}LBH$. *If it is piled as in (b) the formula is* $V = \frac{1}{3} \times H \times$ *base area.*

As the next stage will be further excavation for foundations and/or footings for walls, the essential principles may be indicated here: they are the same for a great range of wall sizes.

If the foundation is to be without footings, then the thickness of the foundation and the amount it projects on each side of the wall should not be less than the wall thickness. This is illustrated in Fig. 9. It may occur to you as you look at this figure that there is a good deal of concrete which is really wasted—the two triangular parts outside the 45-deg. lines. (What proportion of the total do you make it?) This can only be avoided by a troublesome arrangement for casting the concrete with a trapezium-shaped section, and the saving is not considered worth the trouble.

The use of footings with foundations is best understood from Fig. 10. The required increase in area is obtained gradually by stepping out with widening brick courses. The rule is to do this by a total of half a brick per course, or a quarter brick each side, until the course is twice as thick as the wall, and then comes the concrete.

For walls 9 in. thick or more, the amount of concrete is determined as in Fig. 10. Compare this with Fig. 9 for a 9-in. wall, and verify that, allowing 3 in. of height per course of bricks, footings save about 20 per cent of the concrete.

What is the extra cost of bricks? Fig. 10 shows two extra courses, $3\frac{1}{2}$ bricks in section as for house walls; for less height one extra course is enough, making $2\frac{1}{2}$ bricks in section. These are repeated every $4\frac{1}{2}$ in. What is then the total of extra bricks per yard?

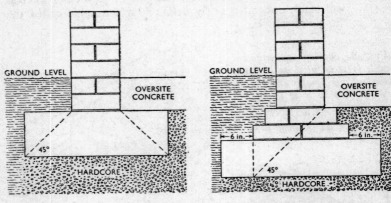

FIG. 9. *Foundation without footings. How much of the concrete is wasted?*   FIG. 10. *Foundation with footings. This method uses up less concrete.*

Allowing £5 per 1,000 for the bricks, this means 2s. extra per yard length of wall for bricks. Comparing this with 20 per cent of the concrete in a yard of foundations as in Fig. 9, what should be the price of concrete per cubic foot to make the two methods about equal? Is there anything in it at 1s. 6d. to 2s. per cubic foot—a fair price for foundation concrete?

For small jobs on good soil it is theoretically sound to excavate, compact and level the sub-soil and put footing courses of bricks straight on the earth. The practical difficulty is then to get a reliable base from which to start bricklaying: foundation concrete is poured and then levelled off to the tops of carefully driven pegs, thus giving a true and level base. That is the other reason for having concrete foundations.

Hardcore is the name given to the layer of broken brick, rubble, and so on, used to keep the concrete out of contact with the earth. When it is being ordered, 20 per cent must be added to the calculated volume to allow for consolidation.

Concrete and hardcore quantities for the foundations in Fig. 6 offer a practical problem. The suggestions there are one course of footings and 1 ft. 3 in. foundation, with 1 ft. 6 in. foundations and no footing below 9-in. portions.

From the illustration it can be seen that there is the equivalent of 40 ft. 6 in. of 4½-in. wall and 6 ft. of 9-in. wall. At 2s. per cubic foot this comes to £3 for the concrete: the hardcore, at 6d. per cubic foot, amounts to about 8s. 6d.

CONCRETE AND MORTAR CALCULATIONS

Concrete is the most misused material in building, and this misuse would almost entirely disappear if the user would follow the cement manufacturer's figures in the same way as a housewife follows a recipe in making a cake.

Concrete has four components. Coarse aggregate, fine aggregate (or sand), cement and water. Ideally, the spaces in the coarse aggregate are filled by the sand, those in the sand by the cement, and those in the cement by water, if the components are in the right quantities. Using too much water means that the excess is not taken up chemically and has to dry out subsequently, leaving the concrete porous.

With concrete quantities you get some queer addition. Using a 1 : 2 : 6 mix, 1 cu. ft. cement + 2 cu. ft. sand + 6 cu. ft. "ballast" + water = approximately 6 cu. ft. concrete, as in Fig. 11. The strongest concrete in general use (as for beams) is a 1 : 2 : 4 mix : this works out not quite ideally, but roughly so that 1 + 2 + 4 = 5 (more nearly about 4⅔)! For that reason mixing machines are listed as 5/3½, 7/5, and so on. You put in 5 cu. ft., for example, and get out 3½ cu. ft. The exact data appear in the table on page 279.

"All-in" aggregate has the sand and "ballast" already mixed, so that the reduction in volume has mostly happened already. If you wanted to make something like a 1 : 2 : 6 mix, but were using all-in aggregate, you might think that this corresponds to a 1 : 8 all-in. You now see that this is wrong. What should it be?

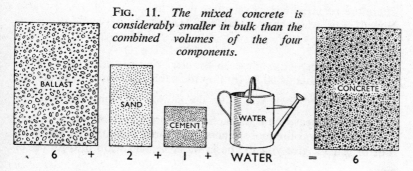

FIG. 11. *The mixed concrete is considerably smaller in bulk than the combined volumes of the four components.*

BALLAST   SAND   CEMENT   WATER   CONCRETE

6   +   2   +   1   +   WATER   =   6

When materials for concrete are being bought, the cost quotations show some significant variations. For example:

Cost of 1 cu. yd. gravel £1 7s. 6d.

Cost of 5 cu. yd. gravel £3 5s. 0d.

These figures show the relative importance of the cost of transport for a substance basically so cheap. Also, as gravel will not deteriorate, they indicate the value of bulk buying.

WATER/CEMENT RATIO

You will always make a better concrete by calculating the amount of water instead of guessing it, but unfortunately no one can lay down hard and fast figures for this amount, as aggregates have a varying "blotting-paper" action and rob the cement of some water. The basic rule is that the water/cement ratio, ideally about 0·5 by weight, should be kept down as nearly as possible to this figure. By "possible" we mean that in most cases, when this amount of water has been added, the concrete is usually still too stiff to handle, and in practice more has to be added; but remember that from this amount onwards all extra water added for your immediate convenience is making the final concrete weaker and more porous. If you are doing a big job, such as a drive-in, yard or long path, vary the amount of *sand* used to get the mix workable with a low water/cement ratio.

We have just referred to a water/cement ratio in terms of *weight*, and while sand is measured by volume, cement is always sold by weight. We must, therefore, see how to fit together volume and weight. All you need is the density of water and of loose cement:

Water weighs 62·3 lb. per cu. ft.

Loose cement weighs 90 lb. per cu. ft.

Suppose you have used 1 cu. ft. of cement and want to measure out the amount of water to give the 0·5 water/cement ratio by weight.

Weight of cement = 90 lb.

Therefore required weight of water = 45 lb.

Now 62·3 lb. water has a volume of 1 cu. ft.

Therefore 45 lb. water has a volume of $1 \times \dfrac{45}{62·3}$ cu. ft.

In practice, it can be made even simpler. You can read the 62·3 lb. per cu. ft. of water as 60 lb. (noting the percentage error in so doing: $\dfrac{2·3}{62·3} \times 100$) and then you have the simple relation that water is two-thirds as heavy as cement. So three measures of water to two of cement give you equal weights, and three measures of water to four of cement give you the basic water/cement ratio of 0·5.

For the materials, you must follow a "recipe" such as those given in the table. You could make this table for yourself given only one figure for each mix: you must have that because only experiment will show how much the volume is reduced by the finer material filling up the voids in the coarser.

Materials needed to make 1 cu. yd. of concrete

Type of Job	Mix by Volume (sand, dry)	Volumes in cubic feet		
		Cement	Sand Dry/Damp	Gravel Ballast
Large masses	1 : 3 : 6	3·72	11·2/14·6	22·4
Paths, floors, small foundations	1 : 2½ : 5	4·36	10·9/14·2	21·8
Paths, floors, small foundations	1 : 6 all in	4·98		31
Structures : beams, lintels	1 : 2 : 4	5·33	10·6/13·8	21·2

The two figures for sand may puzzle you, but you can soon solve the puzzle by measuring out a bucketful of absolutely dry sand, damping it thoroughly, and trying to get it all back into the bucket. The two columns represent the same weight of sand, but a fixed-percentage increase in bulk has been allowed for in the damp-sand column: estimate this percentage for yourself. Notice also how the total of material is always more than 1 cu. yd.

Suppose, now, you want to concrete a shed floor 9 ft. × 16 ft., to a thickness of 4 in. as in Fig. 6, using a mix of 1:2½:5 over 4-in. hardcore. You have

(1) to find the volumes of the layers;
(2) to allow for consolidation of hardcore; and
(3) to take figures in the proportion of your concrete volume to that in the table—1 cu. yd.

In stage (3) you will have, for example, an amount of ballast given by $21 \cdot 8$ cu. ft. $\times \dfrac{\text{required volume}}{1 \text{ cu. yd.}}$. Since your volume is 48 cu. ft., and 1 cu. yd = 27 cu. ft., this comes to $21 \cdot 8 \times \dfrac{48}{27} = 38 \cdot 8$ cu. ft., or rather less than $1\frac{1}{2}$ cu. yd.

As an example of the strongest mix, take the case of a concrete step 3 ft. × 8 in. × 6 in. in 1 : 2 : 4 mix. The cement volume will be $5 \cdot 33$ cu. ft. $\times \dfrac{\text{volume of step}}{1 \text{ cu. yd.}}$, which comes to ·2 cu. ft. For small quantities like this, it is useful to remember that 1 cu. ft. = $6\frac{1}{4}$ gall. almost exactly, so that ·2 cu. ft. is about 5 quarts.

Calculations of mortar quantities can be based on the standard 1 : 3 mix, meaning one part (volume) of cement to three of sand. The only value you cannot then calculate for yourself is the volume of placed mortar that results, which is about 2·7 volumes.

In practically every case, however, the one part of cement can and should be partly replaced by hydrated lime. So you will need mixes such as 1 : 1 : 6, 1 : 2 : 9 and 1 : 3 : 12—all 1 : 3 mixes "gauged" with lime, the cement being given first. As it is best to soak the lime overnight, you need to think about the measuring.

Take the job of plastering a garage wall 8 ft. × 15 ft., $\frac{1}{2}$ in. thick, in 1 : 2 : 9 mix. You have to find:

(1) the total volume of mortar;
(2) the volume of sand, given, as above, that 2·7 volumes of mortar need 3 volumes of sand.
(3) and (4) the volumes of cement and of lime, which come quite easily from the 1 : 2 : 9 proportions.

A sound, if rough, idea of costs often encourages the amateur to use unfamiliar materials. If cement costs 6s., lime 8s. per cwt. and sand 28s. per cubic yard, verify for yourself that the material for this last job would cost less than £1. The building in Fig. 6 would have to be rendered in this way, as it is of only half-brick thickness.

BRICKWORK CALCULATIONS

We have gained some idea of the calculations involved in the foundations of a house. Now what about the walls? Here, you may be surprised at the fact that there is no fixed size for the common brick. The only absolute essential is given by a formula based on the dimensions in Fig. 12: the length L, the width W, and T the thickness of the mortar joint.

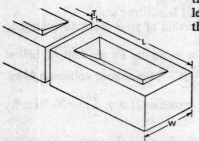

FIG. 12. *Whatever the exact size of the brick, the three essential dimensions are related by the formula* $L = 2W + T$.

The relation between these measurements has to meet the requirements of what is called *bonding*—the pattern formed by the vertical joints between bricks. Consider the two patterns in Fig. 13.

In both cases the applied load is carried by the shaded bricks. In the first case, with a correct "broken bond," the load is carried by

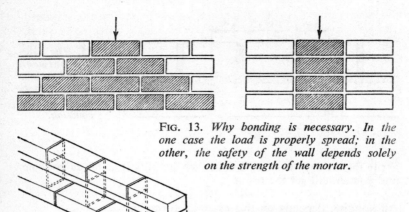

FIG. 13. *Why bonding is necessary. In the one case the load is properly spread; in the other, the safety of the wall depends solely on the strength of the mortar.*

FIG. 14. *Three-quarter bond, laid in this way, is a variant of stretcher bond, seen in the example above it.*

an increasing number of bricks per course; in the second, showing "straight joints," the load is not spread at all.

Bonding has value also on grounds of appearance.

Stretcher bond, as shown in Fig. 13, is the simplest pattern it is possible to obtain.

Three-quarter bond is sketched in Fig. 14. The joints are displaced a quarter length of a brick. You should sketch the elevation for yourself to see how it compares with Fig. 13 for appearance. These two are the only bonds used for a wall as thick as the width of a brick—a "half-brick" wall.

You cannot build to any appreciable height with a wall as thin as this: you will be limited by what is called the slenderness ratio— the height of the wall divided by the thickness. For brickwork this is usually taken as 12 : 1. (Work out the maximum height you can build with a brick not more than $4\frac{1}{2}$ in. thick.)

To build a higher wall, or a stronger one even of this height, part or all of the wall must then be twice this thickness—a "one-brick" wall. This does not as a rule merely duplicate one of the patterns above. Instead, a certain number of bricks are laid across the thickness of the wall and are called *headers*. The lengthwise bricks are called *stretchers*. That is how the formula arises.

In Fig. 15 two consecutive courses are shown, one of headers and one of stretchers. If the pattern is to be maintained, you will see that the distances between the vertical lines must be equal to each other.

281

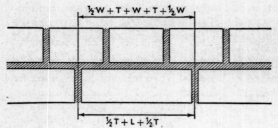

FIG. 15. *The relationship between bonding and the size of any brick is established by this equation.*

Write them down as an equation, then simplify it as far as possible, and you should get the result

$$L = 2W + T.$$

All bonding depends on this essential formula.

In most, though not all, brickwork the distance marked out on Fig. 15, called the *unit of bond*, and equal to $L + T$, is 9 in. That gives two equations: as there are three unknown quantities, L, W and T, a third equation is needed.

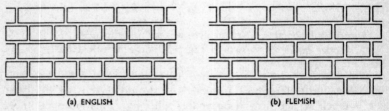

FIG. 16. *English and Flemish bonds. Which of them uses more headers? If facing bricks cost more than common bricks, which bond is the cheaper?*

For instance, if the unit of bond is 9 in. what are the dimensions of a brick to give a $\frac{1}{4}$-in. mortar joint?

Here we have $L = 2W + T$ as always

$$\left.\begin{array}{l} L + T = 9 \text{ in.} \\ T = \tfrac{1}{4} \text{ in.} \end{array}\right\} \text{ just given}$$

Substituting for T gives the two equations

$$L + 2W + \tfrac{1}{4} \text{ and } L + \tfrac{1}{4} = 9,$$

from which you can easily find L, and then W by substitution. You should get the size $8\frac{3}{4} \times 4\frac{1}{4}$ in. Try this again for a $\frac{1}{2}$-in. mortar joint.

In practice the different shrinkage in the kiln makes the bricks vary in size: this is taken up by varying the thickness of mortar.

Besides the bonds shown in Figs. 13 and 14, there are two other standard patterns, shown in elevation in Figs. 15 and 16. You will find it increases interest in brickwork to spot these patterns in buildings. In these elevations the wall is supposed to be a one-brick or 9-in. wall. In comparing them, remember therefore that behind each stretcher there is another you cannot see.

The usual form of *English bond*, with one header course to one stretcher course, is shown in Fig. 16a. It is sometimes modified by giving one header course to a larger number of stretcher courses. What do you think is the reason for the latter being always an *odd* number? More detail of this bond appears in Fig. 18. *Flemish bond* is shown in Fig. 16b.

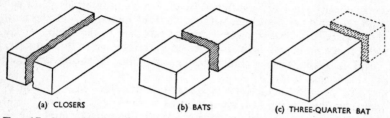

(a) CLOSERS   (b) BATS   (c) THREE-QUARTER BAT

FIG. 17. *Special bricks which are sometimes needed to complete a course.*

Try, by drawing or with model bricks, to keep to the bonding rule—no straight joints—in these details: (1) The end of a wall, in any bond. (2) Turning a corner, in any but stretcher bond.

You will find it cannot be done. To cope with these and other problems, bricks have to be cut in halves—lengthwise, making a *closer*, and crosswise, making a *bat*, as in Fig. 17. The use of a closer at a corner or "quoin" is shown in Fig. 18. Other specials include a *three-quarter bat* (Fig. 17c) and bricks with curves and bevels.

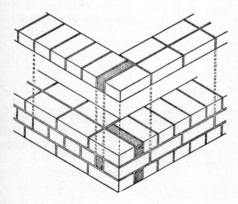

FIG. 18. *On the left are closers in use. Below is a scheme for a 4½-in. wall with a 9-in. pier, using three-quarter bats and headers. Try sketching the courses in plan.*

A				¾
B		½	H	H	
A				¾
B		½	H.	H	
A				¾
B		¾	H	H	
A				¾

Make sketches to show how to bond in the details which follow, noting what special bricks you would need.

(1) The end, or "stopped end," of a half-brick wall in stretcher bond, and in three-quarter bond.

(2) A quoin in three-quarter bond.

(3) A 9-in.-square pier bonded to a half-brick wall. This is a useful exercise for the amateur, as the need for it arises in small construction jobs, as when a garden store or a piece of walling is done mainly in $4\frac{1}{2}$ in. and it is desired to build higher than the maximum allowed under the 12 : 1 slenderness ratio without making a 9-in. wall throughout. The wall is stiffened by 9-in. piers at intervals. You will find that this can be done, without straight joints, only if the half-brick part is in three-quarter bond, at any rate in the region of the pier. If the main wall is in stretcher bond the change to three-quarter bond is made with a three-quarter bat. Fig. 18 shows one way of doing this.

For overall calculations in brickwork, besides the 9-in. unit of bond we must bring in a measurement so far neglected—the height of the brick when laid in courses. With the mortar joint this is taken as 3 in., the brick itself being about $2\frac{5}{8}$ in. There is a difference of tradition over this point, the figure being $2\frac{7}{8}$ in. in the North of England. If you observe accurately you may be able to detect this on your travels.

Taking the 3-in. overall measurement, calculate, first accurately and then in round numbers, the number of bricks per square yard of walling in (1) half-brick and (2) one-brick or 9-in. walling.

An old tradition still used in some parts expresses brickwork in the *rod*. This is the amount needed to make a square rod of wall $1\frac{1}{2}$ bricks thick. Remembering that a rod is $5\frac{1}{2}$ yd. you can find the number of bricks involved—it is over 4,000. This rod is a *volume*, so that in one-brick or half-brick walling the area will be proportionately larger.

Try These

(1) I have three builder's bricks, each measuring 9 in. long, $4\frac{1}{2}$ in. wide and 3 in. deep. How many different heights can I build up with them?

(2) A sash window with a semicircular top is 2 ft. 6 in. wide. If the top sash is lowered 1 ft. what is the area of the opening?

(3) Arrange six matches together to form four triangles.

Solutions on page 444

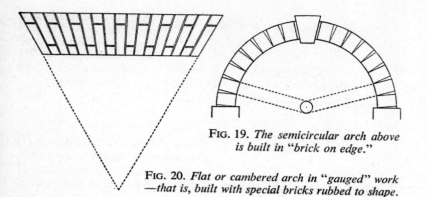

FIG. 19. *The semicircular arch above is built in "brick on edge."*

FIG. 20. *Flat or cambered arch in "gauged" work —that is, built with special bricks rubbed to shape.*

Here are some further examples:

(1) Find the number of bricks needed to build a pair of 5-ft. gate piers 9 in. square.

(2) How many bricks and bats, or closers, are needed for two piers for a porch, 7 ft. high and 13½ in. square? Set out two consecutive courses to give a good bond.

(3) Allowing for a joint ⅜ in. thick, what volume of mortar do you need per square yard of wall, half-brick thick? What, in fact, is the percentage of mortar in a given volume of wall?

(4) Estimate the number of bricks you would require, and the number of cubic feet of mortar, to build the outhouse in Fig. 6.

For the last example, use the approximations arrived at above —for a square yard of wall, 50 bricks for half-brick and 100 bricks for one-brick walling. Don't forget those below floor level—there are about 350 there, besides about 2,250 above.

THE GEOMETRY OF BRICK ARCHES

While you are not likely—unless you are very ambitious—to build your own brick arches, you may find much interest in the geometrical constructions used.

The flat or cambered arch, and the semicircle, as in Figs. 19 and 20, look simple enough; but a closer look at the brickwork of Fig. 20 may increase your respect for the man who built it. The dimensions of every brick had to be geometrically determined by setting out the radii from the centre, and then each brick was cut roughly and finally rubbed down exactly to shape. That is why the bricks used are called rubbers.

Fig. 21 shows the segmental arch. The two dimensions which usually determine the curve are *AB*, the span, and *HM*, the rise.

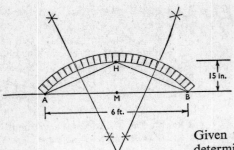

FIG. 21. *Construction of a segmental arch. The perpendicular bisectors of the two chords meet at the centre from which the arc may be described.*

15 in.

A   M   B

6 ft.

Given these, how would you (1) determine the centre and radius, and (2) actually draw the curve?

The first seems easy enough to answer if you have remembered the simplest part of circle geometry—the centre lies on the perpendicular bisector of any chord: where any two such bisectors meet is the centre. This is easy enough on paper, but there are practical difficulties—*AB*, and the radius, may be several feet long. You can probably counter this quite soundly by working to scale; this gives you a measure of the radius. Even then, how do you set to work? You will not have a pair of compasses of the length you have determined.

The calculation of the radius can, in fact, be made without any of these hindrances, by using one of the most attractive propositions in all geometry—the theorem of intersecting chords. This is illustrated in Fig. 22. *AOB, COD* can be any two chords in any circle, and always $AO \times OB = CO \times OD$. If you imagine the curve of the segmental arch to be completed, and *HM* produced to make a diameter to the other side of the circle, you should be able to calculate the value of the rest of the diameter and so find the radius. (It is 4·225 feet.)

This still leaves us with the practical difficulty about compasses for a radius of over 4 ft., and this is solved in the setting out of

FIG. 22. *The theorem of intersecting chords (right) gives us the radius of the arch.*

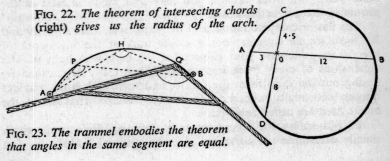

FIG. 23. *The trammel embodies the theorem that angles in the same segment are equal.*

286

arches by bringing in another very attractive geometrical theorem—
that concerning "angles in the same segment." Both theorem and
application are illustrated in Fig. 23. The theorem states that if *A*
and *B* are joined to *H*, *P*, *Q* or any other point on the curve, the
angles *AHB*, *APB*, etc., are all equal. The carpenter who has to
make the wooden formwork for the arch fixes pins at *A* and *B*, the
springing points, and lays battens against the pins to meet in an
angular point at *H*, the crown of the arch. A cross-batten fixes the
angle as in Fig. 23. If the formwork, or "trammel," slides round so
that the lengths of batten are held against *A* and *B*, the angular
point will move on the required segmental curve.

Elliptical arches are much in favour with the designer in brick,
and the curve is in demand in a variety of crafts—for screens,
lampshades, leather handbags, panels, and so on. When an ellipse
or part of one has to be drawn, the conditions given are usually

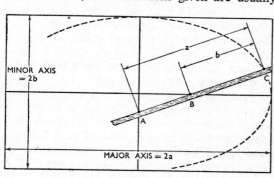

FIG. 24. *Forming
an ellipse by means
of a trammel. So
long as* A *is on the
minor axis and* B
on the major axis,
C *represents a point
on the ellipse.*

that it is to have a certain value for the greatest and least breadth,
called the major and minor axes. A simple method of drawing the
curve is then to use a trammel, as illustrated in Fig. 24. At its
simplest, this is a straight-edge of stout paper with three marks,
A, *B* and *C*, such that $AC = a = \frac{1}{2}$ the major axis, and $BC = b = \frac{1}{2}$
the minor axis. If the trammel takes up successive positions so that
A is on the minor axis and *B* on the major axis, the position of *C*
is a point on the curve.

WHEN TO USE TIMBER

So much for brickwork; but we shall not get very far in building
our house without another useful material—timber. One of the
oldest, wood is also one of the best of building materials. Its use in
Great Britain since 1939 has been determined almost entirely by
the limited supplies available.

The following table shows up the merits of wood from one important aspect—the strength/weight ratio.

	Ultimate Strength in tons per sq. in.		Density in lb. per cu. ft.	Relative cost per cu. ft.
	Tension	Compression		
Mild Steel	35	—	490	£16
Concrete	—	1·1 (7 days)	140	2s. 4d.
Common Brickwork	—	0·7	125	1s. 10d.
Pine	5·8	—	40	16s.

These figures are only approximate, and those for cost are of course liable to change; but we may agree on certain general lines for planning our choice of materials after a thoughtful study of this little table. What will you use, for instance, if you want (1) bulk only, (2) strength, (3) strength and lightness? What does the absence of tensile figures suggest in the case of concrete and brick?

The general conclusion might be that steel and wood are the structural materials essential for beams or any other feature in tension, but to be used in quantities as small as possible. Concrete and brick are the bulk materials, ideal for walls and piers. How, for instance, does 1-in. timber compare with 4½-in. brickwork for cost of materials if used for walling?

Planning of this sort will help to avert extremes such as are suggested in Fig. 25. Nobody *intends* to perpetrate such horrors as are seen in hundreds on our public allotments; things like that usually come into being with no kind of plan behind them. On the other hand, good building is much too expensive to be wasted—the alternative structure below, far too strong for an allotment shed, is therefore much too costly.

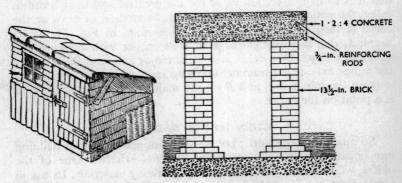

FIG. 25. *In rejecting the dubious architecture of the shed, we may consider how to replace it. The second structure is clearly unnecessarily sturdy.*

Wood is measured in cubic feet, but other units are used, one at least for no other material. An amount having an area of 1 sq. ft. and a thickness of 1 in. is called a foot super (superficial). This is not the same as a super foot, though builders are very easy-going about these and other terms; a super foot is meant strictly to specify any area of 1 sq. ft. Flooring is measured by the square—100 sq. ft. Lengths cut to one of the standard sections used—2 × 1 in., 7 × 2 in., etc.—are sold by the foot run.

The *standard*, a unit used only for wood, means nowadays a Petersburg Standard (not the English Standard, a term no longer in use) and equals 165 cu. ft.

You would do well now to improve your grasp of all these terms by checking the nature of the units involved.

Of what nature—the correct term is dimensions—are these: the foot super, the foot run, the square? (They are units of volume, length and area respectively.) In what class is the standard?

Here are further questions you should be able to answer.

What price per cubic foot are you paying in the following cases?
(1) Parana pine at 1s. 10d. per foot super.
(2) Red deal scantlings: 2 × 2 in. at 8d. per foot run,
                             9 × 3 in. at 3s. 6d. per foot run.
(3) Hardboard $\frac{3}{16}$ in. thick at 30s. per sheet 10 × 4 ft.
(4) Wood-waste board $\frac{3}{4}$ in. thick at 13s. 6d. per square yard.
(5) Softwood at £125 per standard.
(6) Flooring, 1 in. thick, at £6 per square.

In making such calculations, use plenty of space and write down just what is known at each stage. Craftsmanship in calculating partly consists of delaying the actual calculation and so saving labour. Consider the case of the hardboard in (3):

$$10 \text{ ft.} \times 4 \text{ ft.} \times \frac{3}{16} \text{ in. cost 30s.}$$

$$10 \times 4 \times \frac{3}{16} \times \frac{1}{12} \text{ cu. ft. cost 30s. (bringing everything to ft.)}$$

$$\frac{10}{16} \text{ cu. ft. cost 30s.}$$

$$1 \text{ cu. ft. costs 30s.} \div \frac{10}{16} = 30\text{s.} \times \frac{16}{10} = 48\text{s.}$$

In order to group varied lots of wood under a single figure, common practice, especially in periods of shortage, is to measure up, convert to cubic feet and divide by 165 to bring to standards to one decimal place.

In a small job there will be much less than a standard. See if you can estimate whether a whole house uses more or less than a standard.

Then try a rough estimate of the amount of wood needed to build a garden store or garage such as in Fig. 6.

We shall need softwood for doors and frames. Doors can be made by the amateur but are better bought ready made. In case a timber licensing regulation is in force, the makers' catalogue will usually give the number of standards to three or four decimal places. You can calculate the timber needed for a 7 by 7 ft. pair of doors of framed and braced construction as in Fig. 26, and compare the cost of doors

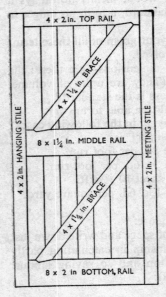

you see advertised with the cost of the timber. In making such calculations you may well follow the practice of the experienced woodworker. He collects together the various lengths of each section. For example, there is a

FIG. 26. *How many cubic feet of softwood are required for a pair of framed and braced doors like this one? How much is this in standards? The overall dimensions of the doors are 7 by 7 ft.*

good deal of 4×2 in. in these doors —more than you would think when the tenons have been allowed for, as in Figs. 39 and 40. Suppose there is about 35 ft. of this section.

The carpenter takes 12×1 in. as a kind of unit section, with any other section of equal area, such as 4×3 in. or 6×2 in., treated as equivalent. Such sections give him a foot super per foot length (or running foot) of board.

Any other sections are related to the unit section. How does our 4×2 in. compare? It is taken as $\frac{8}{12}$ or $\frac{2}{3}$ of unit section, so 35 ft. of 4×2 in. is said to amount to $35 \times \frac{2}{3}$ ft. super.

For a large area of board, as used to face these doors, the calculation proceeds by the square, or the reduction to feet super is made from the area in square feet times the thickness in inches. It should be fairly clear that 7×7 ft. of $\frac{3}{4}$-in. board is equivalent to just over 36 ft. super.

When all the feet super have been collected up, how will you find the volume in cubic feet? Remember the foot super is really a volume unit and twelve of them make a cubic foot. You should get about 9 cu. ft., or ·055 of a standard, for these doors. Some thought should also be given to construction with a timber frame; and $\frac{1}{8}$-in. hardboard or $\frac{1}{2}$-in. wood-waste board, available in 8×4 ft. sheets, may be cheaper than timber and will serve well if you buy a weatherproofed variety. As you look at Fig. 26, decide where the hinges will be—they must be placed so that the braces are in compression. Consider what use the braces would be if the hinges were on the right.

If the doors are 7×7 ft., how much 4×3 in. timber is needed for the framing in which the doors are to be hung?

MOISTURE CONTENT AND SEASONING

Green wood contains a great deal of moisture, much of which dries out whatever the subsequent history of the wood—even if it is out in the weather. When the amount still held is down to about 20 per cent of the dry weight, further change in moisture content is a matter of equilibrium between the wood and the atmosphere in which it is kept. If, then, you have to define what you mean by "seasoning" of wood, what answer do you give? It must include reference to the conditions in which the wood is to remain; boarding which is in ideal condition for internal flooring is not right for an outside door or for the roof of a garden shed. Some idea of the variations is given in the graph in Fig. 27. The common-sense procedure, which is not often possible, is to let the wood adjust itself by storing it for as long as possible beforehand in the place where it is to live.

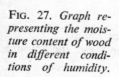

FIG. 27. *Graph representing the moisture content of wood in different conditions of humidity.*

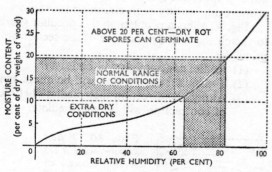

It is a well-known fact that the size of a piece of wood varies very much with the moisture it contains. It is less well known that the movements are different according to the direction. Fig. 28 shows the position of a piece of wood in relation to the original tree-trunk. With change in moisture content, the wood will move. The amount

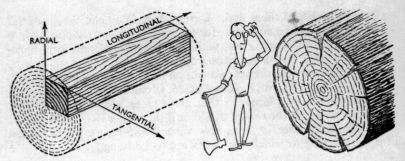

FIG. 28. *The three ways in which a piece of wood is liable to shrink.*

FIG. 29. *What makes a log split in this way?*

of movement depends on the type of wood and the change in moisture, but in all cases it will vary with the direction in this order:

Longitudinal—least (so little that it is usually neglected)

Radial

Tangential—roughly twice the radial movement. The actual amount varies with the kind of wood and ranges from 4 per cent to 14 per cent for the total tangential movement.

One familiar result of this difference is illustrated in Fig. 29.

When the radius of any circle in the log is reduced by radial shrinkage, by the formula *circumference = 2π × radius*, we can say that to be free from stress the circumference should shrink in the same proportion. Actually, however, it shrinks in about twice that proportion, putting each circumference into a state of stress.

Fig. 30 offers a problem in this peculiar geometry. It is interesting to sketch the final appearance of the section following these geı eral principles:

(1) Radial contraction will be least;

(2) Tangential contraction will be about twice radial;

(3) Along any direction intermediate between these, the amount of contraction will be intermediate.

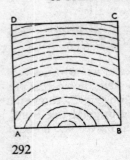

FIG. 30. *What shape will this section assume as the wood dries?*

FIG. 31. *How will this cut alter in shape as it shrinks?*

292

This means that *DC* will shrink twice as much as *AB*, and the other two sides by an intermediate amount. If you have worked on these lines you should have a trapezium, with *DC* parallel to *AB* but shorter.

Fig. 31 gives another example. The answer is first, roughly diamond-shaped. If you had imagined or drawn that shape, which would then be the long diagonal? It should be *KM*.

Another practical problem is illustrated in Fig. 32, which shows four possible sections for, say, 6 × 1 in. boards for flooring. Section (*b*) would give most movement; sections (*a*) and (*c*) would give about half as much. Only (*d*) would show distortion, and the results can be so inconvenient that they are considered further in Fig. 33.

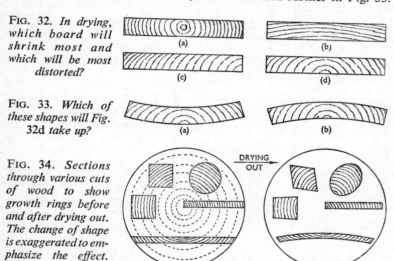

FIG. 32. *In drying, which board will shrink most and which will be most distorted?*

(a) (b) (c) (d)

FIG. 33. *Which of these shapes will Fig. 32d take up?*

(a) (b)

FIG. 34. *Sections through various cuts of wood to show growth rings before and after drying out. The change of shape is exaggerated to emphasize the effect.*

DRYING OUT

Fig. 33*a* is the correct answer; the movement is a shrinkage and the top (tangential) moves more than the bottom (radial, or nearly so), making the board narrower at the top than at the bottom. This effect is so important in joinery that it is remembered in terms of a rule that, on shrinkage, a board curls the opposite way to the curve of the annual rings.

How would you cut up a log—this is called conversion of the timber—or, if you can do so at a timber yard, how would you select boards for yourself? Fig. 32 hints at the answer; in cutting, the trunk is quartered and the boards are cut off alternate cheeks. This is rarely done, however, because it costs too much.

As a summary of the results of this property of wood, draw, perhaps rather exaggeratedly, the subsequent appearance after shrinkage of the sections cut as in Fig. 34. The results will ignore, as we have done, such refinements as the difference between heartwood and sapwood, but they will be approximately correct.

MOVEMENT IN DOORS AND FLOORS

Returning to our door problem, we may now find it easier to understand why doors are made of frame construction. Looking at Fig. 35a, you will see that if a door were made in a continuous sheet, then all across one measurement we should get either the radial or the tangential movement. Fig. 35b shows how this is replaced to give a movement which both ways is mainly longitudinal. Remembering that the latter

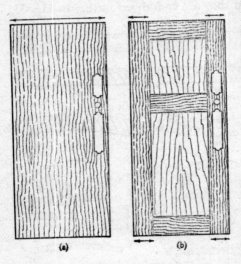

FIG. 35. *Two doors compared. Arrows show where there will be most movement.*

(a) (b)

can be practically ignored, you should be able to compare the total change in width of the two doors for, say, 3 per cent movement across grain.

Clamps and battens are cross-pieces to stiffen a piece of boarding. Their small longitudinal movement cannot keep place with the greater movement of the boards, which will range from radial to tangential. Fig. 36 shows how grooves, or slotted screw holes, allow for this. Some such provision should always be made when cross-bracing, otherwise Fig. 36c might happen!

It may, however, be recognized that movement will occur and that the boards must be fixed to the cross-members—for example in flooring, when the cross-members are the joists, or in a framed, ledged and braced door. In Fig. 37 you can see how a considerable movement can occur without undue disfigurement. The opening between boards has been made a feature of the work, and the tongue closes the actual crack.

294

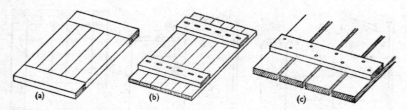

FIG. 36. *Methods of stiffening.* (a) *Clamps.* (b) *Battens with slotted screw-holes.* (c) *An unsatisfactory method which does not counteract shrinkage.*

Another question arises with flooring. Since it is the size of the cracks which spoils their appearance, which width of board would you prefer, 6 in. or 3 in.? The answer is, of course, that the narrower boards lead to narrower cracks. On the other hand, tongued and grooved flooring uses more wood at 3 in. than at 6 in. We could make a calculation of this by expressing the waste as a percentage of the whole. As shown in Fig. 38, the waste is equal to a strip of board as wide as the tongue for every board, and that is about $\frac{3}{8}$ in. wide.

This subject of wasted wood becomes most important whenever timber is scarce, and two economical kinds of jointing may be mentioned here.

For flooring, you can compare, for waste, the ploughed and tongued type in Fig. 38 with the tongue and groove. What is the actual waste now? It is clearly limited to the tongue itself, a strip $\frac{3}{4} \times \frac{1}{4}$ in., as compared with the $\frac{3}{8} \times 1$ in. which is wasted in tongued and grooved 1-in. flooring. The difference in percentage waste in, say, 4-in. floor boards is quite substantial.

Of similar importance is the replacement of mortise and tenon joints by dowels, as illustrated in Fig. 39. Try to estimate the waste on mortised joints in a four-panel door, as in Fig. 40. It is about 14 per cent; that partly explains why such doors are less often produced now.

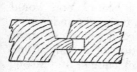

FIG. 37. *Effect of movement in a tongued and grooved joint.*

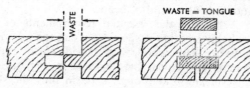

WASTE = TONGUE

FIG. 38. *Amount of wastage in a tongued and grooved joint compared with the wastage in a ploughed and tongued joint.*

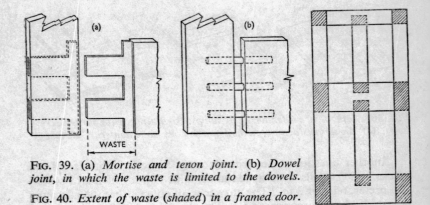

FIG. 39. (a) *Mortise and tenon joint.* (b) *Dowel joint, in which the waste is limited to the dowels.*

FIG. 40. *Extent of waste (shaded) in a framed door.*

If you are using fibreboard, a very popular material with the handyman, similar provision must be made for movement with moisture change. You will get an even larger movement, in fact, for, as noted above, the change in width is proportional to the original width, and fibreboard is used in large sheets (that is what makes it so handy). How will 5 per cent movement on 4 ft. compare with 5 per cent movement on 6 in.? Moreover, fibreboard has a higher percentage of movement than wood for the same change in moisture, being more porous.

In practice these considerations are so formidable that to offset them it is necessary to restrict the use of fibreboard to places where the humidity does not vary much.

MATHEMATICAL FACTS ABOUT BEAMS

A beam is meant to carry a transverse load. In so simple a building as a garden store you can think of several details where a beam is placed though under a different name. Door and window lintels, rafters, shelves, bench tops and (if there is a suspended wood floor) floor joists are all examples. Even a solid concrete floor acts as a kind of beam.

What are the essential requirements of a beam? You would probably say that it should not sag too much, or break, under load. If we are using wood, with its wide elastic range, it will sag far more than is convenient before there is any question of actual failure. That means that though a beam must be stiff enough and strong enough to carry our load, with wood the stiffness is what matters. With concrete it is all too easy to have a beam stiff enough but not strong enough. Fig. 41 indicates the possibilities.

296

What would you expect to determine the stiffness of a beam of rectangular section? There appear to be four factors: (1) the span, (2) the breadth of section, (3) the depth of section, and (4) the nature of the material.

Using a given timber and a given span determined by the plans, that leaves only the breadth and depth to vary. It is fairly easy to see that the stiffness is proportional to the breadth: at its simplest, if you double the breadth you double the weight needed to cause the original sagging. The effect of changing depths is not so simple, and we must quote higher authority and say that the stiffness varies as the cube of the depth.

STRONG ENOUGH—
STIFF ENOUGH

STIFF ENOUGH—
NOT STRONG ENOUGH

STRONG ENOUGH—
NOT STIFF ENOUGH

FIG. 41. *Strength and stiffness are both essential requirements of a beam.*

Compare these pairs of beam sections for stiffness, the breadth being always given first, and the measurements being in inches:

(1) 1×2, 2×2.　　(2) 2×1, 2×2.

Notice that though in each case the second beam has twice as much wood, in (1) the stiffness is doubled and in (2) it is increased eight times. Fig. 42 suggests what happens if you are using the same section, 3 by 1 in., but use it the wrong way round for stiffness.

(3) 2×3, $1\frac{1}{2} \times 4$.

These two sections are the same in one respect—they contain the same amount of wood. This makes a comparison of stiffness more interesting. Since we are only comparing, not calculating, actual stiffness, we have only to compare 2×3^3 with $1\frac{1}{2} \times 4^3$.

(4) 2×7, $1\frac{1}{2} \times 8$.

These are quite practicable alternatives for load-bearing floor joists. Compare (*a*) the amounts of wood, (*b*) the stiffnesses.

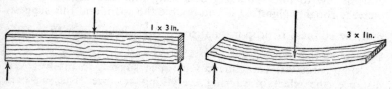

1 x 3 in.

3 x 1 in.

FIG. 42. *Effect of breadth and depth on stiffness. How much greater is the sag in the second board than in the first?*

Now consider the effect of a stiffening piece under a shelf. Fig. 43 shows the alternative sections. If the stiffener is screwed and glued to the shelf we have really to compare $7 \times (\frac{1}{2})^3$ with $6 \times (\frac{1}{2})^3 + 1 \times (1\frac{1}{2})^3$, for the stiffened part behaves as a solid beam 1 in. broad and $1\frac{1}{2}$ in. deep. Compare the two total cross sections and the relative stiffnesses. You may like to verify that even a piece $1 \times \frac{1}{2}$ in. underneath more than doubles the stiffness.

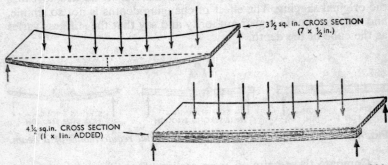

FIG. 43. *With a stiffener added, the sag of the shelf is reduced to one-fifth.*

If you can handle logarithms expertly you can find out how much the overall thickness would have to be increased to produce the same stiffness as the added 1 in. × 1 in. batten. If d is the resulting depth, you want $7 \times d^3$ to equal $6 \times (\frac{1}{2})^3 \pm 1 \times (1\frac{1}{2})^3$, and this ultimately gives the equation $d^3 = \frac{33}{56}$. This suggests one way in which to avoid or cure the sagging bookshelf so often produced by the beginner in woodwork.

EFFECT OF SPAN ON SAGGING

In all these calculations it has been assumed that we are dealing with beams of equal span. To compare beams of different span we need a law like that about the *(depth)*³. It is not a particularly difficult law to infer—the sag of a long thin lath can be seen to increase roughly eightfold if you double the span, and this suggests that the stiffness is proportional to $\dfrac{1}{(length)^3}$, which can be verified by trebling the span.

Many practical consequences at once suggest themselves: for instance, the effect of varying everything at once. The sag of a beam, as we have seen, varies as $\dfrac{1}{breadth}$, as $\dfrac{1}{(depth)^3}$ and as $(length)^3$;

we have, of course, been making the "common-sense" assumption that it varies as the weight—a risky sort of assumption, although true in this case.

All these variations can be combined. Using the initial letters, we should say sag varies as $\dfrac{WL^3}{BD^3}$, or equals $\dfrac{KWL^3}{BD^3}$, where K is a constant number as long as we don't change anything else—the material, for instance, or the kind of loading (point loading or spread-out loading) or the kind of support.

Fig. 44 indicates the startling effect of applying the (*length*)^3 principle. If a bookshelf is sagging badly—an inch, say—and we arrange midway support, which can look very nice anyway, how should we expect this to reduce the sag? Would you expect it to be cut down to $\frac{1}{16}$ in.?

Looking at the formula, you see that L is halved and so is W, for each half span; so that with WL^3 in the formula the halving acts four times over, giving $\frac{1}{16}$ in.

If we increase the span L, and want to avoid increased sag, we can see what to do by rewriting the formula thus: $Sag = \dfrac{KW}{B}\left(\dfrac{L}{D}\right)^3$ (verify that it is still the same formula). This shows that an increase in L if balanced by a proportional increase in D leaves the sag unchanged.

Notice also that the load or weight W may be simply the load of the material of the beam itself. For instance, how would the

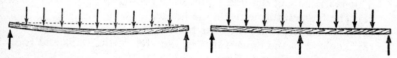

FIG. 44. *Halving the span by a central support reduces sag to one-sixteenth!*

sagging of these two beams of the same wood compare even without any added load: 10 ft. × 4 in. deep × 2 in. broad, and 15 ft. × 6 in. deep × 2 in. broad? We must make a ratio, or a fraction, of these two and work out $\dfrac{W_1 L_1^3}{B_1 D_1^3} \div \dfrac{W_2 L_2^3}{B_2 D_2^3}$, which comes to $\dfrac{W_1}{W_2} \times \dfrac{L_1^3}{L_2^3} \times \dfrac{D_2^3}{D_1^3} \times \dfrac{B_2}{B_1}$. Since $\dfrac{L_1}{L_2} = \dfrac{D_1}{D_2}$ and $B_1 = B_2$, this all "goes out" except $\dfrac{W_1}{W_2}$, which is the ratio of the volumes, or $\dfrac{10 \times 4 \times 2}{15 \times 6 \times 2} = \dfrac{4}{9}$. So the longer beam will sag more than twice as much under its own weight.

7

Heating and Water in the Home

ANY building which is warmer than the surrounding air will lose heat. If this state of warmth is to be maintained the loss must be made good by burning fuel and producing heat as fast as it is lost. In Great Britain we still do this in the vast majority of houses by burning soft coal in open grates. Until recent years we have had a cheap and plentiful supply of coal, which we have been content to waste in two ways:

(1) Through the shell of the house; the walls, with their doors and windows, and the roof have allowed much unnecessary loss of heat.

(2) We have burned our coal in open grates which send most of the heat up the chimney. Many open fireplaces give to the room only 20 per cent or less of the heat produced by the fuel.

Since fuel is now expensive and scarce, it is high time we looked into the possibility of getting better comfort value out of what we can still buy. Loss of heat from a house depends on a number of factors all of which can be measured with fair accuracy. Before reading further, see how many you can write down for yourself.

This is the sort of list you might have produced:

(1) The temperature outside the house.
(2) The temperature inside the house.
(3) The size of the house; that is, the area of the walls and roof and of openings in them.
(4) Thermal conductivity of different materials and methods of construction.

We can make a good start with these four, although there are others also. In looking for a formula to express the relation between them, it is common sense to expect that the temperatures will affect heat loss according to the difference between them, and that the bigger the area the greater the outward heat flow. Here is the formula:

$$H = U(T_2 - T_1)A$$

The symbols speak for themselves, except the letter U, which must be the one expressing the variations between different kinds of material. It is defined as the thermal transmittance, though it is always called the U-value. Fig. 1 gives some of these values.

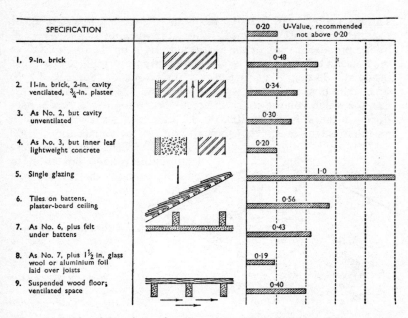

SPECIFICATION		0·20 U-Value, recommended not above 0·20
1. 9-in. brick		0·48
2. 11-in. brick, 2-in. cavity ventilated, ¾-in. plaster		0·34
3. As No. 2, but cavity unventilated		0·30
4. As No. 3, but inner leaf lightweight concrete		0·20
5. Single glazing		1·0
6. Tiles on battens, plaster-board ceiling		0·56
7. As No. 6, plus felt under battens		0·43
8. As No. 7, plus 1½ in. glass wool or aluminium foil laid over joists		0·19
9. Suspended wood floor; ventilated space		0·40

FIG. 1. *Table of U-values of various materials and forms of construction.*

Now apply this to a room such as there may be in your house, with two outside walls, 15 × 8 ft. and 12 × 8 ft., made of 9-in. brick, as illustrated in Fig. 2. From the illustration you can get the data for the calculation: T_2 and T_1, the inside and outside Fahrenheit temperatures, and A, the total area we are considering, in square feet. The value of U is found from the table in Fig. 1, in which the figures have been chosen so that H comes out as the heat in British thermal units (B.Th.U.) per hour.

If you have done the arithmetic correctly, the loss of heat through these two walls should come to 3,110 B.Th.U. per hour, leaving out the fractional bit of the answer (and ignoring the fact that one of the walls includes a window).

It will be interesting to find out what it costs in coal to make up this heat loss, supposing the fireplace is 20 per cent efficient—that is, it gives to the room 20 per cent of the heat it produces. Coal actually produces about 14,000 B.Th.U. for every pound burned. (This number is called the calorific value of the fuel.) So, with this fireplace

$$\text{heat given to room} = 14,000 \times \frac{20}{100} = 2,800 \text{ B.Th.U. per lb.}$$

301

To make good 3,110 B.Th.U. per hour, therefore, about 1·1 lb. of coal per hour must be burned. (Check the working mentally.)

To practise the use of the U-formula, try it on the room you live in. You can take 65 deg. F. as the minimum comfortable temperature inside and 35 deg. F. as that of a cold day outside. Sources of heat other than coal are wood, which gives about 8,000 B.Th.U. per lb.; gas, for which you are charged directly according to the heat it produces—a therm is simply 100,000 B.Th.U.; and electricity, of which the same is true except that the unit you pay for equals about 3,400 B.Th.U. There are some very interesting calculations easily to be made about the relative cost

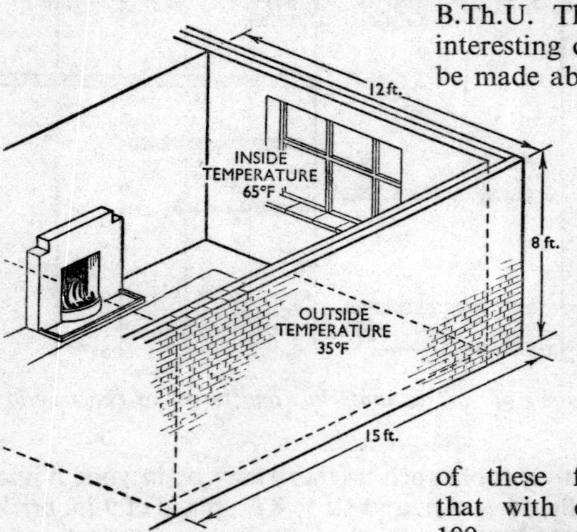

FIG. 2. *From the information already given it is easy to calculate the loss of heat through the two outside walls and the amount of coal required to make good the loss.*

of these fuels. Remembering that with electricity absolutely 100 per cent of the heat you pay for is given to the room, and with gas also (unless there is a flue), you might prepare a graph to show the relative merits of different fuels.

Loss through partitions is not, however, the whole picture. Your earlier list probably included such causes of trouble as: cracks round doors and windows and in floors and roofs; wind blowing on the house; and loss of hot air up the chimney. These are important because if a room feels warm it is usually because the air in it has been warmed, and as a result of these last factors the warmed air is constantly being replaced by cold air from outside (see Fig. 3).

There are really two questions here: how does the rate at which the air is changed compare with what is desirable on health grounds?; and how does the heat loss involved compare with what we lose through partitions?

The first question is in two parts. The recommended air changes are based on a generally accepted figure of 600 cu. ft. of air per

302

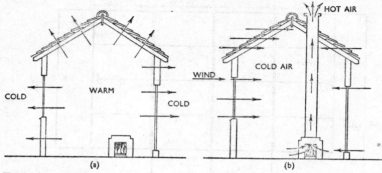

FIG. 3. *Heat is lost in two ways, which combine to give the true picture.*

person normally in the room, but they are usually expressed in the number of air changes per hour. To switch from one statement to the other, you must know the volume of the room. The following table gives figures for one small house; you can check these easily enough, and better still make a table for your own house.

	Living room	Bedroom	Bedroom	Kitchen	Bathroom
No of persons	3	2	1	—	—
Volume in cu. ft.	1,440	1,440	512		
Air changes per hr.	1·25	0·83	1·17	Standard total 1,000 cu. ft./hr.	Standard changes 2·00 per hour

So much for what is desirable. Now we will consider what often happens. Cold air comes into the room from outside when a wind blows on the walls. Very conveniently it happens that the rate at which air comes in is roughly proportional to the wind speed. If the wind blows at an angle it has the same effect as if it were blowing directly on the wall but at a reduced speed, as in Fig. 4.

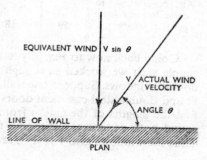

FIG. 4. *Effect of a wind blowing on to a wall at an angle.*

303

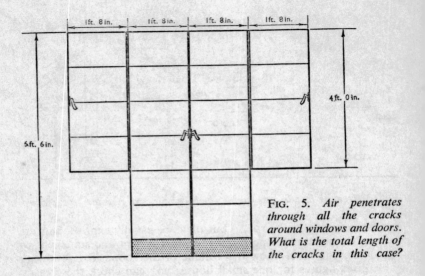

FIG. 5. *Air penetrates through all the cracks around windows and doors. What is the total length of the cracks in this case?*

WINDOW AND DOOR DRAUGHTS

As to where the air comes in you will know from experience, but you may not have realized how extensive is the air penetration through the cracks round doors and windows. In the next table are some data for windows found by measurements. They give a rough estimate of the number of cubic feet entering per hour per foot of crack. They are given for a wind blowing square to the wall at $8\frac{1}{2}$ miles an hour (an average wind speed). Bear in mind that for other wind speeds the air penetration is roughly proportional.

Type of window:	Wood Sash		Steel Casement		
Fit:	Poor	Average	Poor	Average	Good
Air penetration in cubic feet per hour per foot length	59	18	92	27	15

Going back now to Fig. 2, you may have noticed that to make a simple start we worked as though neither of the outside walls had door or windows. Suppose one wall has two steel windows of average fit and double steel-casement doors of poor fit, as in Fig. 5. You can find the lengths of the cracks from the given dimensions, going all round both windows, but taking the join of the doors only once. Thus the windows give 4 × 4 ft. and 4 × 1 ft. 8 in., which comes to

304

22 ft. 8 in. of cracks, giving at average wind speed a penetration of $22\frac{2}{3} \times 27$ (for average fit, see table) = 610 cu. ft. per hour. The doors admit much more air; if you work this out on similar lines, you will find the total is over 2,900 cu. ft. per hour.

The last figure can be applied, together with the volume of the room, to work out the air change due to wind alone. You may, however, have been asking yourself another question: if all this air comes into the room, where does it go to? There is no difficulty about the answer: it goes partly through the communicating door into the rest of the house, but mostly up the chimney.

Now we started on this problem as one of fuel economy, so that our interest will include the condition that there is a fire burning.

Our calculations so far have covered the fact that a wind on the outer wall causes air to be "pushed" into the room.

When a fire is burning, the flue action causes the pressure in the room to fall below normal, so that air is "pulled" into the room. When both wind and flue are operating, the total intake of air will be approximately the sum of the amounts due to the "push" and the "pull" acting separately. The flue action varies widely, but on the average should be taken as equivalent to a wind of 11 m.p.h.

The quickest way to deal with this is to apply the powerful method of simple proportion. Since we know that air penetration is proportional to wind speed (never try to apply simple proportion unless you have quite clear grounds for doing so) we take it that the effect is to bring in another amount made up of a figure of 2,900 cu. ft. increased in the proportion of 8·5 to 11; that is, $\times \dfrac{11}{8\cdot5}$. If you work this out and add the air forced in by the wind, you should reach the formidable figure of 6,700 cu. ft. per hour, with an air-change rate which you can again calculate and compare with the table.

Better still, make a few measurements of your own living-room. When you do so, remember that the flue action also pulls in air through the door into the hall; you must make a guess as to the kind of fit of this door.

But again, what does this cost in coal? Cold air comes in, to an extent that we have estimated in cubic feet and at a temperature we can guess. To keep the room warm this air must be heated to, say, our minimum comfortable temperature of 65 deg. F. How much heat is needed? Clearly one more piece of information is required—a figure for the heat needed to warm up a certain amount of air.

The value usually taken is about ·02 B.Th.U. for each cubic foot of air per degree Fahrenheit. This figure is related to, though not exactly the same as, what is called the specific heat of air. With the same values of inside and outside temperatures as before, you can now work out the cost in coal of the draughts in the room of Fig. 2. If it takes ·02 B.Th.U for one cubic foot to be heated through one degree Fahrenheit, what does it take in B.Th.U. for 6,700 cu. ft. through 30 degrees Fahrenheit?

A useful comparison is to set this figure (which should come to about 4,000 B.Th.U. per hour) against the heat needed to make up what is lost through the walls (p. 301) and to do the same for your own room, with its different measurements.

You can also follow this up by considering the saving you can achieve by reducing the air change, which is clearly the chief source of loss. Weather-stripping the cracks round doors and windows can certainly cut out "poor" fitting and can probably bring them into the "good" class. Some handymen have claimed to have sealed up the cracks so efficiently that they have to open the door to let the fire draw! For this reason under-floor ducts are sometimes fitted, because whenever the fire gets air from the room for burning purposes, for each cubic foot used in combustion 15 or 20 cu. ft. go *over* the fire and up the chimney. With even the most modern design of fireplace over 50 per cent of the heat is lost in that way. You may have heard of an open fire which claims to be more than 50 per cent efficient. If so, you can be sure that it must be using heat from the flue, probably by leading hot gases round a back boiler.

A very practical calculation follows on a visit to the ironmonger to find the cost of weather-stripping material. If you estimate how much cold air it will keep out, how many B.Th.U. that represents, and the cost of fuel to provide these B.Th.U., how soon will the cost be recovered? It is estimated that one air change per hour costs in a small house about £5 per winter. Can you check that estimate?

ROOFS: KEEPING OUT THE COLD

The handyman cannot do much to alter the U-value of the walls of his house, but the roof offers considerable possibilities in this direction. Reference to Fig. 1 shows (1) that the roof may have a very high U-value in a modern house, and (2) that this value can easily be reduced, if after calculation you think it is worth while.

The reduction achieved by a loose covering over the joists is quite remarkable, and if aluminium foil is used the reduction is very surprising. The foil acts by reflecting radiant heat downwards and, if it has a double surface, by a very low rate of re-radiation upwards. This is illustrated in Fig. 6.

To make the calculation, besides the area of the roof (which you can easily estimate by taking the area of top-floor ceilings only) we

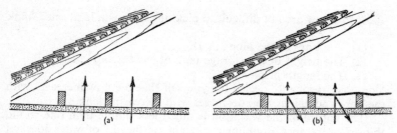

FIG. 6 (a) *Heat loss through plaster-board ceiling.* (b) *Reflection of much of the heat by aluminium foil laid over the ceiling joists.*

need use only the *difference* in U-values. Much time is often wasted by calculating in full two separate sets of figures in order to subtract (or add) the answers when a common factor might be realized [$abc - abd = ab(c-d)$]. Here the area, length of time, temperatures, and so on, are the same for both conditions, but you want to know the effect of reducing the U-value from, say, 0·43 to 0·19. So just find the difference of these first, and then find the advantage, expressed finally in weight of coal, of this U-value difference.

You might take an average upper-floor temperature of 50 deg. F. and an average outer temperature of 40 deg. F. over 35 weeks of the heating season. If your roof has 500 sq. ft. you should get from our U-formula, when multiplied by the number of hours in 35 weeks, something like 700,000 B.Th.U. saved. This can be expressed either as coal, which in a 20 per cent efficient fire gives about 2,800 B.Th.U. per lb., or (for a change) as therms of gas-heat.

Of course, in practice our U-formula must balance. If the calculations require a certain heat-supply to keep up a certain temperature difference, and that heat-supply is not forthcoming, there is only one other factor that can alter—the temperature difference will fall and you get a room colder than need be.

Though we have dealt only with heat lost to a cold atmosphere, the formula also works in reverse—a low U-value in the roof helps to keep up a high temperature difference in summer; that is, it helps to give you cool bedrooms.

ABOUT THE WATER SUPPLY

Before we proceed to deal with the loss of heat from hot-water pipes and storage cylinders, it may be as well to consider a few mathematical facts relating to the water supply generally. Few things are taken more utterly for granted in Britain than the copious supply of pure water that comes at the turn of a tap. The factors that

307

affect this flow are not difficult to pick out. You would at once think of

(1) The bore of the pipe ... D.
(2) The height of the storage tank above the tap ... H.
(3) The length of pipe ... L.

You could probably decide for yourself that the flow increases with the bore and height, and decreases with increasing length.

The nature of the variation is much less simple than one would think. For instance, doubling the height, or "head," of water does not double the rate of flow. The reason can be grasped with an effort: it is that the energy of water (or anything else) in motion is proportional to the *square* of the speed, so that to double the rate of flow needs four times the energy, and so four times the height.

Again, the rate of flow is not proportional to the diameter of the pipe. It is not likely to be, for the issuing stream of water has an area proportional to the square of the diameter; moreover, we have said nothing about the frictional resistance to flow. The factors are numerous and complex. The simplest expression, known as Box's formula, is written:

$$G = \sqrt{\frac{(3D)^5 \times H}{L}}$$

where G is the flow in gallons per minute; the other units are inches for D, feet for H and yards for L.

If you wanted to run a pipeline into a garage or greenhouse you would find some difficulty in applying this formula, because you would probably not connect straight to a tank at a certain height. There is much that is interesting without such direct calculation; for instance, you can consider the effect of variation in D, H or L separately. Suppose we have a certain head and length fixed, and we are concerned only with the variation in flow due to pipe size. As only G and D vary, we may say $G = a\sqrt{D^5}$. Comparing, for example, 1-in. with 2-in. pipe, where a is a constant number, we should say

$$\frac{G_2}{G_1} = \frac{a\sqrt{2^5}}{a\sqrt{1^5}} = \frac{\sqrt{32}}{\sqrt{1}} = 5.65$$

Now the area of the pipes depends on D^2, so that the cross-section of 2-in. pipe is greater than 1-in. by 2^2, that is, four times; yet it will permit 5·65 times more flow. Try comparing $\frac{1}{2}$-in. with $1\frac{1}{2}$-in. pipe and see how the larger pipe has an even greater relative efficiency.

To deal with the heat loss from hot-water pipes or storage cylinders we need nothing more except the appropriate U-value, which for a single surface of metal may be taken as 1·4, and the remaining figures of the U-formula—the area and temperatures.

What, for example, is the heat loss from an uncovered hot-water storage tank, and is it worth while doing anything about it? The area is found easily if the tank is rectangular, and the cylindrical type can be taken as a true cylinder with fair accuracy. If the tank is on brackets the whole surface is included; if it stands on the floor, omit the base.

Fig. 7 illustrates an actual case. For the area you will need the formula $A = \pi R^2$ for the top and $S = 2\pi RH$ for the curved side. You will find that the loss is not far short of 2,000 B.Th.U. per hour. With the practice you had earlier on you should be able to express this in terms of gas, coal or electricity.

If it is proposed to deal with this by lagging, say with glass wool at 4d. a square foot, there is no need to go through the calculation in full. Use the method of simple proportion again—since the glass wool changes the U-value to about 0·3, the loss is altered in the ratio $\dfrac{0\cdot3}{1\cdot4}$; or the saving is $\dfrac{1\cdot1}{1\cdot4}$ of the original B.Th.U. lost. How long would it take for the saving to pay for the glass wool?

The question of lagging pipes is less simple. Look at the sketch of a water-supply system on page 267. Which pipes are worth lagging? Hot-water piping is in two main sections—a run from the boiler to the storage tank, and the draw-offs to bath, basins and sinks. Would you lag either or both of these?

Look first at the run from the boiler, in what is called the primary circulation. This must be full of hot water all the time if the system is to work at all. Using similar temperatures and U-value to those of

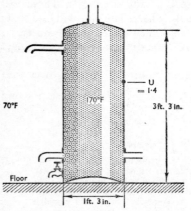

FIG. 7. *How much heat is lost through this hot-water storage cylinder?*

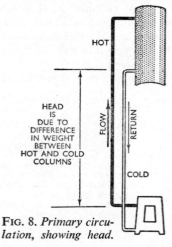

FIG. 8. *Primary circulation, showing head.*

309

Fig. 7, what is the heat loss? The pipe will have a bore of $1\frac{1}{4}$ in.; the length in the diagram is about 12 ft. This gives an hourly loss much less than before—you should get a figure in the region of 500 B.Th.U. per hour—though still appreciable. It must be emphasized again, however, that the formulae rarely work as simply as that.

Here is the U-formula again. $H = A(T_2 - T_1)U$.

However the various factors change, this equation must balance. We have assumed that if U is high, A and $(T_2 - T_1)$ will remain the same, and H will be high. In practice a compromise will occur. If U is high and H, the heat available to waste, cannot reach the value required to balance the equation, what else can happen? The area is fixed: this means $T_2 - T_1$ must be less, and as T_1, the general surrounding temperature, is fixed, T_2 must fall. This was suggested earlier in connexion with room temperature.

In this case another consideration appears. The primary circulation is sketched by itself in Fig. 8. Apart from vague phrases such as "heat rises," what reason would you give for the flow of water? Look at Box's formula again: it requires a definite head H to maintain a given flow G. Where in this closed system do you get a head?

The answer lies in the fact of expansion. The expanded hot water is lighter, and the head is provided by the difference in weight of the columns of water. If the expansion is proportional to the difference in temperature $(T_2 - T_1)$ then the head will be also proportional to this difference. This is a more important reason for lagging—to keep up the difference $(T_2 - T_1)$ and so maintain a good primary circulation.

Now consider what waste there is in the draw-offs. These will have $\frac{3}{4}$-in. pipe to the bath and $\frac{1}{2}$-in. elsewhere. The pipe will lose heat; in this case the lost heat is not made good by changing the water, so the temperature will fall. What then is the difference between lagged and unlagged pipe?

The answer is that the rate of temperature fall will be lower with lagging—lower in the ratio of the U-values, $\frac{0 \cdot 3}{1 \cdot 4}$. If, however, the tap

Carpenter's Jig-Saw

Mallet had four pieces of 8-in. board, respectively 5, 6, 7 and 9 ft. long. From this timber he wanted to construct a rectangular board, strengthened by three battens, making the fewest possible cuts. He found he could do it without wasting any wood. How many saw-cuts did he make and what were the length and breadth of the finished board?   *Solution on page 444* is turned on at long intervals, the water will in either case have cooled and the next user will run all the cooled water out anyway.

The rate of temperature fall can be quite easily calculated for a given temperature difference. $H = U(T_2 - T_1)A$ and the resulting temperature fall is this heat loss in B.Th.U. divided by the weight (in lb.) of water, which weighs $62\frac{1}{2}$ lb. per cu. ft. Thus, if temperature difference is 90 deg.

$$\text{Temperature fall} = \frac{U \times (90) \times 2\pi \times \text{radius (feet)} \times \text{length}}{\pi \times \text{radius}^2 \times \text{length} \times 62\frac{1}{2}}$$

For an unlagged $\frac{1}{2}$-in. (*diameter*) pipe this is about 200 deg. F. per hour, or over 3 deg. F. per minute. If lagging reduces U to about 0·3, the rate is still too fast for the water to stay hot for any length of time. Both heat and water are wasted with every use of the tap and the only remedy is to restrict this "dead" water to short runs.

CALCULATION OF THE PRIMARY CIRCULATION

For this we refer again to Box's formula, the pipe size being the usual $1\frac{1}{4}$-in. diameter. The most interesting feature of this calculation is its simplicity. Since we need to know only $\frac{H}{L}$, we have to remember there are two lengths, and that L is meant to be in yards. The drawing in Fig. 8 will help.

This is how it is done. Suppose the column of hot water to be equivalent to a certain height of cold water:

Effective head = height of cold column − equivalent height of hot

$\qquad$ = height of cold − height of cold × $\dfrac{\text{density of hot water}}{\text{density of cold water}}$

$\qquad$ = height of cold $(1 - \dfrac{\text{density of hot water}}{\text{density of cold water}})$

$\qquad$ = height of cold column $(1 - \dfrac{\text{volume of cold water}}{\text{volume of hot water}})$

Note the inversion: as the volume is greater, the density is less. To make the writing more concise, let h ft. be the height of the columns and V_1, V_2 the volumes at the lower and higher temperature.

Then Head $= h (1 - \dfrac{V_1}{V_2})$

$\qquad = h (\dfrac{V_2 - V_1}{V_2})$ $\qquad$ It does not matter which volume we take now, as the expansion is

$\qquad = h \times \dfrac{\text{expansion}}{\text{volume}}$ $\qquad$ not large.

Now expansion is always given by volume × expansion coefficient × temperature rise, so $\dfrac{\text{expansion}}{\text{volume}} =$ coefficient × temperature rise.

If we suppose a temperature difference of 100 deg. F., and look up the average expansion coefficient for water, which is ·00017 over this range, we have

Head = $h \times$ ·00017 $\times$ 100.

Both up and down pipes make up the length, so

L (in yd.) = h (in ft.) $\times 2 \div 3$; and

$$\frac{H}{L} = \frac{h \times ·00017 \times 100}{h \times 2 \div 3} = \frac{3}{2} \times ·017 = ·025$$

Now for Box again. We have $D = 1\frac{1}{4}$ and $\dfrac{H}{L}$ just found; it only remains to apply the formula, using logarithms for preference. The flow in the case suggested comes to well over 2 gall. per minute; as a gallon of water weighs 10 lb. and the suggested temperature difference is 100 Fahrenheit degrees, you can also work out the B.Th.U. per hour which could be fed into the tank. The figure is far in excess of the B.Th.U. per hour obtainable from a domestic boiler, for which the claims are never above 20,000 B.Th.U. per hour. With the figures we have used there is clearly nothing wrong with the primary circulation!

If there is something wrong, where would you look? The only variables are D and the difference of temperature. You can reassure yourself by feeling whether the flow pipe is substantially hotter than the return; if it is, and yet you don't get a quickly heated storage tank, D is suspect—lime has reduced your pipe bore below a reasonable minimum.

MEASURING GAS CONSUMPTION

You will probably not want to do amateur gas-fitting—it is not easy and not safe. But there is interesting information to be had from your gas meter if you know how to read it. Fig. 9 shows the meter dials. What do you make the main reading? (It is over 156,000 cu. ft.)

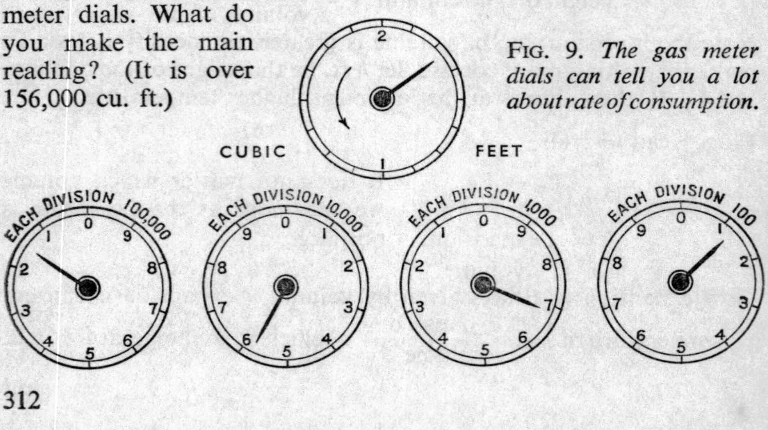

FIG. 9. *The gas meter dials can tell you a lot about rate of consumption.*

CUBIC   FEET

312

Of rather more interest, however, is the single or test dial, from which we can read with considerable precision, using only a watch with a seconds hand, the rate in cubic feet at which any appliance consumes gas. Among other things we can get a definite answer to the question of how gas compares with electricity in the cost of boiling a pint of water. Find out from the gas bill: (1) how many cubic feet go to a therm, and (2) how much a therm costs, and apply these to the cubic feet used in your experiments.

Here are some recorded figures:

Gas Ring: Test Dial Reading = ·50 cu. ft.

    Time   = 65 sec.

Therefore rating of ring = ·5 cu. ft. in 65 sec. = 27·7 cu. ft. per hr.

Time to boil 1 pint of water from 50 deg. F. = 4 min. 15 sec.

Therefore No. of cu. ft. = $\frac{27·7}{60} \times 4\frac{1}{4}$ = 1·96 cu. ft.

Rating of gas   = 500 cu. ft. per therm

    = 500 cu. ft. per 100,000 B.Th.U.

    = 1 cu. ft. per 200 B.Th.U.

Therefore No. of B.Th.U. supplied = 392.

Cost of gas = 1s. 6d. per therm = $\frac{18}{500}$ pence per cu. ft.

Therefore cost of boiling 1 pint = $\frac{18}{500} \times 1·96$d.

    = *·07d.*

Electric Kettle: Test Dial   = 6 revolutions

    Time   = 56 sec.

300 revolutions of this dial = 1 unit = 3,400 B.Th.U.

Time to boil 1 pint from 50° F. = 4 min. 50 sec. = 290 sec.

Therefore No. of revolutions = $6 \times \frac{290}{56}$

No. of units at 1d. per unit = $\frac{6}{300} \times \frac{290}{56}$

Therefore cost of electricity = *·103d.*

The efficiency of the appliances can also be compared:

    300 revolutions of electric meter = 3,400 B.Th.U.

Therefore $6 \times \frac{290}{56}$ revolutions = $\frac{3,400}{300} \times 6 \times \frac{290}{56}$ B. Th. U.

    = 352 B.Th.U.

Actual amount of heat supplied = $1\frac{1}{4}$ lb. × No. of degrees rise

    = $1\frac{1}{4} \times (212 - 50)$

    = 202 B.Th.U.

The gas is thus both cheaper and quicker in this case. The electrical appliance is more efficient than gas—352 B.Th.U. as against 392 B.Th.U. are supplied, for 202 B.Th.U. absorbed by the water.

8

Mechanics for the Layman

ACCORDING to the dictionary the word mechanics means "the laws of rest and motion of matter." The subject is usually divided into two branches, statics and dynamics, but with one or two small exceptions the craftsman and the handyman are interested only in the first branch. Statics covers the laws relating the forces which keep matter at rest, and that is where our interest lies. Once motion has occurred our work is a failure and, if we are builders, we are not much interested in the dynamics of how fast it moves.

Here are two very simple problems in the combination of forces. Suppose that the coils in Fig. 1 represent spring balances light enough for their own weight to be neglected. What would be the weights recorded by *A*, *B* and *C*? What weights would be recorded by balances *D*, *E* and *F* if they are so hung that the readings of all three are equal?

A grasp of mechanical principles depends more on your being clear about these simple fundamentals than on ability to make complex calculations. Make sure that you have thought out for yourself the answer to these two questions. Before seeking confirmation, answer also this further question: what modification of your answers occurs in each case if the spring balances, instead of having negligible weight, themselves weigh $\frac{1}{4}$ lb. each?

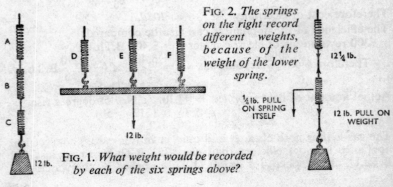

FIG. 2. *The springs on the right record different weights, because of the weight of the lower spring.*

12¼ lb.

¼ lb. PULL ON SPRING ITSELF

12 lb. PULL ON WEIGHT

12 lb.

FIG. 1. *What weight would be recorded by each of the six springs above?*

A

B

C

12 lb.

D E F

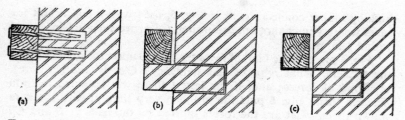

FIG. 3. *Three ways of fixing a wall plate. How do they compare for strength?*

It makes no difference to D, E and F, which remain at 4 lb. each. A, B and C become $12\frac{1}{2}$ lb., $12\frac{1}{4}$ lb. and 12 lb., instead of 12 lb. each. The tension in the line of springs and hooks is at all points the same where the line itself is taken as having no weight. If parts of the line have weight of their own, the tension above such a part is greater than that below by the weight between, as suggested in Fig. 2.

Fig. 3 shows alternative methods of fixing a wall plate. You can probably guess that the first way would be called bad, and the others better, but could you state exactly why?

In this example, the first method relies on the force exerted by the nails on the wood. The problem here is not that of pulling out; if it were, screws could be used instead. What causes the wood to

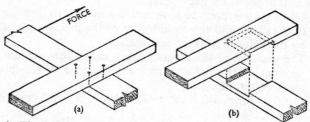

FIG. 4. *The halving joint in (b) is far stronger than the nailed joint.*

give is not *force* but *pressure*, that is, the ratio force/area. Nails, screws or bolts carry the load on a small area, so force/area is larger. In the alternatives the load is supposed to be the same. In Figs. 3*b* and 3*c* the wall plate, instead of being spiked to the wall, is carried on brick or steel corbels. In Fig. 4*b* the timbers are housed, so that any tendency to alter the angle is resisted by wood against wood, instead of wood against nails as in Fig. 4*a*.

Other load-spreading devices will occur to you; for example, wooden plugs to take a nail or screw in soft wall blocks; and

315

bulldog timber connectors, as in Fig. 5, used with a coach bolt for cases where you cannot cut a housing. Compare even a ½-in. dowel with a ⅛-in. nail.

Fig. 4 suggests the kind of force tending to upset the joint between the timbers. What opposes this tendency? Clearly another force, or group of forces; and, if the latter, there will be some relation between them. Fig. 6 puts the problem very simply: with the data shown there, what are the forces exerted by the nails at B and C? This problem has been faced since very early days. Archimedes of Syracuse, who died in

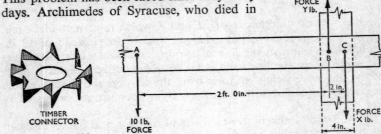

FIG. 5. *Bulldog connector for joining timber.*

FIG. 6. *We have to determine the forces exerted by the nails which join the two pieces at* B *and* C.

212 B.C., wrote a book on it, and a solution along the lines originated by him depends on two ideas:

(1) Consider the forces to have each a tendency to turn the article in question, and the equilibrium of the article to be decided by the balance of these tendencies.

(2) The measure of the turning effect, called the moment, is the product of the force X and the distance of the proposed pivot of turning.

Taking B as the pivot, it means that 10 lb. × 2 ft. must be equal to the force at C × 2 in.

This and all similar calculations can be dealt with far more efficiently if you are not afraid of using the most elementary algebra. Give the unknown force a letter, and apply the rule:

clockwise moment = anti-clockwise moment.

In this case what is the clockwise moment if B is the pivot? The unknown force of X lb., at C, would tend to turn the arm clockwise; the known force of 10 lb., at A, would turn it anti-clockwise. This gives the equation X lb. × 2 in. = 10 lb. × 2 ft.

Reducing all to the same unit—a step often forgotten, with disastrous results:
$$X \times 2 = 10 \times 24$$
giving
$$2X = 240, \text{ or } X = 120.$$

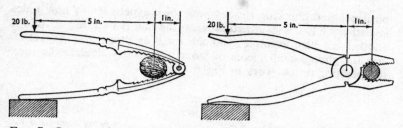

FIG. 7. *Compare the two methods of gripping, assuming a force of 20 lb.*

120 lb. is a big force to be exerted by a nail against softwood. If you pursue this subject further, you might ask why take B as the pivot? Why not C? The answer illustrates the freedom of this method, for since the assumption is that the bar is not to turn you can take any point as a point about which it does not turn.

Take C as the pivot then, and let the force at B be Y lb. Note that the 10 lb. is now at 2 ft. 2 in. from the pivot, and you should have no difficulty in finding $Y = 130$. There are two points to note:

(1) $Y = X + 10$; that is, the total upward force on the bar equals the total downward force. Y could, in fact, have been more easily calculated from that principle.

(2) Y is more than X. You will find that in a joint of this kind the nail at B will show up the weakness more than that at C.

Compare the forces exerted on the object by a grip of 20 lb. applied in the alternative case in Fig. 7. It is in no way necessary to have the points of application of the forces in line. Consider the claw hammer in Fig. 8, comparing the effectiveness of the two

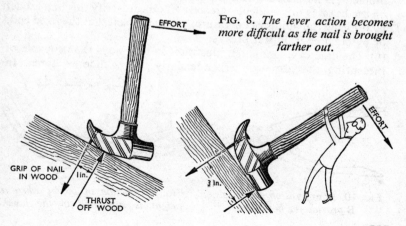

FIG. 8. *The lever action becomes more difficult as the nail is brought farther out.*

317

positions and checking this by your own experience of how much less effective is the lever action when the nail is well out. A door is another excellent example; you can use it as a very good makeshift vice for gluing small pieces of wood together. Calculate the force so operating on the work in Fig. 9.

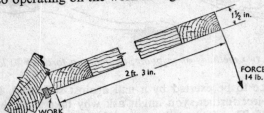

FIG. 9. *The door is being used as a vice to glue two pieces of wood. What is the force operating on the work?*

Here are other examples:

(1) Assuming the tool does not slip out of the screw-head slot, what determines the effectiveness of a screwdriver? What do you think of the assertion frequently made that, all other things being equal, a *long* handle makes for an easier turning action?

(2) Using the gas pliers in Fig. 10, where would you put the work for maximum grip—*A* or *B*?

(3) Referring to Fig. 11, which shows how the biceps lift the fore-arm, verify for yourself that if the hand supports 20 lb. there is in these muscles a force equal to the weight of a man.

(4) How much weight is the man supporting, apart from the weight of the wheelbarrow itself, if the latter is loaded as in Fig. 12?

(5) Such a simple cantilever beam as a diving board tends to turn under the load as in Fig. 13. The tendency, called the bending moment, is measured by the "force × distance" rule. At what point on the beam is this tendency greatest? You can verify this in a model by noticing the radius of curvature, which is greatest at the fixed end, or by bending it until it breaks.

(6) The case of a tennis net illustrates in two ways the principle of measuring the distance perpendicularly to the line of force. In

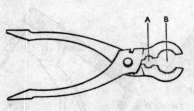

FIG. 10. *Does position* A *or position* B *provide the better grip?*

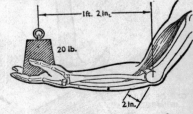

FIG. 11. *Action of biceps when a weight is supported in the hand.*

FIG. 12. *What weight is he lifting?*   FIG. 13. *Bending of a diving board.*

Fig. 14a the base of the post acts as the pivot, and the force at the head of the earth screw can easily be calculated if it is realized that only the perpendicular distances—3 ft. and 1 ft. 6 in.—matter. In Fig. 14b the anti-clockwise moment, 500 lb. × 3 ft., is opposed by *T* lb. × *d* ft., so that *T* × *d* must equal 1,500. To keep *T* low, clearly *d* must be made as great as possible, and it is the perpendicular or shortest distance from the pivot to the guy rope which counts as *d*.

(7) A weight is lifted by a simple lever as in Fig. 15.
   (a) $AC = 3 \times AB$, and the load is 120 lb. What is the effort, if there is no friction and the lever weighs nothing worth counting?
   (b) If the point *B*, where the load is hung, moves to B^1, 1 in. above *B*, how high must *C* rise in moving to C^1?
   (c) If you multiply the force by distance in each case, you have
      (i) for the load, 120 lb. × 1 in. = 120 lb. in.
      (ii) for the effort, 40 lb. × 3 in. = 120 lb. in.

This is a simple example of a rule found to apply to all simple frictionless and weightless machinery: the product *force × distance* is called the *work*, and, as there is nothing wasted, *work got out* (load × load distance) = *work put in* (effort and effort distance). If the contrivance is not frictionless, or has dead weight to be lifted,

FIG. 14. *Two ways of securing the posts of a lawn tennis net, involving separate methods of calculating the forces.*

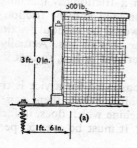
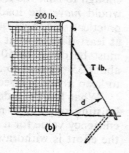

319

this rule will not apply: $\dfrac{work\ got\ out}{work\ put\ in}$ will not equal 1 (or 100 per cent) but some ratio less than 1. This ratio is called the *efficiency*.

The ideas embodied in example 7 make calculations on a more complicated tool, such as a vice, as easy as those on a simple lever. The work-principle above gives a ceiling figure for the work got out; the efficiency can by design be brought near to 100 per cent or 1, but can in no case exceed 100 per cent. You cannot get something for nothing in the physical world.

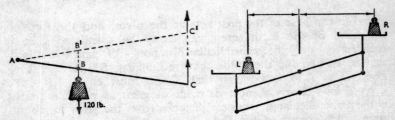

FIG. 15. *The case of a weight lifted by the action of a simple lever.*　　FIG. 16. *Wherever placed on the pans, the two weights always balance.*

In the case of a vice, look at the pitch of the screw. If this is, say, $\frac{1}{8}$ in., what do you know about the load distance?—that the load moves $\frac{1}{8}$ in. for each turn of the handle, say 6 in. long, where the effort is applied (for $2 \times \pi \times 6$ in. of effort distance, that is). Since the effort moves $2 \times \pi \times 6 \div \frac{1}{8}$, or over 300 times as far as the load, what force, or load, would a frictionless vice exert on the job if your effort on the handle was 15 lb.?

Before you decide that a force of this size—over 2 tons—is actually operating, think what would happen if the vice were in fact frictionless. It would move backwards as soon as your effort was withdrawn from the handle. Since the frictional force alone is enough to *hold* the load, it must be at least equal to the force which would *move* the load in a frictionless machine. Your effort in a practical vice, against the load and the friction, must therefore be at least double what it would be without friction, or the efficiency must be down to 50 per cent or less. Actually it may vary from about 35 per cent to 5 per cent or less, so that it is well worth while to keep a vice greased.

What has been demonstrated for a vice is true of any gripping, hoisting or similar machine. What, then, can you say about the efficiency value for a machine which does, in fact, "run back" when the effort is withdrawn? It must be over 50 per cent.

320

This distance principle helps to explain the apparent exception to the law of moments in a balance working on the lines of Fig. 16. The balance has two identical beams pivoted centrally and moving parallel. In the illustration it looks at first as though the weight R should exert far more moment as it is much farther from the pivot than L. In fact it does not do so, and equal weights will balance wherever placed on the pans.

Using the work principle, the geometry of the illustration shows that if R descends, L rises by an equal distance, so that if $R = L$, *work got out = work put in*, and there is balance. This short cut is mathematically as sound as, and is far simpler than, attempts to trace the various forces and moments involved.

Wedges to cramp up flooring boards before nailing are shown in Fig. 17. Using the relative-distance principle, it is easy to see what determines the gain: the smaller the angle of the wedge, the less the load moves for a given effort, so the greater the gain in force. The customary taper is about 1 in 10, so that the gain is not spectacular; but the effort, applied as a blow, is far greater than any normal steadily applied force. For this reason, floor boards must be wedged against a nailed board. The house wall can be quite easily forced out of true if used as a base.

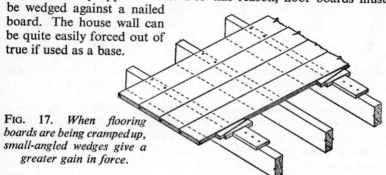

FIG. 17. *When flooring boards are being cramped up, small-angled wedges give a greater gain in force.*

We had an agreement that our main interest in mechanics was in the relation between forces which were in equilibrium—that is, when there was no motion. The mechanics of motion are, however, important to anyone using a hammer. Why does a blow from a hammer weighing, say, 1 lb. drive in a nail when perhaps a steady force of 50 lb. weight would fail to move the nail? The reason is that the hammer has a certain amount of momentum, measured by *mass × velocity*, and can be stopped only if the stopping force multiplied by the time it operates equals this momentum.

A 1-lb. hammer moving at 20 ft. per second requires a force of 60 lb. to stop it in about a hundredth of a second. To stop it more quickly—in a thousandth of a second—would need 600 lb., usually much more than the force resisting penetration by a nail. Why, then, is it almost impossible to knock nails into a light board not supported immediately behind the blow?

The mass free to move is not large, so that the force needed to set it moving along with the nail and the hammer may well be less than the force resisting penetration of the wood. The hammer, nail and board all move off as one, sharing the momentum of the hammer and being retarded relatively slowly by the developing force due to the spring of the board.

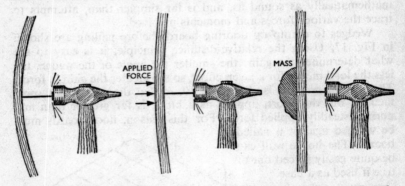

FIG. 18. *The first method is not likely to drive in the nail successfully. The second is better, but the third is the only really satisfactory way.*

Following this line of reasoning, what is the practical solution—(1) to press hard against the back of the timber, or (2) to hold, without much effort, a massive object against it? The second method is the answer; by adopting this method you greatly increase the mass which has to be got under way, hence the force required to do this quickly will rise to a value above that needed to make the nail penetrate the wood. (Fig. 18.)

The weight in Fig. 19 is supported by the tension in two strings. What decides how great these tensions will be? Obviously the value of the weight is of the foremost importance; after that there are only the angles of slope of the strings. The way in which the angles operate is not obvious; but it can be calculated from the principle of moments with the aid of a little trigonometry, and a quite new rule about forces then emerges.

To appreciate this principle, consider first how a force may best be represented. Are a number and a unit adequate? The wind on a roof may exert a force of 200 lb., but to design the roof we must

322

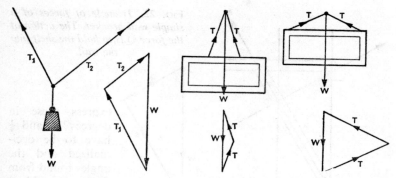

FIG. 19. *Tension represented by the triangle of forces.*

FIG. 20. *The force diagrams show that the tension is greater in the shorter cord.*

know in what direction the force is exerted. This requires a certain line, and a symbol to know which way along that line.

To meet these needs, the only way is to use an arrow, of correct length according to scale; and the triangle principle then states that if three forces act on a body in such a way as to balance, the three arrows representing them can be drawn so as to make an exactly closed triangle, as in Fig. 19.

This is the easiest way to show that when you hang a picture, the longer the cord the less likely it is to break. Fig. 20 illustrates this fact. In each case the three forces acting on the picture are the weight and the two pulls of the two parts of the string. The triangle starts with a downward line drawn to scale to represent the weight; the arrows needed to close the triangle have to be much longer (indicating much greater tension) when a shorter string is used. When the string is nearly flat the tension is very great indeed.

The case of the dovetail joint leads to similarly contrasted triangles. The slope varies from a minimum of 1 in 9 for hardwood to a maximum of 1 in 4 for softwood. (How would you

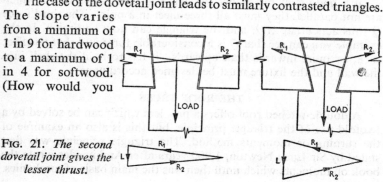

FIG. 21. *The second dovetail joint gives the lesser thrust.*

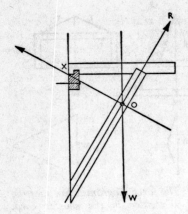

FIG. 22. *Triangle of forces of a simple wall bracket. The action of the force Q is to hold the shelf into the wall.*

express these in degrees? $\frac{1}{9}$ and $\frac{1}{4}$ have to be decimalized and the angles found from the tangent tables.) One reason for this is that as the joint is pulled with a load *L*, considerable thrusts R_1 and R_2 come on the faces. Fig. 21 shows how the greater pitch gives less thrust.

For many other examples of this rule it is necessary to make a decision as to the line of action of one of the unknown forces. Consider the case of the forces exerted on the shelf supported by the simple bracket in Fig. 22. You can be certain about the lines of action of the load *W*, vertically downwards, and of the thrust *R* acting along the strut. You cannot so simply decide the direction of the unknown force *Q* acting at the inner edge *X*; the line starts at *X* but where else does it go?

If the third force *Q* went in any but one direction, it would have moment, or turning effect about *O*, where the other two meet. They can have no moment about this point—they go through *O*, and have no distance from it—so *Q* can have no moment about *O* either, and must pass through *O*.

If a body is at rest under the action of only three forces which are not parallel, they must all three meet in a point. The third force *Q* thus acts along *XO*, and the triangle can now be drawn. In the example you can see that *Q* is a considerable force and that its effect is rather more inwards than upwards—it has to hold the shelf into the wall and the fixture must be designed accordingly.

THE ROOF TRUSS

A double-pitched roof offers a problem which can be solved by a twofold use of the triangle principle, but this is also an example of the turning or moments method. The triangle principle was first stated by Sir Isaac Newton, 1,900 years after Archimedes wrote the book on moments which until then was the main basis of mechanics.

Fig. 23 shows a pair of rafters which may be regarded as representing the two parts of a roof. Each part has a weight W, so that the walls have to exert an upthrust also each equal to W and shown by the upward arrows.

Suppose now that there is no strength to speak of at B, where the rafters are spiked to a ridge board, and that the feet of the rafters are not secured at A and C. What would happen to your roof? You can probably guess that A and C need to be tied together. What your guesses will not tell you is the force required to tie them.

Why does AB tend to rotate? The load W tends to turn it anti-clockwise about B, and the upthrust W tends to turn it clockwise. To find the moments, you need the *force × distance*, and this problem is a good example of the need to use always the perpendicular or shortest distance.

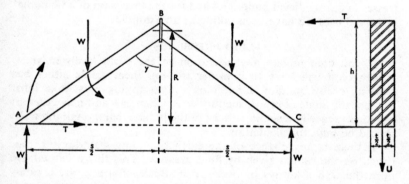

FIG. 23. *Forces operating on a pair of rafters and* (right) *on one of the walls.*

The net clockwise moment on AB is thus $W \times \dfrac{S}{2} - W \times \dfrac{S}{4} = W \times \dfrac{S}{4}$. This must be made up by resistance to turning at B, which will not amount to much, or by the foot A being held by the wall. To avoid it, you may supply anti-clockwise moment by a tie attached, preferably, to A, and the tension T in this tie will be given by making $T \times R = W \times \dfrac{S}{4}$.

Notice (1) the value of $T = \dfrac{W}{4} \times \dfrac{S}{R}$; (2) $\dfrac{S}{2R} = \tan y$.

As the roof gets flatter, angle y increases and so does $\tan y$, so that for the same weight the flatter the roof the greater the need of a tie. You should be able to verify that if the pitch is 30 deg., and the

325

angle y thus 60 deg., the tension T in the tie is not much short of the weight of the roof.

If you had no tie, expecting—as is sensible—no restraining effect at B, what is going to hold up the roof? Only an inward thrust exerted by the top of the wall, which is possible because the weight U of the wall prevents the outward thrust T from turning the wall about the point O, as in Fig. 23. It will be seen that this gives another moments equation:

$$T \times h = U \times \frac{t}{2}.$$

Since the height of a wall may well be twenty or more times its half-thickness, it is necessary for U, the weight of the wall, to be twenty or more times T—more than ten times the weight of a half-roof. This accounts for the massive masonry buttresses and flying buttresses in our medieval buildings; and for the provision of a tie in the proposed roof we have been taking as an example.

FLUID PRESSURES

If you contemplate any alteration of the earth levels in your garden, you will have to consider making them stable either by banking or by building a retaining wall. Banking must take into account the angle of repose mentioned in Chapter 6 and may take up too much space in a small garden; in the latter event a retaining wall should be built to calculation.

If there is any chance of the earth becoming waterlogged, the thrust on the wall is given by fluid pressure. This thrust can either push the wall sideways or overturn it. Buried footings are a safeguard against the first contingency. Overturning will occur if the moment of the thrust exceeds the moment of the weight, as demonstrated in Fig. 24.

To calculate the moments, take the wall first and deal with a 1-ft. length of it:

Force = weight of one foot length of wall

    = depth × breadth × 1 × density of brickwork in lb. per cu. ft.

    = d × b × 120 lb., say.

Moment = d × b × 120 × $\frac{b}{2}$ *(force × distance) = d ×* $\frac{b^2}{2}$ *× 120.*

To find the moment of the fluid thrust, we must first establish three things:

(1) The density of the fluid. At a guess, this would be somewhere between the densities of water and of masonry—between $62\frac{1}{2}$ and 120 lb. per cu. ft. or, say, 90 lb.

(2) The average pressure over the wall. This is simple enough—take the pressure half-way down, at depth $\frac{d}{2}$.

(3) A position at which to pinpoint the total fluid thrust. Since the lower components are at greater pressure than the upper, this position is not half-way down, as might be imagined: it is actually two-thirds down, or $\frac{d}{3}$ up from the bottom.

$$Pressure = average\ depth \times density = \frac{d}{2} \times 90$$

$$Force = pressure \times area$$
$$= \frac{d}{2} \times 90 \times d \times 1 \text{ (taking 1-ft. length of wall)}$$

$$Moment = \frac{d}{2} \times 90 \times d \times 1 \times \frac{d}{3} \text{ (force} \times \text{distance)} = d^3 \times \frac{90}{6}$$

When these are just balanced,
$$\frac{db^2 \times 120}{2} = \frac{d^3 \times 90}{6} \text{ or } \frac{b^2 \times 120 \times 6}{90 \times 2} = d^2$$

This gives $d = 2b$. If the wall is retaining a fluid of three-quarters the density of the masonry, the depth should not exceed twice the breadth of the wall. In fact, you can build higher than this without the wall overturning. Where does the extra stability come from? There are two factors:

(1) the earth, not in fact a simple fluid, is partly held up by its own internal friction.

(2) The wall, built in cement mortar, will tend to hold together more than we have assumed, pivoting about O, at the footing which gives double the moment arm for the weight.

To offset these, however, more advanced calculations show that before it topples over the wall is liable to crack because of bending. This takes place at about two-thirds of the load which would cause overturning.

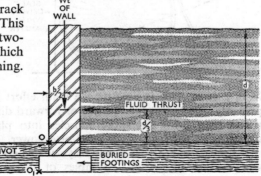

FIG. 24. *Force problem of a wall which is to retain water-logged soil.*

9

Bicycles and Motor-cars

THE invention of the wheel ranks probably second only to that of fire in importance to human society. You could sum up the position by saying that fire is a means of obtaining energy and the wheel a means of saving energy.

To compare walking (or running) with cycling, consider the position when both walker and cyclist have acquired some velocity on the level. The cyclist can retain his speed by only such further output of energy as is needed to overcome wind resistance and the small amount of rolling friction. The walker has a very high frictional force on the ground (notice that this is essential to walking—imagine trying to walk without it!); so he must continually lift his weight from one foot to the next. Since the human muscular system operates solely on contraction, the energy of each lift is totally lost when the muscles go slack again.

You may have noticed that the man on foot can beat the cyclist under two conditions: up a very steep hill, or in rapid acceleration

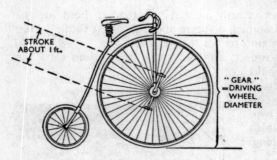

STROKE ABOUT 1 ft.

" GEAR " =DRIVING WHEEL DIAMETER

FIG. 1. *In what way would you modify the penny-farthing, or "ordinary," bicycle so as to improve its performance?*

from a start. This is because the main effort is in these two cases properly directed in the upward or forward direction, and then the runner can bring far more muscles into play. A man running upstairs can work at nearly one horse-power.

Earliest applications of the bicycle were concerned only with the conservation of energy. Examples of this are the hobby horse,

328

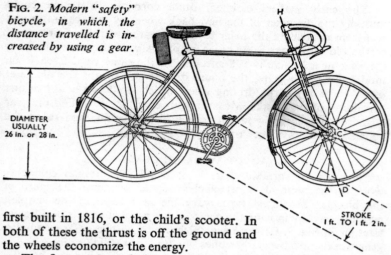

FIG. 2. *Modern "safety" bicycle, in which the distance travelled is increased by using a gear.*

DIAMETER USUALLY 26 in. or 28 in.

STROKE 1 ft. TO 1 ft. 2 in.

first built in 1816, or the child's scooter. In both of these the thrust is off the ground and the wheels economize the energy.

The first true crank-driven bicycle was made in Paris in 1865 and has left a permanent mark on cycle technology in this way. The machine developed quite naturally into what we now call, for obvious reasons, the penny-farthing, as in Fig. 1. Looking at this machine, how would you modify it to improve the speed attainable? To simplify the problem, notice that the size of the crank is roughly fixed at about 6 in., because the human machine seems to work at highest power with a total stroke of about 1 ft. This leaves only the size of the driving wheel to play with; that was made as big as practicable and the model was designated by this all-important dimension—a "52-in. machine" referred to the diameter of the front wheel. The possibilities here are limited by the anatomy of the rider; the tailor's "inside leg" measurement is connected with this limit, together with the extra reach to tip-toe, but minus the margin needed for the crank and the saddle clearance. At this stage the advantage lay heavily on the side of the tall riders!

When the bicycle much as we know it now was invented in 1876 it was called the "safety," as distinct from the former or "ordinary" type, but the makers' chief appeal was in the "gear" as it was, and is still, called. Looking at the modern example in Fig. 2, how would you find the distance travelled by one rotation of the cranks? In the early type in Fig. 1 this is simple enough: the circumference of the driving wheel. You will have corrected this for Fig. 2 by multiplying by the gear ratio: $\dfrac{\text{number of teeth in large wheel}}{\text{number in small wheel}}$.

The early makers claimed, quite correctly, that you could multiply the diameter of the new back wheel by the gear ratio and so get an equivalent diameter to be compared with the front wheel of the old "ordinary." So much emphasis was placed on this that the gear of a bicycle is still specified in the same way. Even when modified by hub-gears, the figure quoted still means the diameter of an "ordinary"-type driving wheel which would go as far in one revolution of the cranks. Measure your own bicycle to find the gear —and then measure yourself to see if you could even reach the pedals of an equivalent "ordinary" bicycle!

ABOUT VARIABLE GEARS

The aim of variable gears is to enable the human engine to work at the same, its most efficient, speed whatever the speed of the bicycle. The latest types vary the gear ratio in the simplest possible way, by moving the chain on to sprocket wheels of different sizes, as in Fig. 3. Extreme examples use up to five different smaller gear wheels and two larger ones, giving ten possible ratios.

Hub gear boxes, giving two, three or even four changes of gear, work on the epicyclic principle, which means that one wheel rolls round another. This rolling motion is worth looking into.

Look at Fig. 4, showing a wheel rolling along a straight line so that the centre C has a speed V units. What would you say is the speed of the points A and B at the instant when they are in the bottom and the top positions?

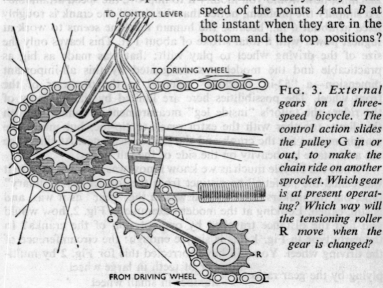

TO CONTROL LEVER

TO DRIVING WHEEL

FROM DRIVING WHEEL

FIG. 3. *External gears on a three-speed bicycle. The control action slides the pulley* G *in or out, to make the chain ride on another sprocket. Which gear is at present operating? Which way will the tensioning roller* R *move when the gear is changed?*

If you cannot answer this at once, the following may help you to think it out.

Consider the rolling motion as made up of two parts: (1) a rotation with a stationary centre in which the speed of the rim is V units, and (2) a sliding motion, without rotation, at a speed V, as shown in Fig. 5. To find the actual motion of any point, combine

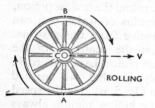

the two motions as shown in the drawing. Doing this for the point C, which has no motion in part (1) and a forward velocity V in part (2), the resultant motion is, of course, the forward velocity V, as we knew already.

FIG. 4. *What are the momentary speeds of A and B above?*

FIG. 5. *Spinning and sliding motions combine in a rolling wheel.*

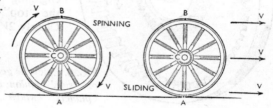

Now apply the principle to the points A and B, and you will obtain two less obvious but valuable results: point B is moving forward with velocity $2V$ and A is for this instant stationary.

The motion of B has a consequence well known to carters who occasionally have to man-handle a stranded vehicle. As there is double the motion, the load can be moved with only half the force if this is applied at B instead of pushing the cart itself.

Before applying the principle further to the three-speed hub, you could with advantage experiment on a bicycle to determine the gear ratios practically. This can be done with a good deal of precision by taking always one revolution of the cranks and finding out the number of turns of the rear wheel, fractions or decimals of a turn being easily determined because there are forty spokes. Here are some actual figures, all for one rotation of the cranks, with a wheel of diameter 26 in.

Low gear:	1 turn + 39 spokes	= 1·975 revs.	Gear	1·975 × 26	= 51·4
Normal gear:	2 turns + 24 ,,	= 2·6 ,,	,,	2·6 × 26	= 67·5
High gear:	3 turns + 18 ,,	= 3·45 ,,	,,	3·45 × 26	= 90

(Imagine trying to ride an "ordinary" bicycle with a front wheel of 90 in. diameter!)

331

Now we can look at the mechanism which produces such a result. Fig. 6 is a sketch of the epicyclic gear used. In this very simple case, the centre (or "sun") pinion, of radius R, is fixed, being a part of the back spindle. Around it roll four "planet" pinions of

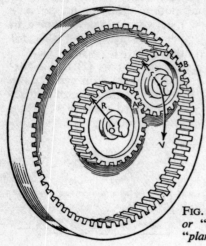

radius r, of which only one is shown; as they travel they drive round the hollow pinion, the radius of which you can determine from the drawing.

Let the centre C of the planet pinion have a speed V. Applying what we learned from Fig. 5, what is the speed of the hollow pinion, always engaging with a point B, the "top" point of Fig. 5? Clearly $2V$.

FIG. 6. *Epicyclic gear showing the centre, or "sun," pinion and one of the four "planets" which revolve around it.*

For the rates of revolution, we have only to divide these speeds by the circumferences, which can be seen from Fig. 6 to have radii $(R + r)$ for C and $(R + 2r)$ for B. This means that if the four planet pinions are on a framework making $\dfrac{V}{2\pi(R + r)}$ revolutions, the hollow pinion makes $\dfrac{2V}{2\pi(R + 2r)}$ revolutions. The gear ratio is thus $\dfrac{2V}{2\pi(R + 2r)} \div \dfrac{V}{2\pi(R + r)}$, which cancels to the simple expression $\dfrac{2R + 2r}{R + 2r}$, the hollow pinion moving faster in that ratio.

The simplest possible figures are produced when $R = r$, when the gear ratio becomes $\dfrac{4}{3}$. You will find that in most models the fixed sun pinion and the four planet pinions are in fact of equal size. All that remains is some contrivance so that for high gear the slower unit, with its four planet pinions, is coupled to the rear sprocket and the faster hollow pinion to the wheel, making a high gear faster than normal in the ratio 4 to 3; while for the low gear the coupling is reversed and the faster unit drives the slower, giving a gear lower than normal in the ratio 3 to 4. Now compare the ratios 90 to 67·5 and 51·4 to 67·5 as measured practically, and you will see how far this agrees with the theory just described.

Some makers supply a hub with sun and planet pinions in different proportions, giving what is called close-ratio gears. Look at Fig. 6, and at the ratio $\dfrac{2R + 2r}{R + 2r}$, and answer the following questions:

(1) If instead of the ratio 4 to 3, given by $R = r$, you want something nearer to 1 : 1, how would you alter the proportions of the pinions? Which would you make larger?

(2) The ratio $\dfrac{2R + 2r}{R + 2r}$ can vary only between two simple limits. What are they?

Most people attempting question (1) by a look at Fig. 6 above give the wrong answer.

CHOOSING A GEAR

External gears present no such problems as those described above, but as each rear sprocket is screwed directly on to the hub, the cyclist has the free choice of each gear. In such selection the principle to be followed applies widely in the theory of machines and is bes illustrated by examples.

Take the case of rear sprockets with 14 and 24 teeth, giving high and low gears respectively. What size of intermediate sprocket is most suitable for the middle gear?

The easiest answer to give is a number midway between 14 and 24—that is, $\dfrac{14 + 24}{2} = 19$. This gives three sprockets, with teeth 14, 19 and 24, with a common difference. The three numbers make the simplest kind of series you could think of, and are said to be in arithmetic progression, or A.P., and 19 is the arithmetic mean of 14 and 24. But though it is the simplest it is not the best answer. For one thing, the resulting gears will not be in the same progression. If the back wheel is of 26 in. diameter and the chain wheel has 48 teeth, the gears are $26 \times \dfrac{48}{14}$, $26 \times \dfrac{48}{19}$ and $26 \times \dfrac{48}{24}$, and you can verify that they are not in A.P. Better still, satisfy yourself as to the general principle that by dividing any fixed number of three others in A.P., the quotients are not in A.P. For instance, divide 24 by 2, 4 and 6: the quotients 12, 6 and 4 have not a common difference. (Try it for any other convenient numbers.)

What is wanted, within the range in which the gears are effective, is that each change should produce the same feeling of re-arrangement of effort on the part of the rider. This can only be done if each change alters the gear by an equal ratio.

Referring to the reversible uses of the epicyclic gears of Fig. 6 you will notice that this mechanism invariably gives an equal ratio for low : normal and normal : high.

Three gears, or any numbers which alter by a common ratio, are said to be in geometric progression, or G.P. Unlike those in A.P., numbers in G.P. if divided into a common numerator give quotients still in G.P. Try this, for example, on the numbers 4, 6 and 9 (varying in the common ratio 3 : 2); divide them into, say, 72 and you see that the quotients 18, 12, 8 still change by a common ratio (2 : 3).

What is then needed is a number of teeth N given by the equation $\frac{24}{N} = \frac{N}{14}$. N is said to be the geometric mean of 24 and 14, and the equation becomes $N^2 = 336$ or $N = \sqrt{336}$, to which the nearest whole number is 18. The three numbers 24, 18 and 14 are then nearly in G.P., and the resulting gears depending on division by 24, 18 and 14 will also be nearly in G.P. Such a set of sprockets appears in Fig. 3, shown in low gear.

Working on this principle, what numbers of teeth would you suggest to complete the missing gear in the following cases?

(1) 15, ?, 25; (2) ?, 20, 25; (3) 15, 20, ?.

HOW A BICYCLE WORKS

Perhaps the most remarkable fact about a bicycle is that it can be ridden at all. Almost everyone in Great Britain, except infants, can ride, but the processes are automatic and unconscious. To explain the mechanism it would be as well to ask yourself first what the facts are and apply them to the basic principles of motion. What are the facts? Beginning with the most obvious, you might say:

(1) You cannot maintain balance on a stationary bicycle.
(2) The faster you go the less effort is needed in balancing.
(3) If you tend to fall sideways you re-act by a turn as in Fig. 7 and so keep your balance.

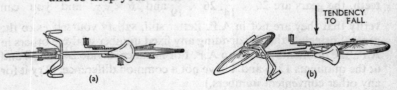

TENDENCY TO FALL

(a)   (b)

FIG. 7. *The steering in* (a) *is undisturbed, but in* (b) *a natural reaction on the part of the rider turns the handlebars as he tends to fall.*

These are enough to explain the bare fact that a bicycle can be ridden, if they are combined with the basic principle known as Newton's First Law of Motion. This states that a moving body persists with the same velocity in the same direction unless it is forced to change. This is sometimes called the inertia principle.

In Fig. 7b the cycle is tending to topple to the left. The front wheel is turned and the machine goes to the left. The mass of the rider, however, tends to go straight on, so sooner or later his body will be more to the right of the machine and he will tend to the right.

As to the effect of speed, we said that "sooner or later" the straight course of your body will swing over the path of the cycle and correct the toppling tendency. Whether it is sooner or later is entirely a question of speed—of two speeds, rather. Have you the double answer to that problem? It is, of course, the speed of the machine combined with the speed (and control) of the rider's reaction. All of this is easily verifiable by comparing slow cycling with fast, and a skilled with a clumsy cyclist.

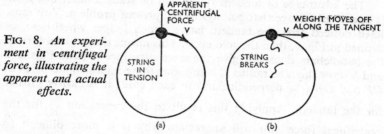

FIG. 8. *An experiment in centrifugal force, illustrating the apparent and actual effects.*

The inertia principle as stated fully explains all these problems of curved motion. Sometimes, however, the principle is stated in terms of a fiction called centrifugal force, which means a tendency to fly out from the centre. This is the force you feel in the string holding a weight whirled round at speed. It seems as though the weight would fly outwards, but that is quite untrue, as you can verify with the aid of Fig. 8: if the string breaks, the weight flies off along the tangent, thus verifying the first law of motion. Nevertheless, the fiction is a convenient one and gives quite correct results. For a given mass, the value of the force (the tension in the string in Fig. 8a) is proportional to the square of the speed and, for a given speed, is inversely proportional to the radius of the curve; that is, the force is proportional to $\frac{V^2}{R}$. Applying this to Fig. 7b, the tendency to topple is corrected by going into a curve, thus producing a "centrifugal force" to correct the topple.

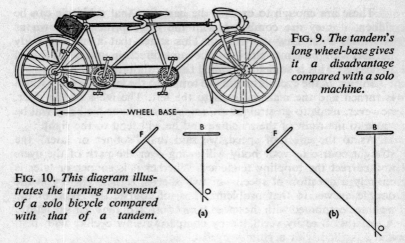

FIG. 9. *The tandem's long wheel-base gives it a disadvantage compared with a solo machine.*

WHEEL BASE

FIG. 10. *This diagram illustrates the turning movement of a solo bicycle compared with that of a tandem.*

(a)

(b)

The advantage of tandem riding can be studied later, but there is one disadvantage that belongs to the present problem. You must have noticed that the tandem has a much longer wheel-base, as defined in Fig. 9, than the solo cycle. This means that a given turn of the handlebars does not give the same curvature of path. Figs. 10*a* and *b* show this, the radius R being something intermediate between OF and OB (the perpendiculars) in each case; it is clearly greater for the tandem. Applying this result to the expression $\frac{V^2}{R}$ for the centrifugal force you will appreciate why it is more difficult to control a tandem; for the same speed V, a given amount of turn to the handlebars results in a curve of longer radius R, so $\frac{V^2}{R}$, which measures the balancing centrifugal force, is less.

GYROSCOPIC EFFECT

You have probably played with or seen a toy gyroscope top. If there is one available, hold it lightly by the screw knobs, when it is spinning well, and gently try to move these so as to incline the axle. You will find (1) that it seems very stiff, and (2) that as it gives way under your gentle pressure the knobs move at right-angles to the way you push them, as in Fig. 11.

A spinning cycle wheel acts as a gyroscope. The mathematical theory of these bodies is very complicated to work out but some of the results are most simple. One of them has been indicated above. It can be summarized simply if you are prepared to specify any rotation of a body by an arrow pointing along the axis. If you have caught this idea, what line represents the rotation of a cycle wheel? The answer is, of course, the line of the spindle.

If anything tends to topple the cycle, that is a second rotation; have you in mind a line to represent that? It should be drawn along the forward motion of the machine—that would be the axis about which the cycle would turn if it fell over. We have now two rotation axes—the axle line of the wheel as it spins, and the fore-and-aft line as a possible toppling axis; and the two axes are at right-angles to each other.

The simple result promised is that the resultant turning of the body (in this case the bicycle) will be about a third axis perpendicular to each of the others. If you have kept up with these directions you should have the answer ready—the third axis will be an upright one. To check this, hold the thumb, forefinger and middle finger of your left hand at right-angles to the other fingers, as in Fig. 12. Set the middle finger as if it were the wheel spindle, and the forefinger pointing fore and aft (the axis of possible toppling). Now which way is the thumb pointing? It should be vertical. That means that the result, where the bicycle is concerned, is for the whole machine to tend to slew round sideways about the third, vertical, axis. If the tyres grip well and the handlebars are held, this tendency is resisted by the ground, so the gyro effect has acted at a stabilizer.

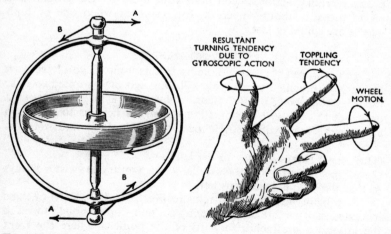

FIG. 11. *If you try to tilt the spinning top along the lines AA, it will actually move along BB.*

FIG. 12. *Holding the thumb and two fingers as shown above we see an analogy with the spinning cycle wheel.*

There is great precision in these thumb-and-two-finger rules, another pair of which features prominently in electromagnetism. The rule just given can handle also the sense of the rotations—a finger representing an axis of rotation can be regarded as a normal screw; if the finger direction gives the axial movement of a screw, then the associated rotation is in the sense in which that screw would turn.

Applying these more exact principles, if your left hand is held in the most comfortable position with the middle finger horizontal across the body and the forefinger pointing away from you, then

(1) the middle finger represents wheel motion bringing the bicycle towards you;

(2) the forefinger represents a toppling tendency clockwise as you look at the oncoming cycle; and

(3) the thumb represents a turning tendency in which the front of the machine would move from your left to your right.

Compare this with the idea of turning motion required in centrifugal-force reasoning and you will appreciate that if there is any gyroscopic turning result about the third axis it will be such as to restore balance.

The gyroscopic effect is proportional to the speed and amount of mass in motion, and does not amount to much for a pedal cycle till speeds are of the order of 20 m.p.h.; but it is a powerful factor in stabilizing a motor cycle. You can get further experience of its peculiar cranky action if you hold your cycle off the ground and try to move it about—invert it, for instance—when one or both wheels are spinning fast.

"LOOK, NO HANDS!"

We have been some time coming to this topic. If you have been thinking in practical terms, you will long ago have wanted to raise this question: how, on the theory above, can a bicycle be steered no-handed? A little experimenting will again help us to approach an answer. Take your bicycle out, stand beside it and note the effect of

(1) tilting it side-ways, say to the left; and

(2) holding it upright by the saddle, which you try to twist sideways so that the saddle nose turns left.

To explain what happens, refer to Figs. 2 and 13. Each of these indicates that the line of the steering column slopes enough to reach the ground some inches forward of the point A where the front wheel touches. Let us consider (2) first. The arrows at the saddle in Fig. 13 indicate your twin forces trying to twist it; supposing the saddle pin is secure, what, if anything, is going to give way?

338

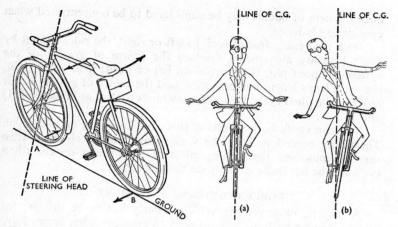

FIG. 13. *Arrows show the forces involved in steering a cycle by tilting it and by twisting the saddle.*

FIG. 14. *In steering no-handed, the rider turns the front wheel by displacing the centre of gravity.*

If the ground is not slippery the tyres will not give sideways; the rear wheel is rigid in the frame; the only lateral motion possible is that the front wheel, fixed to the ground at *A*, pivots about the line of the steering axis with *A* fixed and the front swinging left.

The result of tilting as in (1) is similar, the ground at points *A* and *B* supporting the weight of the machine, now partly sideways, at the rims; at *A* the support is behind the pivoting line of the front-wheel unit, which can therefore fall a little and twist left.

All problems of this sort become much simpler to think out if use is made of another principle, called Newton's Third Law of Motion, which states that "to every action there is an equal and opposite reaction." Applied to the facts above this would lead us to say that the pair of forces at the saddle, tending to turn the machine, set up a pair at the ground points *A* and *B* with an equal but opposite turning effect; and the one at *A*, being to the rear of the steering axis, swings the wheel round.

If you wheel a bicycle, methods (1) and (2) are both available to steer it without using the handlebars. If you are riding it no-handed, effect (1) occurs to some extent automatically, setting up the correct turn to restore balance as in normal riding. This effect can also be produced to order, as is shown in Fig. 14.

This illustration uses the expression "centre of gravity" (C.G.), simply defined as the point at which all the weight of a body or linked system of bodies may be considered to be concentrated when considering balance.

With the system free to rock to left or right, the rider cannot by normal steady movements displace the centre of gravity of the system—himself plus the bicycle—to left or right: if he leans right, the cycle leans left in compensation and the centre of gravity is not moved. The tilted cycle, however, now tends to turn as in method (1) above.

You can verify both aspects of this effect by riding on one pedal. The tilting needed to keep the C.G. above the wheel-line is then very obvious, and the turning effect of the ground on the tilted cycle can be felt quite strongly on the handlebars.

FORCES OPPOSING MOVEMENT

A bicycle, or any other vehicle, clearly has to be driven; for calculations on such a topic we need to consider what forces have to be overcome, what is available for the purpose, and how to express our measurements.

What opposes the movement of a vehicle? On the level, you will suggest: (1) friction in the bearings; (2) friction at the road surface; (3) resistance of the air.

Against motion up a hill there will be a force due to the earth's pull on the machine and rider; it will not be equal to their joint weight, but a fraction thereof called the "component" acting down the hill. The value of this component is most easily deduced from the work principle described in Chapter 8.

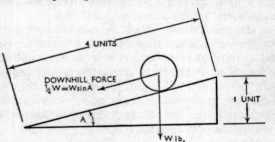

FIG. 15. *Diagram illustrating the downhill force opposing the movement of a vehicle travelling uphill.*

A hill is said to have a gradient of 1 in 7, 1 in 12, and so on. What does this mean? Fig. 15 shows a gradient of 1 in 4, with 1 unit of vertical rise to 4 units along the sloping roadway; a very steep hill, though it may not look so. This means that to rise 1 ft. in the true direction of the weight, that is, vertically, you must move 4 ft along the slope—an increase of four times. Likewise there will be

340

╳ ÷ ╳ ÷ ╳ ÷ ╳ ÷ ╳ ÷ ╳ ÷ ╳ ÷ ╳ ÷ ╳ ÷ ╳ ÷ ╳ ÷ ╳ ÷ ╳ ÷ ╳ ÷ ╳ ÷ ╳ ÷ ╳ ÷ ╳ ÷

The Milk-and-Water Puzzle

A glass containing a quantity of water stands next to a glass containing an equal quantity of milk. Young Timothy, who dabbles in experiments, transfers a spoonful of the milk to the glass containing water. After stirring the mixture he transfers a spoonful of it back to the other glass. Is there now more milk in the water than there is water in the milk, or vice versa?   *Solution on page 444*

÷ ╳ ÷ ╳ ÷ ╳ ÷ ╳ ÷ ╳ ÷ ╳ ÷ ╳ ÷ ╳ ÷ ╳ ÷ ╳ ÷ ╳ ÷ ╳ ÷ ╳ ÷ ╳ ÷ ╳ ÷ ╳ ÷ ╳ ÷ ╳

a 4 to 1 reduction in the effective downhill force—for a weight W the downhill component is $W \times \frac{1}{4}$.

Applying your trigonometry, the connexion with the slope of angle A is clear from Fig. 15. Sin $A = \frac{1}{4}$, so that the downhill component is also $W \sin A$—a widely applicable rule.

Like all frictional forces, those in (1) and (2) above are usually measured in terms of the load, in this case the weight. We say that frictional force = load × the friction constant (or coefficient). This coefficient for surfaces sliding over each other may be as much as 1; for wood on wood it is somewhere around $\frac{1}{3}$.

For wheels and roller or ball bearings, however, it is very low; coefficients for the materials used in bearings vary from ·02 down to ·002. In other words, the forces of frictional resistance due to bearings and road may each be equal to from ·002 to ·02 times the weight of machine and rider.

Comparing this with the expression for the component force down a hill, $W \sin \alpha$ or $W \times$ the gradient, you will observe:
(1) How relatively unimportant the total frictional force can be. (It will be mostly ignored in what follows, and considered more fully later in regard to motor vehicles, where it is more important.)
(2) That it may be equated in effect to a gradient of from 1 in 50 to 1 in 500.
(3) That if you have any small measured gradients in your neighbourhood you can estimate the value of the frictional coefficient by finding a hill on which you just keep moving down very slowly in still air without pedalling.

Why slowly and in still air? Both mainly for the same reason, namely, that the air offers considerable resistance to movement. How would you expect this air resistance to operate? See now if you can list the factors that may influence it.

Clearly it will depend on the size of the moving body, the shape and kind of surface and the speed at which the air moves past the body. We cannot do much about the first two of these; we must take them as we find them. In the case of a cyclist, however, the resistance can be considerably varied from moment to moment by lowering or raising the trunk. As to the third factor, the resistance is usually taken to be proportional to the square of the air speed. We write this as $F = kV^2$, where F is the force opposing the motion, V is the speed through the air and k is a number which remains constant for the same cycle and the same rider in the same position.

This is a most important relationship, well worth considering by anyone interested in efficient locomotion. The value of the constant k can be estimated by finding the speed of drifting at a steady speed down a hill of known gradient on a day when there is no wind. For example, you may obtain these figures:

Weight of cycle and rider 200 lb.; gradient 1 in 20; speed 20 m.p.h.; rolling and bearing friction coefficient ·005.

Component of weight acting downhill $= 200 \times \dfrac{1}{20}$ lb. $= 10$ lb.

Of this, friction requires $200 \times ·005$ lb. $= 1$ lb.

Therefore air resistance $= 9$ lb.

Therefore if $F = kV^2$, $9 = k \times 400$, or $k = \dfrac{9}{400}$

$= $ about ·022 with lb. and m.p.h units.

What value of k do you find for a car weighing 15 cwt. which will just move under its own weight against bearing friction down a gradient of 1 in 30, and will coast at 20 m.p.h. down a gradient of 1 in 15? Remember to work in lb. and also to allow for the bearing friction as we did above. As you would expect, k here is much greater —about ·14.

WORK AND POWER

How is the power of a cyclist estimated? When mechanical work is done, it is measured, as we saw in the last chapter, as the product of force and distance. In the example above, the combined force of friction plus the air resistance at 20 m.p.h. is supposed to be 10 lb. What work is done in moving the bicycle for, say, a mile at 20 m.p.h.? Force $= 10$ lb. Distance $= 5,280$ ft. ($= 1$ mile). Therefore work $= 52,800$ "foot-pounds."

At 20 m.p.h. this takes 3 min., or 180 sec., so that the rider is working at 52,800 ft.-lb. per 180 sec., or about 280 ft.-lb. per sec.

This is called the power, or rate of doing work. James Watt, the father of the science of mechanical power, assumed that a draught horse could work at a rate of 550 ft.-lb. per sec. That is what is meant by a rate of 1 h.p.

342

At what h.p. or horse-power would the rider be working in the example above? 280/550 is just over ½, so he would be working at about ½ h.p.

You can estimate your own maximum h.p. very simply. A man can probably work at nearly his highest rate when running upstairs, so you can (1) measure the total rise in feet, (2) multiply by your weight in lb. (3) divide by the time in seconds, thereby obtaining foot-pounds per second, and (4) divide by 550 to get your power in h.p.

Since 1 m.p.h. is 5,280 ft. in 3,600 sec., you should be able to verify the useful rule that 60 m.p.h. = 88 ft. per sec. For all approximate work, take this as 90 ft. per sec., and then you can say that 2 m.p.h. is very nearly 3 ft. per sec.

We can, for example, restate in foot, pound and second units, the case of the cyclist at 20 m.p.h. In the new units we have still $F = kV^2$. F is still 9 lb. but V is now approximately 30 ft. per sec., so that $9 = k \times 900$, which gives, in these units, $k = \cdot 01$.

HOW FAST CAN A CYCLIST TRAVEL?

With the arithmetic thus made a little simpler, the next question to ask is: What is the highest speed a cyclist can achieve against an air resistance such as this, given by $\cdot 01 V^2$? Let us suppose that he will have a maximum working rate of 1 h.p., or 550 ft.-lb. per sec. It is also most convenient to bring in here the direct connexion between power and velocity; for since

$$\text{work} = \text{force} \times \text{distance},$$
$$\text{power} = \text{work} \div \text{time}$$
$$= \text{force} \times \text{distance} \div \text{time}$$
$$= \text{force} \times \text{velocity}.$$

As it is the same cyclist, the air resistance to his motion is still given by $F = \cdot 01 V^2$. If we neglect the bearing resistance altogether we shall get a very simple equation which should be somewhere near the

× ÷ × ÷ × ÷ × ÷ × ÷ × ÷ × ÷ × ÷ × ÷ × ÷ × ÷ × ÷ × ÷ × ÷ × ÷ × ÷

What Do You Make of These?

(1) A railway waggon is moving steadily forwards at 20 m.p.h. Can you say whether any part of it is bound to move faster than this? And is there any point which must frequently travel backwards?

(2) Around a fixed wheel another is to be made to roll so that it makes four full turns in one complete circuit. What is the ratio of the diameter of the rolling wheel to that of the fixed wheel?

Solutions on page 444

× ÷ × ÷ × ÷ × ÷ × ÷ × ÷ × ÷ × ÷ × ÷ × ÷ × ÷ × ÷ × ÷ × ÷ × ÷ × ÷

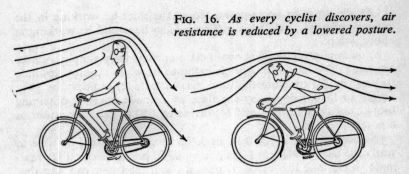

FIG. 16. *As every cyclist discovers, air resistance is reduced by a lowered posture.*

truth, so we take $F = \cdot01\,V^2$ as the only force against which he is working.

Then with the power $= 1$ h.p. or 550 ft.-lb. per sec.

$$550 = F \times V = \cdot01\,V^2 \times V$$
$$\text{or } \cdot01\,V^3 = 550$$
$$V^3 = 55,000.$$

The cube root of 55,000 is about 38, so that, working at 1 h.p., the rider could not exceed 38 ft. per sec., or about 26 m.p.h.

How can a cyclist exceed this speed, if our (velocity)² law is true?

(1) He may exceed 1 h.p. working rate.

(2) He may alter the value of k—the figure which measures the air resistance set up by a given speed. As mentioned earlier, the shape and texture of the whole unit—cycle plus rider—determines this, and k can be reduced by the wearing of a minimum of clothing and by a lowered posture as in Fig. 16.

(3) He can "pace" behind a moving barrier which takes the mass of air along with it, so that his speed *relative to the air*, from which $F\,(= kV^2)$ is calculated, is much less than his speed over the ground. In this way a cycle has been ridden at 66 m.p.h. on the level.

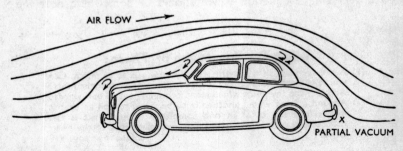

AIR FLOW ⟶

PARTIAL VACUUM

FIG. 17. *The air-flow lines show how a partial vacuum is created.*

344

Wind resistance is partly frictional; there is a viscous drag of air against the moving body. Again, work is done in stirring up eddying air currents. Also, as you can easily verify, it is a matter of air pressure. On the downwind side the pressure is reduced, creating a partial vacuum, and you can see light objects being "sucked" into this region. Fig. 17 indicates the general lines on which this pressure reduction operates; the arrows show the air-flow past a stationary car because it is simpler to think of the air moving relative to the car.

There is a fundamental law about gases in motion which states that where the flow is faster the pressure is lower. In drawing air flow, you represent the unimpeded air motion by a number of parallel lines; when there is an obstacle, the same number of lines must be drawn with the crowding or thinning out evenly shared as far as possible. This results in curvature of the flow lines as in Fig. 17 and as the air mass tends to keep together the particles have to go much faster round the bend to keep up.

To follow this up, you can

(1) sketch the flow lines behind a much longer tail;

(2) draw them also round a section through an aeroplane wing, as in Fig. 18;

(3) work out the explanation of swerve in a ball, as in Fig. 19.

FASTER FLOW, LOWER PRESSURE

FIG. 18. *The air-flow lines round an aeroplane wing show how such a section imparts lift when the plane moves forward.*

LIFT

SLOWER FLOW, HIGHER PRESSURE

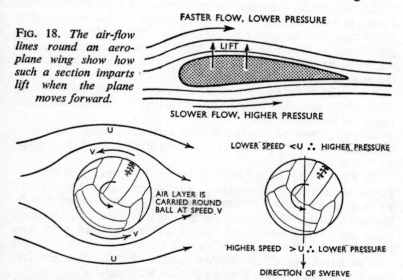

U

V

AIR LAYER IS CARRIED ROUND BALL AT SPEED V

V

U

LOWER SPEED <U ∴ HIGHER PRESSURE

HIGHER SPEED >U ∴ LOWER PRESSURE

DIRECTION OF SWERVE

FIG. 19. *Spin and swerve, illustrating the component speeds of air around a spinning ball and the resultant air speeds and direction of swerve.*

345

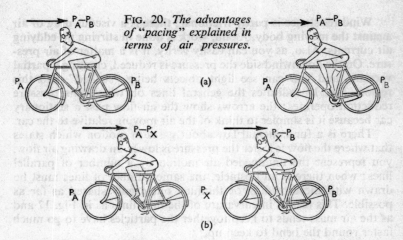

FIG. 20. *The advantages of "pacing" explained in terms of air pressures.*

$P_A - P_B$

P_A P_B (a)

$P_A - P_B$

P_A P_B

$P_A - P_X$

P_A P_X

$P_X - P_B$

P_X P_B

(b)

In this case also it helps to consider the ball as spinning about a fixed point while the air mass moves past. This explanation is more acceptable if checked carefully with experience: from games, especially where the swerve can be considerable as in tennis and football—not to mention the golfer's "slice."

Cycling against the wind one day during the Second World War I enjoyed an easier passage for some distance behind an Air Force pilot; then, coming alongside him, I said: "Thank you for helping me along," to which he replied: "And thank you too for helping me." Was he right? If the second rider is helped, must it not be at the expense of the leader? To work out this energy balance think only in terms of air resistance due to differences of pressure; all the other kinds of resistance are unaffected by having someone just behind or just before you.

In Fig. 20 two independent cyclists each push against a pressure difference $P_A - P_B$, P_A being a little above atmospheric pressure and P_B (rather more) below.

In Fig. 20b the second rider closes up. The pressure in front of him is now also the pressure behind the leader: it can only therefore be something in between P_A and P_B—say P_X, which is more than P_B but less than P_A. (A pleasing example of mathematical shorthand, using the "more than" and "less than" signs, is to write this $P_A > P_X > P_B$.) Now was the pilot right?

The advantage of the tandem follows directly from the last example: the riders have closed right up. Remember also your air-flow drawings; it may well be that the longer tandem gives a better air flow whilst $P_A - P_B$, besides operating only once and having the

346

thrust of two riders to oppose it, may possibly be very little more than for a single cycle. Supposing the air resistance to be the same for a tandem as for a solo cycle, some figures should now be produced. Let us take the constant $k = \cdot01$, working in foot-pounds and seconds.

(1) On the level, speed 20 m.p.h. = 30 f.p.s. (approx.)

$F = \cdot01\ V^2$ (Therefore a solo rider has to deal

$= \cdot01 \times 900$ with 9 lb. wind resistance; tandem

$= 9$ (lb.)   riders share this.)

(2) Up a hill, gradient 1 in 16, speed 8 m.p.h. = 12 f.p.s.

$F = \cdot01\ V^2$

$= \cdot01 \times 144$

$= 1\cdot44$ (lb.)

Weight component $= W \times$ gradient. (Let weight of solo cycle and rider $= 200$ lb.; and let weight of tandem $=$ weight of 2 cycles approx.)

For solo $= 200 \times \dfrac{1}{16} = 12\frac{1}{2}$ lb.

Therefore forces of air pressure + gravity = 14 lb. approx. for one rider, solo; or $26\frac{1}{2}$ lb. approx. for two riders (tandem).

There are also, of course, the frictional forces due to the bearings and road surface; these will be a fairly constant amount per rider.

It is not difficult to see that the advantage of the tandem, so much reduced, may be more than outweighed by the poorer stability shown earlier to result from the long wheel base. Students of records will be aware that these calculations are amply verified by performance.

POWER RATING IN MOTOR VEHICLES

You will be very familiar with the description of a motor-car in terms of its horse-power—for example, a 12-h.p. model. What does this mean in terms of design and performance?

We know already that 1 h.p. means a working rate of exactly 550 ft.-lb. per sec. or 33,000 ft.-lb. per min. Another useful fact is that the energy latent in a gallon of petrol is roughly between $10\frac{1}{4}$ and $13\frac{1}{2}$ million ft.-lb. A petrol engine is a device for turning this into energy of motion.

Several formulae exist for connecting design with performance. The first of these assumed that the only important difference between engines was due to the different areas of the tops of the pistons. This led to the R.A.C. rating, in which the diameter D of the piston was measured in inches: the formula was $h.p. = 0\cdot4D^2$ per cylinder.

Fig. 21 shows a more practical approach to the problem. As the piston moves downward, the amount of fuel taken into the cylinder clearly depends not only on the bore of the cylinder but also on the distance travelled by the piston. The product of these (bore × stroke) gives the swept volume, and the later formula is

$$\text{h.p.} = \frac{\text{total swept volume in cubic centimetres}}{100}$$

Compare the two formulae for a car having four cylinders each of internal diameter 7 cm. and stroke as in Fig. 21 (remembering that 1 in. = 2·54 cm.).

You have probably noticed that it is the total swept volume which is given prominence in distinguishing motor-cycle models, the h.p. equivalent having only unofficial status; the engine is listed as of 500 c.c., and so on down to the tiny 25 c.c., which is typical of engines used to assist pedal cycles.

It may be claimed that an 8-h.p. car develops 24 h.p. This sounds so paradoxical that we are entitled to ask what it means.

Power developed means true horse-power as originally defined—a rate of doing work. The engine is made to drive a wheel against a measured braking force, as in Fig. 22. The calculation is a perfectly easy one if we remember that

(1) work = force × distance,

(2) power = $\dfrac{\text{work}}{\text{time}}$, and

(3) h.p. = $\dfrac{\text{power in ft.-lb. per sec.}}{550}$ or $\dfrac{\text{power in ft.-lb. per min.}}{33,000}$

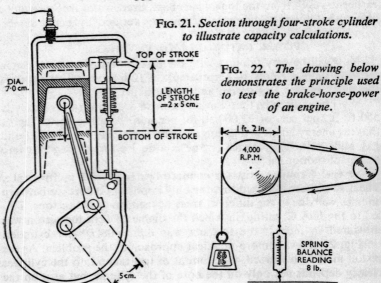

FIG. 21. *Section through four-stroke cylinder to illustrate capacity calculations.*

FIG. 22. *The drawing below demonstrates the principle used to test the brake-horse-power of an engine.*

DIA. 7·0 cm.

TOP OF STROKE

LENGTH OF STROKE = 2 × 5 cm.

BOTTOM OF STROKE

5 cm.

1 ft. 2 in.

4,000 R.P.M.

56 lb.

SPRING BALANCE READING 8 lb.

The "force" in the example is provided by the weight of 56 lb. When the wheel is free, the spring balance takes the weight, but in Fig. 22 the spring takes only 8 lb. and the brake force is therefore 48 lb. The "distance" is 4,000 circumferences in one minute. Since rotation speeds are nearly always given in revolutions per minute, engineers use 33,000 ft.-lb. per min. rather than 550 ft.-lb. per sec. for the horse-power. The engine is working at $21\frac{1}{3}$ h.p.—a figure easily reached by a modern 8-h.p. engine.

How is this done? Early ratings had a basis of reality, and an engine with a capacity or swept volume of 800 c.c. did develop about 8 h.p. You will have noticed that one variable factor is completely ignored in the ratings—how frequently is the volume swept? Work is given out with each stroke and the modern engine achieves the extra power by a much greater number of revolutions per minute than was contemplated in early days.

The modern engine is also probably more efficient than the early internal combustion engines. Supposing the engine in the example above uses a gallon of petrol per hour when running in this way, what is its efficiency? In other words, what is the ratio $\dfrac{\text{energy output}}{\text{energy input}}$?
The input, as indicated earlier, is about 12,000,000 ft.-lb. per hour for a gallon of fuel. Dividing this by the energy output per hour (which we know to be $21\frac{1}{3} \times 33,000$ ft.-lb. per min.) we find the efficiency as a decimal. Efficiency is usually stated as a percentage. An efficiency of 38·5 per cent is high but not unknown.

Actual horse-power can also be estimated from such performances as hill climbing; the speed, however, must be slow. (Why?) For example, if a loaded car weighs 1 ton and climbs a 1 in 5 gradient at 10 m.p.h., what estimate can you make about the h.p.? Before working this out you must recall that

$$\text{power} = \text{work} \div \text{time}$$
$$= \text{force} \times \text{distance} \div \text{time}$$
$$= \text{force} \times \text{velocity}.$$

This is a convenient short cut; using the approximation 2 m.p.h. = 3 ft. per sec., and noting that the downhill component is one-fifth the actual weight, you should obtain the value 12 h.p. This value, however, represents only the work done against gravity; it ignores air pressure, which is not negligible, and all kinds of friction.

To obtain an estimate of what has been ignored, we can restate our previous conclusions about the resistance to car motion. The engine pull has to overcome three forces:
(1) A frictional force due to the bearings and road surface: this is fairly constant over a wide speed range for a given car. Call this A.

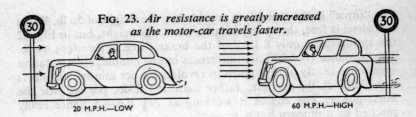

FIG. 23. *Air resistance is greatly increased as the motor-car travels faster.*

20 M.P.H.—LOW   60 M.P.H.—HIGH

(2) Air resistance due to drag and pressure: this, as suggested in Fig. 23, increases greatly with rising speed and is roughly proportional to the square of the speed. Call it BV^2.

(3) Gravity, in the form of the component $\frac{1}{G}$ of the weight (W) for a gradient of 1 in G.

Built into a formula, this would read

$$R = A + BV^2 + \frac{W}{G}$$

In the Journal of the Institute of Mechanical Engineers for April, 1923, Kersey gave the values of A and B for a 30-cwt. vehicle as $A = 70$, and $B = \cdot09$, V being in m.p.h.

On a hill you must add the gradient fraction of the weight. It is most interesting to make for yourself a table of likely speeds and gradients and see how the importance of various factors shifts. A few entries on such a table are shown below.

Conditions		Resistance in lb. due to:			Total force opposing motion	Horse-power (force × velocity)
Gradient	speed m.p.h.	Constant Friction	Air	Gravity		
(1) Level	20	70	36	0	106	5·65
(2) Level	40	70	144	0	214	23
(3) Level	60					
(4) Up 1 in 20	30			118		
(5) Up 1 in 7	20					
(6) Down 1 in ?	5				0	0
(7) Down 1 in 15	60					

In working out the gravity column, reduce 30 cwt. to lb. and divide by the gradient. For a vehicle running downhill that force is *subtracted*, for gravity then operates to reduce the h.p. required, as in Fig. 24. Note also that V is in m.p.h. but the easiest way to work out h.p. is to work in ft. per sec. (using 60 m.p.h. = 88 ft. per sec.) and divide by 550.

Item (6) is of interest in that by writing in 0 for the h.p. and 5 m.p.h. for the speed you are really trying to find out the gradient down which the car will drift at 5 m.p.h. without engine power. Note that in this case the air-resistance term is practically negligible: the point to bear always in mind about any term depending on the square of the speed is that it will usually have vanishing importance at low speeds and will assume chief place at high speeds.

If you know the weight of your own car and the values of a few steady gradients, you should have no difficulty in filling up a table like that above, by finding first some drift speeds on known gradients, and hence the values of A and B.

How does this affect the all-important "m.p.g." (miles per gallon)?

Over a wide range of speeds the efficiency of the engine, which may be from 30 to 40 per cent, will be fairly constant. This means that the work done per gallon of fuel may at a first approximation be taken as the same over a range of speeds. Does this mean that it is as cheap to drive fast as slow?

Referring to our table, we have the tractive force needed on the level varying as follows:

20	40	60 m.p.h.
106	214	394 lb.

How is work measured? Our definition is work = force × distance, so that the work done per foot is 106, 214 and 394 ft.-lb. respectively. If the efficiency is unchanged, these figures may be taken to indicate the amount of energy, that is, of the petrol consumption, required to travel at those speeds for a given distance on the level. You can make them into quite a good graph, filling in the figures for 30 m.p.h. and 50 m.p.h., and so make for yourself a picture of the cost in petrol of high-speed driving. Remember that we assumed constant efficiency, though in fact at higher engine speeds the overall efficiency—work done per pound of fuel—falls, so that the petrol cost rises more sharply than is here shown.

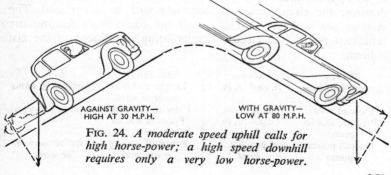

AGAINST GRAVITY—
HIGH AT 30 M.P.H.

WITH GRAVITY—
LOW AT 80 M.P.H.

FIG. 24. *A moderate speed uphill calls for high horse-power; a high speed downhill requires only a very low horse-power.*

10

The Mathematics of Electricity

OF ALL the calculations you make in your home those concerned with electricity can be the most accurate. Even the reason for this is itself a matter of calculation, as we may find out on the way. Electrical units, however, are remote from any other quantities we have so far handled: they deal entirely with the invisible; so we try to imagine what happens by analogy with the flow of water. Let us build this up piecemeal and see how complete we can make it.

What are the conditions for maintaining the flow of water round a circuit—to run a fountain, shall we say—and in what units will they be measured? We shall want the piping, measured in length of pipe of a certain bore. To keep up the circulation we shall use a power-driven pump, said to be capable of maintaining a certain pressure, measured in pressure units such as pounds per square inch or in feet "head" of water. The pipes must run from the pump to the fountain and back again. The fountain will have a flow of water measured, say, in gallons per minute. And we may also want to consider how high it throws the jet of water; of two fountains both delivering a gallon per minute, one throwing the jet 3 ft. high and the other 10 ft. high, the second would clearly need more power though the flow is the same.

How are these features paralleled in an electric circuit running, say, a fan? There must be the cable, with a certain length and gauge of wire; there must be a battery or dynamo to keep the current flowing; the circuit must be complete with a return lead. The systems are sketched in Fig. 1 and the comparable features are tabulated below, the electrical units being introduced in the last column.

WATER	Units	ELECTRICITY	Units
Length and bore of pipe	*ft. and sq. in.*	Length and diameter of wire	*combined as ohms*
Flow of water	*gal. per min.*	Flow of electricity	*amperes (or amps)*
Pressure due to pump	*lb. per sq. in. or ft. head*	Pressure due to battery or dynamo	*volts*
Overall power pump	*gal. per min. × head*	Power of battery or dynamo	*volts × amperes or watts*

Of all these units, the most often misunderstood is the power unit, or watt. Consulting our water "parable," consider pumps delivering:

(1) 1 gal. per min. at 1 ft. head of water
(2) 1 gal. per min. at 3 ft. head
(3) 3 gal. per min. at 1 ft. head
(4) 3 gal. per min. at 3 ft. head.

Would you not say at first glance that (2) and (3) are each three times as powerful as (1), and incidentally equal to each other; or, again, that (4) is three times as powerful as (2) or (3), and therefore nine times as powerful as (1)?

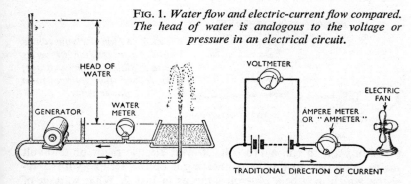

FIG. 1. *Water flow and electric-current flow compared. The head of water is analogous to the voltage or pressure in an electrical circuit.*

These conclusions are summarized in the law that in comparing power ratings, power = flow × head (water), or, colloquially, watts = amperes × volts (electricity).

Being a power unit, the watt may be directly related to any other power unit, for example, horse-power: 1 h.p. = 746 watts.

OHM'S LAW

The law actually stated by Georg Simon Ohm seems now so obvious that he is usually credited with rather more than he actually did say, which was, in effect, that if you change the voltage which is driving current through a given conductor, the current or amperage will change proportionally. Following this lead, we now think of the volts as doing the driving and the length and thinness of the wire as offering a resistance which the drive has to overcome. (The material of which the wire is made can also make a vast difference, and that is something for which there is no obvious counterpart in water flow.)

If 200 volts drive current through a conductor which offers such resistance that 5 amperes of current are flowing, we balance the sum by saying that the 200 volts had been divided by 40 ohms to result in 5 amperes; or, colloquially,

$$\text{volts} \div \text{ohms} = \text{amperes}.$$

This is often spoken of as Ohm's Law.

Here are some familiar examples:

(1) What is (*a*) the current in amperes, and (*b*) the resistance in ohms of a 200-volt, 40-watt lamp?

(2) What is (*a*) the resistance, and (*b*) the power, of a 6-volt, ·04-amp. rear lamp on a cycle?

(3) What current does a 240-volt, 3-h.p. motor take? If you wanted to protect the circuit against excessive current, which fuse wire would you put in: 5-amp., 15-amp. or 30-amp.?

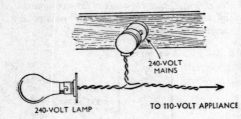

240-VOLT MAINS

240-VOLT LAMP

TO 110-VOLT APPLIANCE

FIG. 2. *A filament lamp can be used as a resistor in series with appliances of low wattage, to reduce the voltage to a lower value.*

(4) You want to run a 110-volt, 30-watt electric razor on 240-volt mains. You can do this by connecting it up in "series" with a resistor, which may be a 240-volt lamp as in Fig. 2. What wattage of lamp should you choose?

The current in a 110-volt, 30-watt appliance is such that $110 \times$ current $= 30$.

Therefore current $= \dfrac{3}{11}$ amp.

The voltage driving this current through the lamp $= 240 - 110$
$$= 130.$$

Therefore the lamp is such that on 130 volts, the current $= \dfrac{3}{11}$ amp.

Therefore on 240 volts, the current $= \dfrac{3}{11} \times \dfrac{240}{130}$ amp.

Therefore the wattage on 240 volts $= \text{volts} \times \text{amperes}$
$$= 240 \times \dfrac{3}{11} \times \dfrac{240}{130}$$

It will improve your grasp of these principles if you work through the example using the idea of resistance. As above, we have voltage 110, wattage 30, and current $\dfrac{3}{11}$ amp.

354

$110 \div$ resistance $= \dfrac{3}{11}$, and $110 \times \dfrac{11}{3} =$ resistance $= \dfrac{1210}{3}$ ohms.

Required *total* resistance must keep current at $\dfrac{3}{11}$ amp. on 240-volt mains.

$$\text{Therefore} \quad \frac{240}{\text{total resistance}} = \frac{3}{11}$$

$$240 \times \frac{11}{3} = \text{total resistance} = 880 \text{ ohms.}$$

Therefore resistance of lamp $= 880 - \dfrac{1210}{3} = 476\dfrac{2}{3}$ ohms.

Used alone on 240-volt mains, the lamp will therefore take a current given by $240 \div 476\dfrac{2}{3} = 0.5$ amp. almost exactly.

Therefore power $= 240 \times \cdot5 = 120$ watts as before.

In this example, it must be noted that lamp resistances vary, usually rising with rising temperature, and that the lamps when being under-run would have a resistance lower than when running normally.

SERIES AND PARALLEL

In the preceding example we have assumed that if two appliances are connected as in Fig. 3a, their combined resistance is the simple sum of the individual resistances. They are said to be connected in "series," the same current flowing through them consecutively. The assumption is perfectly correct.

Fig. 3b shows a different way of connecting two resistances: they are said to be in "parallel." This is the way in which a number of appliances are normally connected to the same source so that the voltage drives a current through each independently, and it is then the total current which is given by $I = I_1 + I_2$. If the voltage is E, we have already used $\dfrac{E}{R} = I$. Since also $\dfrac{E_1}{R_1} = I_1, \dfrac{E_2}{R_2} = I_2$

therefore $\dfrac{E}{R} = \dfrac{E_1}{R_1} + \dfrac{E_2}{R_2}$ or $\dfrac{1}{R} = \dfrac{1}{R_1} + \dfrac{1}{R_2}$ (since $E = E_1 = E_2$).

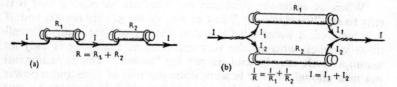

FIG. 3. *Two resistances, or resistors, connected* (a) *in series,* (b) *in parallel, showing the method of calculating the total resistance.*

This is not much used in doing odd jobs, but it is worth noting that in such a simple case as $R_1 = R_2$,

we have $\dfrac{1}{R} = \dfrac{1}{R_1} + \dfrac{1}{R_1} = \dfrac{2}{R_1}$. Therefore R $= \dfrac{R_1}{2}$.

In the above example we wanted a lamp of 120 watts to give the correct resistance. Such lamps are not made. However, a 60-watt lamp, taking half the current, has double the resistance a 120-watt lamp would have, so two 60-watt lamps connected in parallel by a two-way lampholder adaptor would give the theoretically correct figure.

How would you verify the power consumption of an appliance adapted in this way—or of any other circuit? You could do this most directly if you possessed current-measuring instruments. It is, however, quite easy if you use the test dial on your meter, as in the following example, where an American radio set is supposed to work at 30 watts on 110 volts. A series resistance is used. (You can feel the warmth generated by these series resistances, which are in the form of an asbestos-covered resistance wire incorporated in the flexible lead.) Test-dial rating: 600 turns per kWh (*voltage: 200*),

that is, 600 turns per hour at 1,000 watts,
or one turn per 6 sec. at 1,000 watts.

Time recorded for one turn with only radio set working = 110 sec.

Therefore power $= 1,000 \times \dfrac{6}{110} = 54$ watts, at 200 volts.

Therefore current $= \dfrac{54}{200} = \cdot27$ amp.

Correct current, from rated figure of 30 watts at 110 volts,

$= \dfrac{30}{110}$ or $\cdot27$ amp.

Check on meter operation, with new 40-watt bulb in circuit:
Time of one revolution = 2 min. 23 sec.

Therefore power $= 1,000 \times \dfrac{6}{143} = 42$ watts.

THE ELECTRICITY BILL

When we settle the electricity bill what are we paying for? It is easy to say "for electricity," just as we pay the gas bill for gas and, if it is metered, a water bill for water. But we can see, hear or smell these supplies, whereas the very existence of electricity is only an assumption. It may be said we pay for "power." This is nearer but not near enough: power is work done per unit of time and a power rating must be multiplied by the time for which it operates, to give work as the product.

It is, in fact, a bill in respect of work done: power at so many watts has worked for so much time, and since work ÷ time = power, power × time = work. As for the units, you can use the watt and any time unit you please; but the bill for a watt-second would be less than a millionth of a penny. It is usual to take as the power unit 1,000 watts = 1 kilowatt, and as the time unit 1 hour; the work unit is then 1 kilowatt-hour, or 1 kWh. This is the "unit," and any power in watts multiplied by time in hours and divided by 1,000 gives you the work in "units." How many units, for instance, are consumed in the following examples:

(1) Using a 2,000-watt fire for 3 hours.
(2) Leaving a 40-watt lamp on all night (10 p.m.—8 a.m.).
(3) Running a 3,000-watt immersion heater for 50 minutes.

Gas also does work for you, delivering it in the form of heat. It should be noticed that the gas undertaking does not quote a price for gas, but for heat—in "therms." Gas meters are operated by the volume of gas passing through, and the dials would turn whatever gas went through them; the gas undertaking has therefore to see that the gas supplied has a certain heat value (in therms) for a given volume. The usual value is 500 B.Th.U. (British Thermal Units) per cubic foot. Since the therm = 100,000 B.Th.U., you can if you wish convert this into a rough figure of cubic feet per therm.

Of much more interest is the connexion between the therm and the kilowatt-hour. 1 therm = 29·25 kWh, both being taken as energy or heat quantities. For rough calculation the equation 1 therm = 30 "electricity units" will give you a fair idea of comparative cost. This is certainly worth investigating by means of the test dial, for such a job as boiling a quart of water, which can be done equally well by either service.

The cost of supplying electricity is due partly to large capital outlay for plant and transmission lines, which is the same for small or large consumption. In a period of capital expansion it is much to the interest of the undertaking to encourage consumption, and in Great Britain various tariff systems have grown up to favour the heavy

×÷×÷×÷×÷×÷×÷×÷×÷×÷×÷×÷×÷×÷×÷×÷×÷
÷   ×
×   *Grannie's Cakes*   ÷
÷   ×
×   Grannie used to make tall round cakes for tea on Sundays. Now   ÷
÷   she uses the same amount of mixture but a different tin. She says it   ×
×   is easier to cut a flatter cake more fairly when all her grandchildren   ÷
÷   come to see her. Her cakes are now only half as tall as they were.   ×
×   How many times wider are they?   *Solution on page 444*   ÷
÷   ×
×÷×÷×÷×÷×÷×÷×÷×÷×÷×÷×÷×÷×÷×÷×÷×÷

consumer. These include the so-called Norwich system, of a fixed charge plus a very low rate per unit consumed, and the two-part system, with a higher rate for a certain number of units followed by a lower rate for the rest.

Using a recent electricity bill, you can
(1) Divide the total cost by the total consumption and find the true average cost per unit on the system you use.
(2) Find what the cost would be with the same consumption on any alternative system described on the account.
(3) Consider how far any change in your consuming habits, with or without changing to another system, would work to your advantage.

EFFICIENCY OF LAMPS

If you are interested in studying the luminous efficiency of various sources, you may meet a new unit to confuse you, called the lumen.

The theoretical unit of luminous power is a standard candle. Supposed to radiate equally in all directions, it would distribute its light equally over any sphere with the lamp at the centre. Consider a sphere of 1 ft. radius: this would have an area, from the formula $S = 4\pi r^2$, of 4π sq. ft., since $r = 1$. The quantity of light falling on 1 sq. ft. of the spherical surface would then be called 1 lumen. The total illumination from a source of 1 candlepower is 4π times as much, so that a lamp of 1 candlepower gives 4π lumens.

Compare now the luminous efficiency, say in lumens per watt, of:
(1) A 12-volt, 4-amp. car bulb claimed to be of 60 candlepower.
(2) A 240-volt, 15-watt lamp, which gives about $\frac{1}{2}$ candlepower per watt.
(3) A 240-volt, 100-watt lamp, giving about ·9 candlepower per watt.
(4) An arc lamp, giving about 35 lumens per watt.
(5) A gas-discharge lamp, giving about 45 lumens per watt.

Manufacturers usually claim a life of 1,000 hours for a lamp. Consider the case of a 100-watt lamp run on a Norwich system at $\frac{3}{4}$d. per unit over and above fixed charges.
(1) What is the total cost of electrical power over the life of the lamp?
(2) If a cheaper make costs 1s. less and on the average has four-fifths of the luminous efficiency, is there a net gain or loss?

VOLTAGE DROP

The relation between volts, amperes and ohms has been stated earlier in the form $\frac{E}{R} = I$. If this is multiplied through by R it becomes $E = IR$, which is, of course, the same relation but in a different form. Read as it now stands, it says that for any part of a

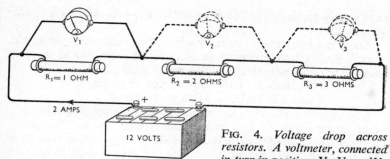

FIG. 4. *Voltage drop across resistors. A voltmeter, connected in turn in positions* V_1, V_2 *and* V_3 *across the terminals of the three resistors, records the voltage drops* E_1, E_2 *and* E_3, *and these are proportional to the respective ohmic resistances.*

circuit, having a given resistance and carrying a known current, there is a voltage difference between the ends of that part measured by current times resistance. Fig. 4 indicates what could be measured if you had a voltmeter, and connected it in turn across the terminals of each resistor.

What would be (1) the total resistance, (2) the current given by the battery, (3) the readings E_1, E_2 and E_3 from the formula $E = IR$?

Notice that $E_1 + E_2 + E_3 =$ the total voltage of the battery— 12 volts. In Fig. 4 we have supposed that R_1, R_2 and R_3 are the only resistances present—that all other parts of the circuit, through which the current must flow, have absolutely zero resistance. This must always be untrue, though with a good accumulator, short leads of copper wire and sound connexions it can be approximately true. If any of the three conditions just mentioned are not all fulfilled, there will be other resistance than $R_1 + R_2 + R_3$, and the current will not be 2 amperes. What will $E_1 + E_2 + E_3$ amount to? Clearly not 12 because I does not equal 2. The difference will be the voltage needed to drive what current you do get through the unknown (and usually undesired) resistance.

This may be (1) somewhere inside the battery, when it is called "internal resistance," or (2) across a connexion—"contact resistance," or (3) in the connecting wires—"line resistance," or any combination of these.

Since the volts represent a driving force overcoming the resistance, work is done in all parts of the circuit. In what form does the work appear? In R_1, R_2 and R_3 it will be given out according to the nature of the appliances—if they are motors, as mechanical energy; if heaters, as heat; if lamps, as heat and light. In all parts offering simple resistance the energy comes out as heat. The measure of the heat is quite simply given by the power in watts: $W = EI$, and as $E = IR$, $W = I^2R$.

There is a conversion factor by which the mechanical power can be expressed as heat: the wattage multiplied by the time in seconds gives the work in watt-seconds, also called joules, and

$$1 \text{ calorie} = 4 \cdot 18 \text{ watt-seconds or joules,}$$
$$\text{and } 1 \text{ B.Th.U.} = 1,052 \text{ watt-seconds.}$$

Consider the following example: A badly fitting plug serving a 5-amp. electric fire sets up contact resistance of $\frac{1}{2}$ ohm. This resistance will not seriously reduce the current; for if the mains voltage is 200, we have, with proper connexions, $200 = 5 \times R$, or $R = 40$ ohms. With the faulty plug, $R = 40\frac{1}{2}$, an increase of one-eightieth. The current will decrease in that proportion; but, at the contact,

$$W = I^2 \times R = 25 \times \tfrac{1}{2} = 12\tfrac{1}{2}.$$

Therefore every second there are $12\frac{1}{2}$ watt-seconds of energy wasted at the plug.

$$\frac{1,052}{12\frac{1}{2}} = 84$$

Therefore every 84 seconds 1 B.Th.U. of heat is produced at the plug. This is very bad for the plug!

There is a certain amount of resistance at any connexion (and anywhere else in a circuit): and you have noted that the heat developed rises with the *square* of the current. For the same resistance, 15 amp. would develop $\frac{(15)^2}{(2)^2}$ times as much heat as 2 amp.; that is, 56 times as much. The 15-amp. plug is made so very much more massive for two reasons: to reduce resistance and so the amount of heat developed, and to be able to absorb and dissipate the heat.

VOLTS DROP ON LEADS

You are not likely to do much installation work with permanent leads. If you do, get the tables giving the right kind of wire for a given load. The amateur is, however, much given to fitting flexible leads to appliances: this should be done to rule, and the following figures are selected to enable you to see the difference between the right and the wrong cable. What you must avoid is such resistance as, with the current you will take through it, will set up undue voltage drop. This would reduce the efficiency of the appliance and also generate undesired heat. In good practice the drop is restricted to 1 volt over all the lead wires.

The basic information regarding the resistance of soft copper is that 1,000 yd. of wire of cross-sectional area 0·1 sq. in. has a resistance of 0·238 ohm.

360

The standard wire used in making flex has a diameter of 0·0076 in. and is sold with 14, 23, 40, 70, 100 or 162 strands. (It is quite easy to check this statement.) To keep the heat developed well below an amount which would damage the insulation, it is found that the current should not exceed 1·8 amp. for the lightest and 17 amp. for the heaviest (162-strand) of these.

What determines the variation of resistance with thickness of wire? Clearly to a first approximation it is inversely proportional to the cross-sectional area, for a doubled area acts like two wires in parallel, with halved resistance. (The gain does not go on unmodified as the wires become very thick, but that qualification can be ignored in considering flexes.)

(1) Calculate the total cross-sectional area of 14 pieces of standard wire.

(2) Compare this with 0·1 sq. in. and so find the resistance in ohms of 1,000 yd. of 14/·0076 flex, as indicated in Fig. 5.

(3) Find the resistance in ohms of the length of lead—say 6 yd. in all; that is, 3 yd. of twin flex.

(4) Using the formula $V = CR$, now find the voltage drop when the maximum safe current of 1·8 amp. is flowing. You should get about $\frac{2}{5}$ volt. The wattage, therefore, is about $\frac{3}{4}$ watt.

Suppose, now, that the current is exceeded by, say, three times what you should allow to pass: notice that the wattage—$I^2 \times R$— will be nine times as great.

Here are a few problems on voltage drop.

(1) A 3-volt dry battery gives the following current readings:
External circuit 6 ohms, current ·48 amp.
External circuit 1 ohm, current 2·4 amp.
Here we have one-sixth of the resistance but only five times the current. What is the reason for this?

 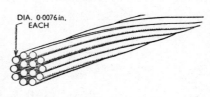

FIG. 5. *Calculation of the resistance of copper cable by comparison with a length of known cross-sectional area and resistance. In this example the total area of section* $= 14 \times \pi \times (\frac{·0076}{2})^2 = 0.000635$ *sq. in. Resistance*

$$per\ yard = \frac{0·238}{1,000} \times \frac{0·1}{0·000635} = 0·0375\ ohm.$$

The cause is clearly a resistance we have not accounted for. If its value is r, we have

$$\frac{3}{6 + r} = \cdot 48, \text{ and } \frac{3}{1 + r} = 2\cdot4$$

These two equations give the same value for r; but even if they did not, it would not follow that our argument was unsound: the resistance will be due to either the connexions or internal resistance of the battery, and the latter sometimes varies with the load.

(2) A home battery charger gives at first an input of 1 amp. to a battery, and this falls overnight to 0·4 amp.

Suppose no change has occurred in the resistances: it is the effective voltage which has fallen. If the charger gives 16 volts and the battery 11 volts at the start, the effective charging voltage is $16 - 11 = 5$. To what value has the effective voltage fallen and the battery voltage risen during the night?

(3) Suppose you have a 12-volt battery and some 6-volt lamps. You can connect these in series and the results will be satisfactory *if the lamps are identical*—both of 3 watts, or both of 12 watts, say. What happens if one is 3 watts and the other 12 watts?

You had better not actually try this out, as it will cost you a bulb: make the calculation instead. Referring to Fig. 6, since the

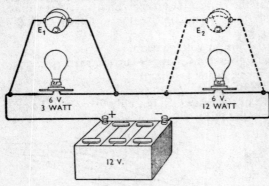

FIG. 6. *When two lamps are connected in series, as here, the voltage drop across them is in inverse proportion to their wattage.*

current is the same through the two lamps, the voltage across them will be in proportion to their resistances; that is, in inverse proportion to their wattages. Working out the shares, you will see that inevitably one lamp will have much more than half of the 12 volts and will soon burn out. This can be confirmed by calculating the correct current for each and then the actual current through the circuit of Fig. 6.

TRANSMISSION OF ELECTRICITY

So far we have taken a mains supply of electricity for granted and have examined some domestic aspects of its use, but it will be interesting to see what happens before the current reaches the consumer.

What are the main sources of the huge amounts of energy in the industrial and domestic life of a modern state? In Great Britain, you will say, mainly coal; in Switzerland, much more comes from water; countries with large forest areas use wood; the future may lie with atomic sources. In all cases the problem is not only the existence of the energy but getting it to the right place. One of the most acceptable features of electrical energy is the economy with which it can be transported. You are probably aware, for instance, of the considerable difference in the economic prices of coal at the pit-head and at your door: it represents the cost of transport. What is the cost of transporting electricity?

Since it seems to weigh nothing, the only cost is the energy lost in voltage drop along the transmission lines, measured as before by Ohm's Law. For example, copper 1·00 sq. in. in cross-section has a resistance of ·023 ohm per 1,000 yd.; the voltage drop per ampere is thus ·023 volt per 1,000 yd.

Suppose, however, a 250-volt supply is required at 200 amp. To send this 1,000 yd. will cause a voltage loss of 200 × ·023, with copper conducting wires of 1 sq. in. section; this is 4·6 volts loss— 1·8 per cent wasted for only 1,000 yd.! In the early days of electric power the distance of transmission was severely limited.

Almost all electrical appliances can now operate with current continually reversing, or "alternating"—A.C. The transmission of such current allows of enormous saving in voltage drops as will be shown presently by reference to examples. First of all, however, we will consider the mathematics of the transformer.

The coal or water energy is converted into mechanical, then to electrical energy in the generator. Suppose this were generated at 250 volts. To send 1,000 amp. for 1,000 yd. with 1 sq. in. conductors would require 23 volts (·023 per amp.) for the transmission lines, and only 227 volts would be available for the consumer. This would impose close limits on the size of the distribution area.

Electrical power is therefore usually distributed at a very high voltage and the amperage is correspondingly small. Suppose the transmission line is to deliver power at the rate of 250,000 watts. At 250 volts the current will have to be 1,000 amp., as we have seen; but if the voltage is raised to 132,000 the current will be less than 2 amp. This alternative is of enormous importance to the electrical engineer, since 2 amp. can be sent 500 times as far along wires of the same thickness as can 1,000 amp. for an equal volts loss. Moreover, a volts loss of, say, 23 volts, which would be serious out of 250 volts, is negligible out of 132,000!

Power at 132,000 volts, however, is not usable by ordinary appliances. The main transmission wires end in one set of coils wound round a soft iron core; separated from these another set of, usually, a quarter the number of turns are wound round the same iron core. As the incoming electricity alternates, usually 50 complete reversals and back again every second, the magnetism in the iron grows, decreases, reverses, and so on, thus inducing electricity in the second set of coils. As there are only a quarter the number of turns, according to Faraday's Law there will be in this coil only one quarter of the voltage in the first—33,000. Since very little energy is lost in this transformer, the output of energy must equal the input; that is,

$$132,000 \times 2 = 33,000 \times \text{output current}$$

Therefore output current = 8 amperes.

This stepping-down process is continued by sub-stations for towns, and so to districts or villages, till the voltage reached is suitable for the user, usually a figure between 200 and 250. As shown in Fig. 7, the distribution is preceded by a stepping-up process, since no dynamo has yet been designed to generate at 132,000 volts. 11,000 volts is the usual output voltage of a generator and 33,000 volts the maximum.

This subject is worth a recapitulation. Taking some very simple figures, let us compare the voltage losses over (say) 10,000 yd. of wire of 1 sq. in. carrying 110,000 watts at (a) 11,000 volts, and (b) 220 volts. You will agree that the resistance of the wire is ·23 ohms. The volts loss for (a) is 2·3 volts, because the current is 10 amp.

$$2·3 \text{ out of } 11,000 = ·021 \text{ per cent.}$$

In the case of (b), do you agree that the loss is 115 volts? This represents a 52 per cent loss!

Most small motors will work on A.C. or D.C. The reason for this is mathematical. A D.C. motor is driven by magnetism; a fixed magnet called the field magnet acts on a moving magnet known as

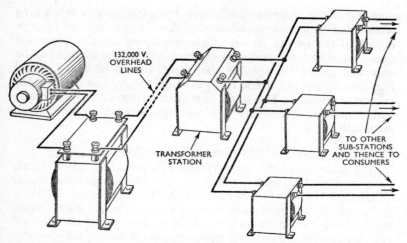

F<small>IG</small>. 7. *Alternating current is generated at a high voltage and stepped up to 132,000 volts for transmission by overhead lines. It is reduced in one or more stages by transformers which supply other sub-stations, which in turn feed the distribution networks.*

the armature. If, as is usual, both are electro-magnets, the current flowing in a direction we may call positive (+) sets up magnetisms we may also call positive (+). The force is measured by the product of these, and (+) × (+) gives (+). Reversing the current gives magnetisms which may be called negative, and (−) × (−) also gives (+): the direction of the force is unchanged.

Used with A.C., the reversing occurs 100 times a second—50 changes and 50 back again, or 50 "cycles." The magnetism in the soft iron also has to change 100 times a second, and in bigger motors the larger masses of iron become heated by rapid "about-face" action on the molecules. Units of more than a small fraction of 1 h.p. have to be proper A.C. motors, working on a somewhat different principle.

You may be interested in continuing the stepping-down process to provide a power unit of very low voltage. Quite useful transformers can be wound using the core and case from one of the larger types of inter-valve transformer. To get the correct power input and output voltage, the rough rule is *nine* turns of wire per volt if the iron core has a cross-section of 1 sq. in. Remember that (a) you must seal off the input wires, which will have mains voltage across them, and (b) you should earth the case by connecting it to the third pin of a 3-pin

365

plug and socket. Another useful step-down transformer is the type often fitted to a moving-coil loudspeaker. These have to be connected to the output circuit of an amplifying circuit, where the resistance is already thousands of ohms, so that the current can be only very small. The speaker coil, which has to vibrate at sound frequencies, has just a few turns of copper wire, and needs a fair current to operate it. This situation is met by a step-down transformer with a ratio of over 100 to 1. It will usually work an electric bell excellently.

WATTLESS CIRCUITS: IMPEDANCE

Fig. 8 shows a step-down transformer, operating a bell circuit, connected to the mains and with the low-voltage output, or "secondary" switched on as required. It also suggests that the input or "primary" will be steadily passing a current which even if small will be ticking off units on your meter. A look at the test dial will reassure you that no power is registering, but it will not tell you why.

To find out why, it must be remembered that A.C. is *changing* current, all the time. This means changing magnetism within the transformer, which again means an induced voltage in the primary due to its own magnetism. The effect depends on a quantity L, called the self-inductance of the coil. L depends on the number of turns and the amount and quality of iron core. The effect depends also on n, the frequency of the A.C. in cycles per second.

There is a relation between the voltage and current similar to that based on Ohm's Law; if we call the voltage linked with current and resistence E_R, and that due to self induction E_L (each of these being the peak values), by Ohm's Law we write $E_R = IR$. Self-induced voltage is given by $E_L = I \times 2\pi nL$, so that $2\pi nL$ acts as a sort of resistance; it is called inductive reactance.

To find the combined effect of resistance and reactance a graphical method is always used. The two voltages E_R and E_L each alternate

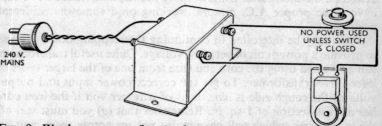

FIG. 8. *Wattless currents flow in the primary coil of the transformer when no current is flowing in the bell circuit.*

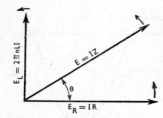

Fig. 9. *Vector diagram showing resistance, reactance, and the resulting impedance in a simple circuit. Mathematical computation can be avoided by the use of a graphical method, as in this example.*

with the frequency n cycles per second, their rise and fall being represented by the rotation of the arrow-headed arms, or vectors, in Fig. 9. (At the instant represented in the figure, $E_R = O$ and E_L has its peak value.) They are out of step with each other, as indicated by the right-angle between them, and they combine to produce a single (alternating) voltage, the peak value of which is given by the diagonal, by the principle of the parallelogram of forces.

By the theorem of Pythagoras, the resultant peak voltage E is given by $E^2 = E_R{}^2 + E_L{}^2$. Also, we represent the combined opposing effect of reactance and resistance by a symbol Z, called impedance; and as this is a kind of resistance (and its value is expressed as a number of ohms) we write $E = I Z$, conforming with $E_R = I R$.

So, then, $E^2 = E_R{}^2 + E_L{}^2$

or $I^2 Z^2 = I^2 R^2 + (2\pi n L I)^2$

Dividing by I^2, $\quad Z^2 = R^2 + (2\pi n L)^2$

or the impedance $Z = \sqrt{R^2 + (2\pi n L)^2}$.

Before we use this formula, it should be noted that there is another one, which needs a good deal of trigonometry to work out, so we will just quote the result. It gives the power operating in this circuit as $\dfrac{E^2}{R} \cos \theta$, where θ is the angle shown in Fig. 9; $\cos \theta$ is called the power factor.

You can verify from the figure that $\tan \theta = \dfrac{2\pi n L}{R}$. If there is only the single coil, of self-inductance L and resistance R, and L is very large compared with R, then $\tan \theta$ is very large and θ is nearly a right-angle. What is the value of $\cos \theta$, the power factor, when θ is nearly a right-angle? Nearly zero. So the power operating in these conditions is practically zero. A highly inductive coil of *very low resistance* left connected straight across the mains consumes no power and is called a wattless circuit.

When you switch on the secondary, the magnetism in that coil neutralizes that in the primary with, in effect, a great reduction in the value of L, so the value of θ falls, the power factor $\cos \theta$ rises (the smaller an angle, the bigger its cosine) and some power is consumed.

367

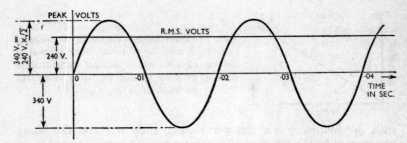

FIG. 10. *An alternating current has, theoretically, a perfect sine-wave form, as illustrated here. A frequency of 50 cycles per second is now standard for transmission and distribution networks.*

Now we can look again at our impedance formula $Z = \sqrt{R^2 + (2\pi nL)^2}$. For very low frequencies, that is, low values of n, the second term is very small and Z is nearly equal to $\sqrt{R^2}$ or R: for high frequencies R^2 is small compared with $(2\pi nL)^2$ and an approximate value for Z is then $\sqrt{(2\pi nL)^2}$, or $2\pi nL$. Thus, in this latter case the impedance is roughly proportional to the frequency.

"PEAK" AND "VIRTUAL" VOLTS

The graph in Fig. 10 shows how A.C. voltage varies with time. If it is desired to compare A.C. with D.C. for effectiveness, some kind of average must be taken. What is the average voltage in Fig. 10? Clearly exactly nil; and yet power is delivered quite effectively by such a voltage.

A basis of comparison suggests itself when we consider the heating effect, which, as we have seen, is for a given resistance proportional to the square of the current (or of the voltage, as you can verify from $E = IR$ and $W = EI = I^2R = \dfrac{E^2}{R}$). Counting the reversed current as negative, its square will still be positive.

The method, then, is
(1) Find an expression for the square of the voltage at every instant throughout the cycle.
(2) Find the mean value of the squares.
(3) Take the square root of this mean.
The root-mean-square, or R.M.S., voltage is used for comparison with D.C. It is also called the virtual voltage and is denoted by $\overline{E}$.

You may be aware, or may recognize at once, that the graph of Fig. 10 is a straightforward sine curve: the voltage E at any moment is related to the peak voltage E_0 by an equation.

368

$E = E_0 \sin 2\pi nt$, where n is the frequency and t is the time in seconds from the beginning of the cycle; the average value of any sine, or cosine, over a complete cycle is 0, because the positive values are all balanced by equal negative values.

However, $E^2 = E_0^2 \sin^2 2\pi nt$

$$= \frac{E_0^2}{2} (1 - \cos 4\pi nt) \qquad \text{(from the standard formula } 2 \sin^2 A = 1 - \cos 2A)$$

The average value of the cosine part is, again, zero; so the average value of $E^2 = \frac{E_0^2}{2}$. Therefore R.M.S. voltage $\bar{E} = \frac{E_0}{\sqrt{2}}$.

When the mains voltage is said to be 240 volts, it means the R.M.S. or $\bar{E}$. You can perhaps see why A.C. is essentially rather more dangerous than D.C.: peak voltage $E_0 = \sqrt{2} + \bar{E}$, so that if $\bar{E} = 240$,

$$E_0 = \sqrt{2} \times 240 = 340.$$

Dangers of shock or insulation break-down should be related to peak rather than R.M.S. volts.

THREE-PHASE DISTRIBUTION

This is an essentially mathematical device which, besides being very suitable for electric-motor operation, saves copper on transmission lines. The power is split into three equal parts, generated one third of the cycle period apart.

The combined effect of the three currents can be seen from Fig. 11, or calculated by trigonometry, to be exactly zero at all times. They are each fed by a separate lead-in, and can be combined in one return lead, which, if the components are equal as shown, would in fact carry no current at all.

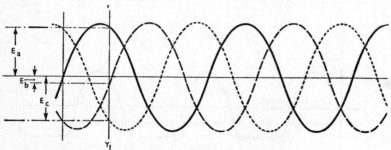

WHEREVER YY IS DRAWN $E_a + E_b + E_c = 0$ (HERE E_b E_c ARE NEGATIVE)

Fig. 11. *With three-phase distribution the maximum voltage in each phase lags behind that of the preceding phase-line by one-third of a cycle. This method economizes in the amount of copper required in cables.*

369

Comparing three-phase with single-phase distribution for, say, 300 amp., the leads for three circuits at 100 amp. each use very little more copper than for one lead at 300 amp. The saving is on the return, which would have to be of full weight for single phase, but need be no heavier than a 100-amp. line if it is the three-phase return: this makes a total requirement of only two-thirds the copper used in a 300-amp. single-phase supply.

RECTIFICATION

What happens if a supply such as suggested by Fig. 10 is connected—with suitable resistance, or after stepping-down—to a battery with a view to recharging? Looking a little way into this question, the answer might be "nothing." This, however, is not true. Suppose the supply to be at 18 volts virtual and the battery at 12. For $\frac{1}{100}$ sec. the battery will be charged by (18 — 12) volts = 6 volts; for the next $\frac{1}{100}$ sec. it will be *discharged* at (18 + 12) volts = 30 volts.

The A.C. must be rectified by including in the circuit a device which either allows current to flow only one way, such as a thermionic valve, or a conductor with much greater resistance in one direction than in the other, such as a plate of copper pressed against a surface of copper oxide. Fig. 12 gives the voltage graph for two such rectifiers: clearly the missing half of the sine wave represents a loss of half the input power.

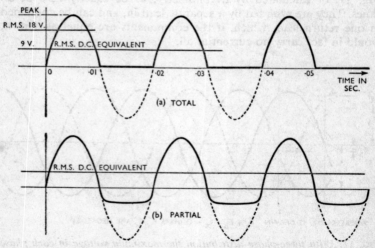

Fig. 12. *Half-wave rectification of 50-cycle A.C.* (a) *Wave-form produced by a valve rectifier.* (b) *Wave-form of a copper-oxide rectifier.*

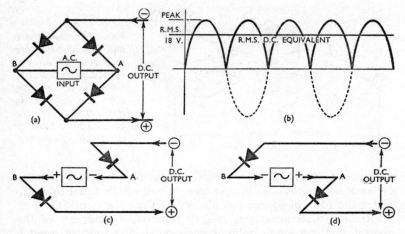

Fig. 13. *Full-wave rectification showing* (a) *four metal rectifiers connected to form a "bridge" circuit;* (b) *the pulsating half-wave of direct current produced by the "bridge" rectifier;* (c) *the path of the current during one half-cycle;* (d) *the path of the current during the reverse half-cycle.*

A network of four rectifiers connected as in Fig. 13a recovers the lost half and gives full-wave rectification, pictured for a 100 per cent type of rectifier in Fig. 13b.

In Fig. 13a the arrows give the direction of current flow (or greater current flow) through the rectifiers: try letting in turn A be $+$ and B $-$, and then the converse, as in Figs 13c and 13d, verifying that in each case the current flows in the same direction in the D.C. circuit.

RADIO

The kind of rectification needed to convert radio signals into audible sound is described later, but first of all we need to be clear about the nature of a radio signal. A glance at your *Radio Times* will illustrate the most essential feature—you will find stations listed as 330 m., 908 kc/s.; 1,500 m., 200 kc/s; and so on. What do these mean? Radio is simply electromagnetic waves, differing from radar, light and X-rays as Atlantic rollers differ from ripples in a teacup; or, more exactly, as deep notes differ from high notes. A constant velocity marks *all* ranges of electromagnetic radiation: waves of length λ go by at a frequency n per second, so that the velocity $c = n\lambda$.

The velocity in free space is 300,000 kilometres per second, or 3×10^{10} centimetres per second. If you look at the radio station, and

371

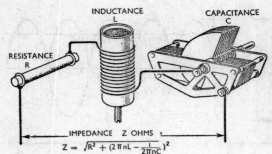

FIG. 14. *Inductance and capacitance are properties of all circuits, and by selective adjustments of the condenser shown in this illustration the circuit can be tuned to a given frequency.*

remember that *m* stands for metres of wavelength and kc/s for kilocycles or thousands of cycles per second, you will find that by multiplying the pairs of figures you always get the velocity of light.

Radio signals are, then, radiating alternating currents of frequency anything up to millions per second. The modern trend is continually to be shortening the waves used, that is, to increase the frequency. Consider, for instance, what must be the frequency of centimetric radar, with wavelengths of a few centimetres. This field is rightly designated that of U.H.F.—ultra-high-frequency. Any exposed conductor, such as an aerial wire, picks up all the currents present in sufficient strength, and the next problem is how the receiver selects the desired frequency. To answer this, our impedance formula needs the addition of another quantity—capacitance—denoted by *C*. This represents the storage or condenser effect on the surface between conductors and any insulating medium, and the presence of capacitance modifies the impedance formula to

$$Z = \sqrt{R^2 + \left(2\pi nL - \frac{1}{2\pi nC}\right)^2}$$

Fig. 14 shows in diagram form a circuit having resistance *R*, inductance *L*, and capacitance *C*, and frequently both *L* and *C* can be varied. To obtain maximum current of any particular frequency, when a medley of frequencies is flowing in the circuit, *Z* is to be reduced to the minimum. From the formula, what values of the variables *L* and *C* give the least value of *Z*? The part in brackets being squared, *Z* is least when this part is zero, or $2\pi nL - \dfrac{1}{2\pi nC} = 0$

that is, $2\pi nL = \dfrac{1}{2\pi nC}$, or $n^2 = \dfrac{1}{4\pi^2 LC}$; *therefore* $n = \dfrac{1}{2\pi\sqrt{LC}}$.

When *L* and *C* are adjusted to the correct value, the impedance is lower for that value of *n* than for any other, and signals of frequency *n* are received at much greater strength than other signals.

372

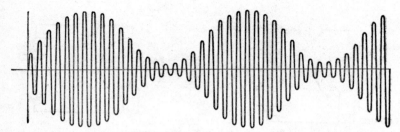

FIG. 15. *The wave-form of a high-frequency carrier wave after it has been amplitude-modulated by an audio-frequency current.*

MODULATION

The next problem is to transmit the radio wave in such a way as to make it carry sounds. Whereas radio waves are at frequencies of millions of cycles per second, sounds are in hundreds or thousands. One method used is therefore to make the peak value of the radio wave—the amplitude—itself vary with sound frequencies. This is called modulation, and Fig. 15 shows the principle: a higher-frequency wave has its amplitude varying regularly, so that the profile of the high-frequency peaks outlines a lower-frequency variation.

In the receiver, such a wave is rectified by cutting off all or part of one half, as in Fig. 16a, the other half, or its margin of excess, being smoothed out as in Fig. 16b to remove the high-frequency component. It is now in effect an A.C. added to a D.C., which is removed by passing through a transformer (which transmits only A.C., as we found earlier on).

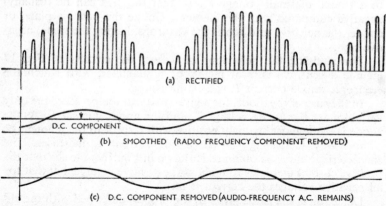

(a) RECTIFIED

D.C. COMPONENT

(b) SMOOTHED (RADIO FREQUENCY COMPONENT REMOVED)

(c) D.C. COMPONENT REMOVED (AUDIO-FREQUENCY A.C. REMAINS)

FIG. 16. *The three stages of rectification/detection of a modulated wave.*

373

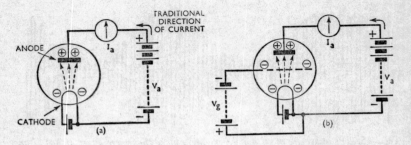

FIG. 17. *Principle of thermionic valves.* (a) *A diode, which has one cathode and one anode.* (b) *The triode, which incorporates a "grid." Control of the valve's operation is given by the potential of the grid voltage* V_g.

THE THERMIONIC VALVE

The word thermionic summarizes the discovery that heated bodies send out a stream of electrified particles. If there is no atmosphere to absorb them they can be received on a metal plate surrounding the emitting source. A thermionic valve contains, therefore, a heated filament to send out electrons, and a metal plate around it to catch them. Usually the plate is connected to the positive side of a battery or other D.C. source, of voltage V_a, so that it can, by attraction of opposites, increase the flow of the negative electrons. Fig. 17a shows the simplest form, the diode, with only the filament (or cathode) and the plate (or anode).

Fig. 17b shows the connexions for a triode when a grid, a perforated screen, is placed between cathode and anode and connected to a source of small voltage V_g, so that the grid can be (usually) negative compared with the filament. Unlike the positive plate, or anode, the negative grid repels the electrons, having the same, negative sign.

For studying the behaviour of valves, the circuits of Fig. 17 include a sensitive current meter, or milliameter, with which the electronic anode current I_a can be measured.

In the case of the diode, for a given filament temperature the only variables are the anode voltage V_a and the anode current I_a. As the anode is made more strongly positive with respect to the filament or cathode—by increasing V_a—the anode current I_a increases. The characteristic curve so obtained is shown in Fig. 18a. Notice that the positive current increases roughly as the positive voltage, but that for all negative voltages the current is zero.

Detection is the name given to the process described with the aid of Fig. 16, in which the modulated radio-frequency wave is rectified,

374

leaving only the audio-frequency modulation. All that is required of a detector, provided that it can conduct these high frequencies, is that it shall have a greater resistance in one direction than in the other. Early radio receivers used a crystal, with a metal contactor; the contact resistance was different in the two directions, giving partial rectification. The diode is much more effective, giving total rectification and having much lower resistance than a crystal. Fig. 18b shows how the modulated signal, if fed in between the filament and the anode, is totally rectified, because in the negative half of the wave the current is zero. The rest of the process as in Fig. 12 then follows.

A triode has an extra variable, the voltage V_g between the filament and the grid. It is usual, therefore, to plot *sets* of curves showing variation of anode current. These can show the effect either of variation of anode voltage V_a for a number of set values of V_g, or, as in Fig. 19, of variation of grid voltage V_g for a number of set values of V_a.

Fig. 19 also shows the simplest, or class A, amplification. For the anode voltage, or high tension (H.T.), in use, a point is selected well in the middle of the straight part. In Fig. 19 the H.T. is 120 volts, and the point chosen requires a fixed negative voltage V_g of about 1·5.

If, now, an alternating voltage of peak value 1 volt is connected between the grid and filament, the value of V_g will vary between

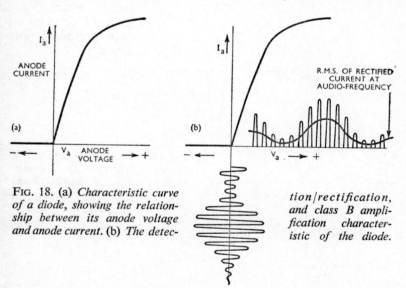

FIG. 18. (a) *Characteristic curve of a diode, showing the relationship between its anode voltage and anode current.* (b) *The detection/rectification, and class B amplification characteristic of the diode.*

375

— 0·5 and — 2·5. Owing to the *straightness* of the characteristic curve, the anode current I_a will vary in proportion to the voltage; and owing to the *steepness* of the curve, the amount of variation is as much as would be produced by an A.C. in the anode circuit of peak value 10 volts, as is shown in Fig. 19. The valve is said in these conditions to have an amplification factor of 10.

It should be noted that if the curve of Fig. 18 is also steep, the signal is also amplified during the detection/rectification process by the diode: this is called class B amplification. Looking again at Fig. 18, you should be able to see that as the signal is amplified in this way, a greater average value results for the anode current I_a: the anode current consumption is thus high for high output, low for low output. Such amplification is appropriate for use in portable radio receivers, where the chief running cost is for the H.T. batteries which supply the anode current.

You can also verify for yourself that a triode can be used for detection/rectification. If the operating point of Fig. 19 is taken further back at a place of sharp curvature, a voltage swing in the grid circuit will have an effect on I_a which is greater in one direction than in the other. That is the only condition required for the detection/rectification effect; this form of the process is called anode-bend detection.

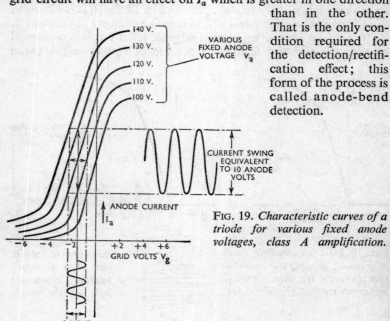

FIG. 19. *Characteristic curves of a triode for various fixed anode voltages, class A amplification.*

11

Chance in Games and Sports

ALMOST every game, however high a degree of skill it demands of the players, has its own elements of chance. The part which chance plays in the final result varies enormously; in some card games and dice games, for instance, the skill of the player has no appreciable effect, while in games such as chess the effect of chance is negligible. It is these elements of chance, this infinite variety of circumstances which may arise by accident, which form part of the appeal of many games; were it not so, it would be useless for players of unequal skill to compete with each other, since the result would be a foregone conclusion. Fortune indeed may favour the brave but it does not of necessity reward the most skilful!

While it is possible in some games to assess numerically the chances of certain situations arising, or of a particular player being successful, in others no amount of calculation can estimate the effects of chance. For example, the odds against obtaining a total of eight with one throw of two dice can readily be calculated, but it is impossible to estimate when a golf ball is driven down the fairway whether it will come to rest in a hollow in the ground or be nicely teed up for the second shot. And yet on this "lie" the whole issue of the game may depend.

We shall consider in this chapter some of the mathematical ideas on which the calculations of chance are based, though we shall not be concerned here with probability as such—a subject already dealt with in Chapter 5.

Some of the earliest gambling games were concerned with coins, cards or dice, and one of the simplest of these was the game of "heads or tails." In this one player spins a coin and his opponent attempts to name the face of the coin which will fall uppermost. The roles are then reversed, and so on. After an agreed number of throws the player with the greatest number of successful calls takes the stake or whatever has been decided by the players themselves. This game is obviously quite independent of the skill of the players, and is a matter of pure chance. Simple though it is, it provides one of the best illustrations of the ideas underlying chance and is moreover closely related to more complicated gambling games such as roulette. We will begin therefore by examining what happens when coins are tossed.

If we toss up a coin it will come down either heads or tails—or it will stand on its edge, which is most unlikely. Disregarding the unlikely, we can say that the event can end in two ways—heads or tails uppermost. A second coin tossed with the first will also fall heads or tails uppermost, and each coin is quite uninfluenced by what happens to the other. Since both coins can fall in two ways independently, when tossed together they can fall in 2 × 2 or 4 ways, as shown in Fig. 1.

It will be seen that the combination of one head and one tail occurs twice, and although we are not concerned here with the probability of this happening it is clear that it is twice as likely as either two heads or two tails. Tossing three coins at a time (or one coin three times in succession) will result in a number of possible arrangements—H.H.H., H.H.T., H.T.H. are three of them: see if you can write down the others. How many can you find? Each toss can end in 2 × 2 × 2 or 8 ways. Did you get them all?

Similar results can be obtained when dice are thrown. One dice can fall with any one of its six faces uppermost. If a second dice is thrown with the first then that too can fall with any face uppermost. Since every number on the first dice can be associated with every number on the second, the dice can fall in any one of 6 × 6 or 36 possible ways. Not all of these will look different as there will be

(a)   (b)   (c)   (d)

Fig. 1. *The four possible results—heads or tails—of tossing two coins.*

378

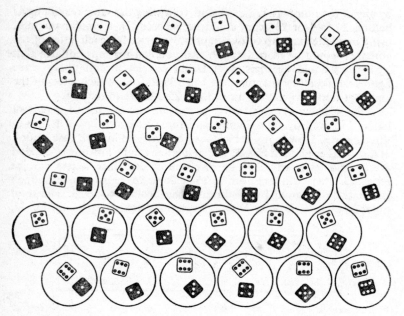

FIG. 2. *The thirty-six possible results of throwing a pair of dice.*

reversals; for example a two on one face combined with a six on the uppermost face of the second will be repeated when a six and two are upwards. Can you find all possible reversals? How many different pairs of numbers can be obtained? Fig. 2 shows all the possible ways in which two dice can fall.

COLLECTING REGISTRATION NUMBERS

A popular game amongst boys (and some quite intelligent adults, too) is to collect the registration numbers of motor-cars, buses or railway engines. Eagerly they search for the next one in the "series." Do they ever stop to consider how many there are and how long it may take them to collect the complete "set"?

When motor-cars were few, the allocation of identity numbers was a comparatively simple matter, but with vehicles now running into millions the problem becomes more complicated. A registration "number" normally consists of certain letters combined with a number of figures. Obviously one of the simplest methods of registration would be to use one letter only followed by a single figure: A 1, B 9, Z 3, and so on. Each letter of the alphabet could be followed

379

by any of the numbers 1, 2 . . . 9 and, following the same reasoning as before, 26 × 9 or 234 cars could be licensed. In a similar manner, using one letter and up to two figures the series for each letter of the alphabet would be from 1 to 99, and you can perhaps confirm that 2,574 cars could be registered. Using one letter and up to three figures would allow the numbers 1 to 999 to follow each letter of the alphabet and so produce more than 25,000 combinations.

Two systems of registration in current use consist of a pair of letters followed by four figures, and three letters followed by up to three figures. How many vehicles can be licensed in each case? Look at the number plate in Fig. 3. The first letter can be any one of 26, and the second letter can also be any one of 26, since letters can be repeated. There will therefore be 26 × 26 or 26^2 pairs of letters. Each pair can be followed by all the numbers from 1 to 9999. The total number of registrations in this series may therefore be 6,759,324.

FIG. 3. *Vehicle registration number formed from two letters and up to four figures. How many registrations are possible with this system?*

Nevertheless, it seems that the series became inadequate long ago, for the three-letter registrations are now even more common. How many three-letter combinations are possible? Now combine with each of them a number between 1 and 999 and what do you get? It might be well to check the size of your number by the mental approximation $(25)^3 × 1,000 = 15,625,000$, which of course will be appreciably less than the correct answer.

If the collectors of registration numbers thought about all this they would probably not be dismayed, because they are not so greedy as to want to bag the whole lot. Assuming that all the two-letter and three-letter combinations are now in use, how many different registration patterns are there of which the number part is 1? We make it 18,252. And how many 999s are possible? (a very easy one), and how many 1000s? What a hobby! Fig. 4 illustrates how all the letters and numbers can be combined in a number plate containing three letters followed by the figures 1 to 999.

In 1953 a new chapter in the history of car number plates was opened with the appearance on the roads of cars bearing four figures followed by a single letter—1234 A, and so on. This need had arisen

380

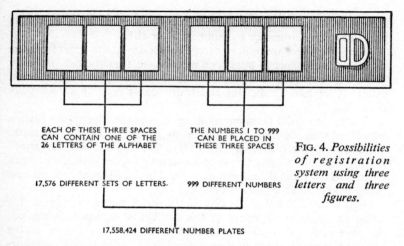

EACH OF THESE THREE SPACES CAN CONTAIN ONE OF THE 26 LETTERS OF THE ALPHABET

THE NUMBERS 1 TO 999 CAN BE PLACED IN THESE THREE SPACES

17,576 DIFFERENT SETS OF LETTERS.

999 DIFFERENT NUMBERS

17,558,424 DIFFERENT NUMBER PLATES

FIG. 4. *Possibilities of registration system using three letters and three figures.*

because of the vastly increased number of vehicles and the exhaustion of the three-letter series allotted to some areas. Although some registration authorities will not exhaust their three-letter combinations for some years, the new system will slowly spread throughout the country. Can you discover how many vehicles can be licensed under this new system, using up to four figures and every letter of the alphabet?

Sometimes motorists seek to secure for themselves a particular letter combination and number. Most famous of these numbers is of course A 1, the first registration ever in the London area. Originally it belonged to the late Earl Russell but in due course it was handed over to the L.C.C. and was the registration number of the car used by the Chairman of the Council. A private motorist bought the old car from the L.C.C. and, realizing the distinction of the unusual number, he paid a fee for the transfer of the number every time he got a new car. Low numbers of any combination are generally prized and in some cases are allocated to people of distinction. For instance, the Lord Mayor of Leeds traditionally uses No. 1 of a series. Originally, when U was the letter for Leeds, he had U 1. Today the number is MUM 1!

If you want a particular registration number the only way to get it is to discover the authority who will issue it in due course and stake a claim well in advance or, if it has already been issued, find the person who owns it and buy his car. Many famous people have obtained appropriate numbers: the Western Brothers have CAD 1, and Harry Tate, famous for his motor-car sketches, had T 8. A few combinations are not regarded as suitable and will not be used at all. There is, as you will realize, romance in numbers after all!

Serial numbers are used so extensively today, quite apart from the registration numbers of buses and motor-cars, that you can probably find a dozen or so about your person—keys, membership cards and tickets of various kinds. Bus and train tickets provide an everyday example.

They often differ from car numbers in that the four spaces for the figures usually contain a figure even if this is 0—for example, AA 0000, AA 0007. Does the use of 0 in this way increase the series? How many tickets using two letters and four figures (including 0) can be printed? If these tickets can be printed in six different colours how many tickets will there be altogether?

It is easy to see that the size of the series is greatly increased if either the number of letters or the number of figures is increased. Suppose you had to allot a serial number to every person in the United Kingdom, using only digits or letters, what number of characters in the pattern is the least that would suffice? And how many for the whole world? Not so many after all!

THE FOOTBALL RESULTS

Tossing coins or rolling dice leads us naturally to that popular pastime of forecasting the results of football matches for the Football Pools. Careful study is made not only of the form of the teams but of the ways in which systematic entries can increase the chances of success. The terms "permutations" and "combinations" are used frequently and often inaccurately in books and newspaper articles. Undoubtedly thousands of "investors" in the Pools make systematic entries without any knowledge or understanding of the principles on which they are based.

Forecasting the result of a number of football matches provides a further illustration of the principle suggested by the examples so far considered—that if one event can occur in *m* ways and a second

More Car Numbers

In Diatonica the alphabet runs from A to G. The Diatonicans have digits 1 to 7 only and use 0 just as we do. In the district of Melodia the car registration letters are FA followed by four digits or fewer, as in this country. How many cars can be registered? Your answer should be written (a) in the style that would be understood by a Diatonican, (b) in our style. *Solution on page 444* independent event can occur in *n* ways, then the two events can occur simultaneously or in succession in $m \times n$ ways.

It is obvious that since any single match must end in a home win, an away win or a draw, the correct result can be obtained with certainty in three guesses. If there are two matches to forecast then each can end in one of three results, and since these results are quite independent of each other there will be 3^2 possible ways in which the results can be combined:

| Arsenal *v.* Tottenham | 1 1 1 | 2 2 2 | X X X |
| Aston Villa *v.* Blackpool | 1 2 X | 1 2 X | 1 2 X |

9 possible pairs of results
(1 = home win; 2 = away win; X = draw)

The correct pair of results is certainly included in the nine forecasts.

Addition of a third match will increase the possibilities to 3^3, since each of the nine forecasts for two matches can be associated with a home win, an away win or a draw for the third game.

Arsenal *v.* Tottenham	111 111 1 1 1	222 222 2 2 2	XXXXXXXXX
Aston Villa *v.* Blackpool	111 222 XXX	111 222 XXX	1 1 1 2 2 2 XXX
Newcastle *v.* Sunderland	12X12X 12 X	12X12X 12 X	1 2 X 12 X 12 X

27 ways of forecasting 3 matches

Ten matches can thus be forecast in $3 \times 3 \times 3 \ldots$ (10 times) ways or 3^{10}—a very large number! In order to be certain of having the correct combination of results in a list of 14 matches the number of entries would have to be 3^4 times as great. This amounts to 4,782,969 forecasts, which, at one penny per attempt, would cost nearly £20,000 and would hardly turn out to be a profitable investment!

Whether it be tossing coins, rolling dice, forming registration numbers from letters and figures, or forecasting the results of football matches, the principle involved is the same—if one event can happen in a certain number of ways, a second independent event in a certain number of ways, then the number of ways they can happen simultaneously or in succession is found by multiplying together the number of ways they can occur separately.

WHAT IS A PERMUTATION?

We referred earlier to the frequent misuse of the terms "permutation" and "combination" in newspaper and magazine articles on football-pool systems. For example, in a pool which requires a forecaster to select any three matches which will each end in a draw it is common to find systems which first advocate choosing seven likely matches and then combining these in all possible groups of three. The investor then writes, quite incorrectly: "Permute any 3 matches from 7"; the total number of such combinations of three is 35. What, then, is a permutation?

Let us turn for an answer to the sport of greyhound racing, in which a number of greyhounds chase a mechanical hare round a circular track. The number of dogs in a given race is usually, though not always, six and they are automatically released from a series of traps numbered 1 to 6 set across the track at right-angles, with No. 1 on the inside. Supposing that all the dogs complete the course, in how many ways can they cross the finishing line? Obviously the race can be won by any one of the six dogs, the second place can be filled by any one of the remaining five, the third place by any one of the other four, and so on. Thus, the race can be won in six ways, the first two places can be filled in 6×5 or 30 ways, the first three places in $6 \times 5 \times 4$ or 120 ways, and all six places in $6 \times 5 \times 4 \times 3 \times 2 \times 1$ or 720 ways. This, then, is the answer to our question: the six dogs can cross the finishing line in 720 different ways.

Clearly this is only the problem of arranging six different things (in this case dogs) in every possible way. One of the "attractions" offered to supporters of greyhound racing, many of whom are interested only in gambling, is the possibility of forecasting in the right order the first two dogs to finish in any particular race. We have already seen that the first two places can be filled in thirty different ways. As it is usual to have a 2s. forecast ticket, the expenditure of £3 would ensure success in every race! What, then, is the snag? Like all gambling systems this offers no opportunity of easy riches, since the average winning amount paid for each race correctly forecast will certainly fall below £3.

In horse racing, in which the number of runners is normally much larger than six, the number of ways in which the field can finish rapidly increases. You may like to confirm that in a Grand National with thirty-six runners the first two places can be filled in 1,260 ways, and if all complete the course, which is most unlikely, they can cross the finishing line in $36 \times 35 \times 34 \ldots \times 3 \times 2 \times 1$ ways. Our greyhound example really illustrated the basic ideas of permutation, which is simply the number of ways in which some or all of a given number of things can be arranged. All six dogs can be arranged in 720 ways, any two of them in 30 ways, any three in 120 ways, and so on.

Another example may help to clarify the idea. Take the four aces from a pack of playing cards and set them out in a line on the table.

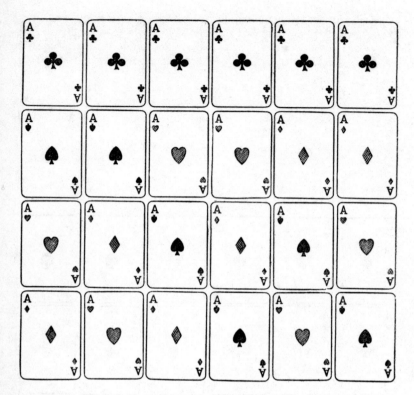

FIG. 5. *Six arrangements of the four aces, with Clubs in the first position. The arrangements can be repeated with each of the other aces in first place.*

In how many different ways can they be arranged? The best method of doing this "experimentally" is to place any one of the four aces in the first position and then make all possible arrangements of the other three alongside it. Since the ace in the first position can be any one of four, the final total will be four times the number of arrangements of the other three. Or, more simply, we can say that the first place can be filled in four ways, the second in three ways, the third in two ways and the final position in one way. All possible arrangements will therefore total twenty-four. Did you get this? Six of these arrangements are illustrated in Fig. 5; the remainder can easily be obtained by putting each of the aces in turn in the first position.

In how many ways can a crew of eight oarsmen fill the places in a racing boat if each of them can row in any position either on the

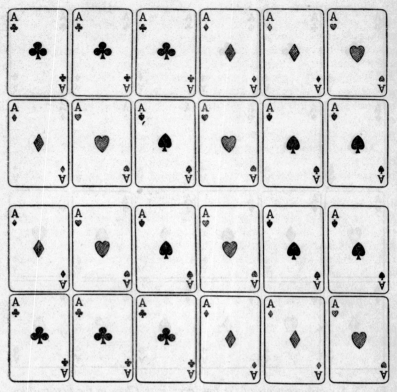

FIG. 6. *All the possible arrangements obtainable with pairs of aces.*

stroke or bow side? Stroke can be any one of eight, the second position can be filled by any one of seven, and so on. Total possible arrangements will be $8 \times 7 \times 6 \times 5 \times 4 \times 3 \times 2 \times 1$—a very large number, you will agree.

Similarly, a football team could arrange itself to fill all positions on the field in $11 \times 10 \times 9 \ldots \times 1$ ways, though this is most unlikely since every player tends to become a specialist in his own position.

These continuous products formed by multiplying any number by every smaller whole number down to unity are known as factorials and are usually written in short as $n!$ or $\lfloor n$. Thus, the six greyhounds can be arranged in 6! (factorial six) ways, the four aces in 4! ways, the racing crew in 8! ways, the football team in 11! ways, and so on.

386

Mathematicians like to generalize their results whenever possible, and it is fairly easy to discover that n different objects, where n is any number, can be arranged in $n!$ ways. For imagine n boxes in a row into each of which one of the n objects is to be placed. The first box can be filled in n different ways and when this is done there remain $n - 1$ objects for the second box. Having filled these two there will be $n - 2$ objects for the third box, and so on until finally one object remains for the last box. It is therefore possible to fill the n boxes in $n(n - 1)(n - 2) \ldots 3 \times 2 \times 1$ different ways. This is $n!$ by our previous definition of a factorial.

The number of arrangements of the cards in a pack of playing cards will be 52! Just consider what a fantastic number this is and how remote are the chances of getting thirteen of a single suit!

When only some, and not all, of the different objects are to be arranged, the total number of arrangements will obviously be smaller. For example, in our previous example from greyhound racing any two of the six dogs could be arranged in 6×5 or 30 ways, compared with a total of 720 different arrangements of all six. Similarly, the number of ways of selecting and arranging any two aces from the four will be 4×3 or 12, compared with the 24 arrangements for all four aces (Fig. 6).

In how many ways can we arrange any three of the five letters a, b, c, d, e? This implies that we must first choose all possible groups of three letters from the given five and then arrange each group of three in every possible way. We might put it another way by asking how many different arrangements of three things can be made from five things. It is like filling three boxes each with a single object when there are five objects to choose from. Any one of the five letters can fill the first place (or box), and then any one of the remaining four can fill the second place and so for the third place. Total number of possible arrangements is therefore $5 \times 4 \times 3$ or 60 (Fig. 7). In these arrangements, a, b, c is different from a, c, b and b, a, c, since we are concerned here with the arrangements of the letters and not merely with the selection of any group of three letters irrespective of order.

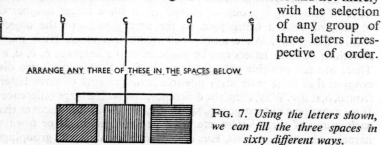

ARRANGE ANY THREE OF THESE IN THE SPACES BELOW

FIG. 7. *Using the letters shown, we can fill the three spaces in sixty different ways.*

All the examples considered so far illustrate the idea of permutation—that is, the number of possible arrangements of all or some of a number of different objects. It is laborious to write in full such statements as "The number of different arrangements of three objects which can be made from six different objects." Mathematics has a shorthand for it. It is $^6P_3$. P stands for permutation, 6 is the total number of objects, and 3 the number of objects which are to be arranged. You will realize that this is the problem of finding the number of ways in which the first three can be placed in a race with six runners. The value of $^6P_3$ is $6 \times 5 \times 4$, or 120. Similarly, the number of arrangements of two aces from the usual four is $^4P_2$ and the number of arrangements of three letters from five is $^5P_3$. Try to find the value of $^7P_4$ and $^{10}P_5$. What meaning can be assigned to $^6P_6$ or ^nP_n?

Let us try as before to generalize the result. In how many ways can we arrange any n different objects taking any number, say r, of them at a time? Imagine r boxes or compartments each to contain one object from the original n. The first box can be filled in n ways, leaving $n - 1$ objects to select from for the second box. There are $n - 2$ possibilities for the third box when the first two have been filled. Continuing this arrangement for each of the r boxes we find that the last box can be filled in $(n - r + 1)$ ways. The total number of all possible arrangements of r objects from the original n objects is therefore $n(n - 1)(n - 2) \ldots (n - r + 1)$, or ^nP_r. This expression is not, of course, the same as the factorial mentioned earlier, since it consists only of the multiplication of r successive numbers starting from n and does not, unless n and r should be the same number, go down as far as unity.

THE IDEA OF COMBINATION

So far we have considered arrangements or permutations of all or some of a number of different objects. What then is a combination? Let us say at once that a combination is merely the number of ways of choosing a group of objects from some larger number of objects, no regard being paid to the arrangement of the objects within the group. An example will make this clear. How many selections of three letters can be made from the letters a, b, c, d, e? There are ten possible groups shown in Fig. 8. Previously we discovered that there were sixty possible arrangements of three letters from a, b, c, d, e. Why, then, the difference, and such a large difference? If we examine a chosen group, say a, c, e, we shall soon discover that each group of three letters can itself be arranged in 3! or 6 ways, namely $ace, aec, cae, cea, eac, eca$. Hence ten different groupings,

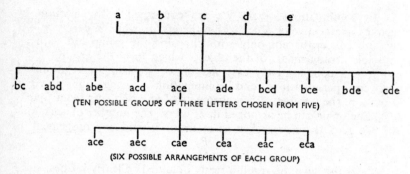

(TEN POSSIBLE GROUPS OF THREE LETTERS CHOSEN FROM FIVE)

(SIX POSSIBLE ARRANGEMENTS OF EACH GROUP)

FIG. 8. *Ten groups of three letters may be chosen from five letters, but there are sixty arrangements of three letters in all.*

each of which is capable of being arranged in six ways, produce a total of sixty arrangements and this agrees with our earlier results.

The diagram below (Fig. 9) illustrates the six ways in which two objects can be chosen from four different objects. There will be six pairs only, since when we select the objects A and B it does not matter whether we choose A first and then B, or vice versa, for A and B together in any order will only constitute one pair. In an earlier problem we saw that there were twelve ways of arranging any two aces from four aces. Common sense suggests that this agrees with our present result, since if there are six pairs, each of which can be arranged in two ways by interchanging the objects, then there will be twelve possible arrangements in all.

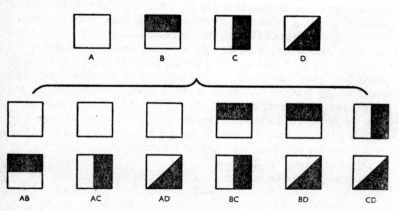

FIG. 9. *From four different objects there are six possible pairs.*

389

In combinations, then, we are concerned with selection of groups irrespective of order within the group, while in permutations we are concerned not only with choosing the group but with all possible arrangements of the objects which form the group.

It is a comparatively easy matter to establish the relationship between permutations and combinations. Using our previous notation, the number of arrangements of any two aces from four is $^4P_2$. Each pair can be arranged in 2! ways. The number of selections of two aces, therefore, when no attention is paid to arrangement, is

$$\frac{^4P_2}{2!}$$

Does this give the result already obtained? Clearly it does, since $^4P_2$ is 4×3 and 2! is 2×1, and hence

$$\frac{^4P_2}{2!} = \frac{4 \times 3}{2 \times 1} = 6.$$

The number of ways in which two objects can be selected from four objects is written $^4C_2$, where C stands for combination (or choice), 4 is the total number of objects and the suffix 2 indicates the number of objects to be selected. Thus, $^7C_3$ stands for the number of ways in which any three things can be chosen from seven different things. Now the number of arrangements of three from seven is $^7P_3$, or $7 \times 6 \times 5$. Each group of three when selected can be arranged in 3! ways. The number of groups is therefore $\frac{^7P_3}{3!}$ and this is $^7C_3$.

$$^7C_3 = \frac{^7P_3}{3!} = \frac{7 \times 6 \times 5}{3 \times 2 \times 1} = 35.$$

Notice that the number of arrangements of any three objects from seven different objects is 210 ($7 \times 6 \times 5$), while the number of ways of selecting groups of three is only 35. You will now realize that the football-pool forecaster often refers to permutations when he really means combinations. In selecting seven matches for the Three Draws Pool and covering for all possible groups of three in thirty-five lines, he is making practical use of combinations. The order of the matches within each group is of no consequence; the results for matches A, B, and C will be the same in whatever order they are given. The instruction therefore to "permute any 3 from 7" is strictly speaking quite incorrect, though no doubt its use is so well established by practice that it causes no confusion to those responsible for checking the coupon!

Let us generalize our results by deriving an expression for the number of ways in which r objects can be chosen from a total of n different objects. It has already been shown that there are $n(n-1)$ $(n-2)\ldots(n-r+1)$ arrangements of r objects taken from n

390

objects. Each group of r objects can be arranged in $r!$ ways. If ^nC_r represents the number of groups, then the total possible arrangements of all groups will be $^nC_r \times r!$ Thus,

$$^nC_r \times r! = n(n-1)(n-2)\ldots(n-r+1)$$
$$\text{or } ^nC_r = \frac{n(n-1)(n-2)\ldots(n-r+1)}{r!}$$

This result can be written in a slightly different form. Notice that the last factor at the top is $(n-r+1)$. The next, if the series were continued, would be $n-r$, and so on. Multiply the top of the fraction by $(n-r)(n-r-1)(n-r-2)\ldots3\times2\times1$ and, of course, in order to compensate for this, introduce the same quantity also into the denominator. Then

$$^nC_r = \frac{n(n-1)(n-2)\ldots(n-r+1)}{r!} \times$$
$$\frac{(n-r)(n-r-1)\ldots3\times2\times1}{(n-r)(n-r-1)\ldots3\times2\times1}$$

The numerator is now $n!$ and the denominator is $r! \times (n-r)!$

$$\text{Hence } ^nC_r = \frac{n!}{r!\,n-r!}$$

We will use the result to calculate $^{10}C_6$. Here $n = 10$ and $r = 6$, so that $n - r = 4$.

$$\text{Therefore } ^{10}C_6 = \frac{10!}{6!\,4!}$$

$$= \frac{10 \times 9 \times 8 \times 7 \times 6 \times 5 \times 4 \times 3 \times 2 \times 1}{6 \times 5 \times 4 \times 3 \times 2 \times 1 \times 4 \times 3 \times 2 \times 1}$$
$$= 210$$

$$\text{Otherwise } ^{10}C_6 = \frac{10 \times 9 \times 8 \times 7 \times 6 \times 5}{6 \times 5 \times 4 \times 3 \times 2 \times 1} \text{ (6 terms)}$$
$$= 210$$

A useful result follows from what has already been said, but an example will serve to illustrate it. In how many ways can a team of

The Hymn Board

New number plates are required for a church hymn board. The board has spaces for four hymn numbers and the book in use contains 700 hymns. In working out the number of plates required, the vicar thriftily decides that the plates for the figure 6 can be inverted to serve for the figure 9. What is the least number of plates he has to buy?

Solution on page 444

eleven players be selected from the fourteen players who are available?

The answer is $^{14}C_{11}$, or $\dfrac{14 \times 13 \times 12 \times 11 \ldots \text{(11 terms)}}{11!}$. But

there is a shorter calculation than this. Each time we select eleven players we automatically reject three players. The problem then is the same as selecting (or rejecting) three players from the fourteen available. It follows therefore that $^{14}C_{11} = {}^{14}C_3$. The calculations below show that this is true.

$$^{14}C_{11} = \frac{14 \times 13 \times 12 \times \cancel{11} \times \cancel{10} \times \cancel{9} \times \cancel{8} \times \cancel{7} \times \cancel{6} \times \cancel{5} \times \cancel{4}}{\cancel{11} \times \cancel{10} \times \cancel{9} \times \cancel{8} \times \cancel{7} \times \cancel{6} \times \cancel{5} \times \cancel{4} \times 3 \times 2 \times 1}$$

$$= \frac{14 \times 13 \times 12}{3 \times 2 \times 1}$$

$$^{14}C_3 = \frac{14 \times 13 \times 12}{3 \times 2 \times 1} \text{ (3 terms)}$$

Generalizing this result, we see that each time we select a group of r things from n different things we are in effect rejecting the remaining $n - r$ things. From this it readily follows that

$$^{n}C_r = {}^{n}C_{n-r}$$

This result is very useful in shortening calculations; in the example above it is easier and quicker to find $^{14}C_3$ rather than $^{14}C_{11}$, and numerically they give the same answer.

EXAMPLES OF PERMUTATIONS AND COMBINATIONS

Let us now apply the knowledge we have so far gained of permutations and combinations to some examples:

A football club has only eighteen full-time professional players on its books, consisting of two goalkeepers, three full backs, five half backs and eight forwards. In how many ways can the team of eleven players be selected if players are chosen only for that section of the team in which they are specialists—that is, forwards are chosen only for the forward line, and so on?

The goalkeeper can be chosen in two ways; the two full backs can be chosen in $^{3}C_2$ ways; the three half backs in $^{5}C_3$ ways and the five forwards in $^{8}C_5$ ways. Since all these selections are independent of each other, the total number of ways in which the team can be picked will be $2 \times {}^{3}C_2 \times {}^{5}C_3 \times {}^{8}C_5$, which you can easily work out. We found the answer to be 3,360.

Each of these teams will contain different personnel. If in addition we regard it as a slightly different team each time the forwards or half backs or full backs are rearranged, this number will be greatly increased. Five forwards can be arranged in 5! ways, three half backs in 3! and two full backs in 2! ways. Counting an arrangement as a new team we should need to multiply the result above by 5! × 3! × 2! or 1,440. A staggering result, is it not? And yet managers of football teams with only eighteen players to call upon would no doubt consider themselves very limited in their choice! It is, after all, the quality of the players for each position which counts.

No doubt our Test team selectors feel that an appropriate team is one which contains six batsmen, a wicket-keeper and four bowlers. How many different teams could they select if they had under consideration ten batsmen, three wicket-keepers and six bowlers?

You should confirm that the answer is $^{10}C_6 \times {}^3C_1 \times {}^6C_4$ and that this produces 9,450 different teams. Of course, in actual practice due regard would have to be paid to the batting order and to the variety and pace of the bowlers, so that the actual choice would be much more restricted than this figure suggests.

The game of snooker is played with fifteen red balls, a black, a pink, a blue, a brown, a green, a yellow and a white ball which is the cue ball. Apart from the reds, which form a triangle at the top of the table, each of the other coloured balls must be placed on its own appointed spot on the table. If a novice is playing who is not certain where the colours go, in how many ways can he place the coloured balls on the six spots provided?

You should consider first whether this problem is concerned with selection or arrangement. Clearly it is a matter of arrangement, since there are six spots on which the six coloured balls have to be placed. Each interchange of balls will be a different arrangement. It is therefore a matter of permutation. Total number of ways will be 6! or 720 different arrangements, and of these only one will conform to the rules of the game!

In a racing crew of eight men the stroke has been chosen but the coach continues to experiment with the seating of the other seven. If the bow-side oarsmen row only on their own side and the stroke-side oarsmen on theirs in how many ways can the crew be arranged? The three remaining stroke-side men can be seated in 3! ways, the bow-side men in 4! ways. Total number of ways in which the crew can be arranged is 3! × 4! or 144. Compare this with the result obtained earlier, when all eight oarsmen could row in any position.

SIMPLE CHANCES AT BRIDGE

Let us consider an example for card players. How many different hands can be held by four men playing bridge or whist (thirteen cards each)?

The first player can receive his cards in $^{52}C_{13}$ ways, the second in $^{39}C_{13}$ ways, the third in $^{26}C_{13}$ ways and the last player in $^{13}C_{13}$ ways.

Total number of hands is therefore: $^{52}C_{13} \times {}^{39}C_{13} \times {}^{26}C_{13} \times {}^{13}C_{13}$

$$= \frac{52 \times 51 \times 50 \ldots 40}{13!} \times \frac{39 \times 38 \ldots 27}{13!} \times \frac{26 \times 25 \ldots 14}{13!}$$

$$\times \frac{13 \times 12 \ldots 1}{13!} = \frac{52!}{13! \; 13! \; 13! \; 13!} = \frac{52!}{(13!)^4}$$

Regard has been paid here to the order in which the hands have been placed on the table. If, however, we are concerned only with dividing a pack of fifty-two cards into a row of four heaps of thirteen cards each, then the order of the heaps is of no consequence. The four heaps can be arranged among themselves in 4! ways. In card playing, however, the four heaps are always arranged to form a ring. The number of different arrangements of four heaps in a ring is of course less than 4! Do you agree that it will be $\dfrac{4!}{4}$?

In the distribution above for card playing, each arrangement of the four heaps is rightly regarded as different since the hand will fall to a different player. The number of ways of dividing the pack into four heaps forming a ring irrespective of order will be

$$\frac{52!}{(13!)^4} \div \frac{4!}{4}.$$

You will agree that the number of possible hands is very large indeed. The chances of holding thirteen cards of the same suit are extremely small and when it occurs it is regarded as very remarkable. It is remarkable in the sense that it is rare, but it is no more remarkable than that you should obtain any hand you care to nominate beforehand. Write down the names of thirteen cards, both suit and denomination. The odds against your holding such a hand are 635,013,559,599 to 1 and these are precisely the odds against your holding thirteen spades!

A hand in bridge that contains no card above a nine is called a Yarborough, after a certain noble Lord who once had the habit of offering bets of 1,000 to 1 against such hands occurring. The chances

Who Married Whom?

Under the terms of a will six separate bequests, totalling £1,000, are made to three husbands and their three wives. The wives receive altogether £396, of which Maud gets £10 more than Mabel, and Martha gets £10 more than Maud. Of the husbands, Bill Brown gets twice as much as his wife, Henry Hobson gets the same as his wife, while John Jones gets 50 per cent more than his wife. What are the full names of the three wives?

Solution on page 444

of holding such a hand are easily calculated. There are thirty-two cards in the pack below the tens from which the Yarborough must be selected. In any deal the chance that the first card will be one of these thirty-two is $\frac{32}{52}$, and the chance that the second card is then also below ten is $\frac{31}{51}$, and so on. The chance that all thirteen will be favourable is $\frac{32 \times 31 \times 30 \ldots 20}{52 \times 51 \times 50 \ldots 40}$, which works out to $\frac{1}{1,828}$. The odds against such a hand occurring are therefore more than 1,800 to 1, and Lord Yarborough was playing safe when he offered only 1,000 to 1. In the long run the odds were in his favour.

There is another way to approach the problem of the Yarborough. The number of ways of choosing any thirteen cards from the pack is $^{52}C_{13}$. If all cards above the nine are removed the number of ways of choosing thirteen cards from the remainder is $^{32}C_{13}$, and all these hands will be Yarboroughs. The chances of a Yarborough occurring are thus $^{32}C_{13}$ in $^{52}C_{13}$ cases, or 1 in 1,828 as above. You should check this calculation for yourself. Calculate for yourself also the chances of holding a hand with no "face" cards—that is, no Aces, Kings, Queens or Jacks.

In the game of poker each player receives five cards. How many different poker hands are possible? The answer is 2,598,960. Can you obtain this figure?

The game of bridge, although demanding a high degree of skill from the players, presents some interesting examples of the working of chance. In fact, compared with the purely intellectual game of chess it is the part which chance plays in the distribution of the cards and the strength of the hands which is one of the attractive features of the game. Whole books have been written on the mathematical theory of bridge and no more than passing reference can be made here to some of the interesting problems the game presents. Most of the problems are best considered under the laws of probability, which are dealt with in another chapter, but in such problems we are constantly required to determine the number of favourable cases compared with the total number of possible cases and this usually involves the combination or permutation of a certain number of things taken so many at a time. It has been previously indicated how rare it is to hold thirteen of one suit or thirteen cards nominated beforehand. What is of greater interest to the player are his chances of holding a hand with a given distribution, say a six-card suit, a five-card suit, a doubleton and a void. This is the distribution 6, 5, 2, 0, where the cards may be in any suit.

Consider this example: What are the chances that a hand will contain a 4, 4, 3, 2 distribution?

The first four cards can be chosen in $^{13}C_4$ ways from any suit, the second four similarly in $^{13}C_4$ ways, the three in $^{13}C_3$ and the two in $^{13}C_2$ ways. The total number of ways in which the hand of thirteen can be selected is $^{52}C_{13}$. We must remember also that the 4, 4, 3, 2 distribution can be regarded as four different objects to be arranged in every possible way, two of the objects—the 4, 4 suits—being similar. The number of possible arrangements is $\frac{4!}{2!}$, or 12. The chances therefore of the required distribution are $^{13}C_4 \times {}^{13}C_4 \times {}^{13}C_3 \times {}^{13}C_2 \times 12$ in $^{52}C_{13}$.

This somewhat large calculation works out to ·2155, or a chance slightly better than 1 in 5. Another way of looking at this would be to say that in any 10,000 hands the theoretical frequency of the 4, 4, 3, 2 distribution is 2,155. Using the above method, you may like to calculate some other frequencies of distribution for yourself. Some of the figures you should obtain are shown in Fig. 10. The chances of holding unusual distributions like 9, 4, 0, 0 or 10, 1, 1, 1, are small indeed, as you can easily confirm for yourself.

Distribution of suits	Frequency in 10,000 hands	Distribution of suits	Frequency in 10,000 hands
4,4,4,1	299	6,6,1,0	7
4,4,3,2	2,155	6,5,2,0	65
4,3,3,3	1,054	6,5,1,1	71
5,5,3,0	90	7,6,0,0	1
5,5,2,1	317	7,5,1,0	11
5,4,3,1	1,293	7,4,2,0	36

FIG. 10. *Frequency with which certain suit distributions are likely to occur in ten thousand bridge hands. Other distributions may be similarly calculated.*

Other simple chances at bridge are of interest to the players. If, for example, the caller and his dummy hold nine of a suit between them, including the Ace and King but not the Queen, what are the chances that the Queen will fall if both the Ace and King are led? Clearly this is the same problem as determining what are the chances of the remaining four cards being equally divided in the opponents' hands or the Queen being singleton in one of them.

Suppose one player A holds all four of the suit and his partner B none. Now A and B share 26 cards between them and the possible number of ways of selecting A's hand is $^{26}C_{13}$. As A already holds four of the required suit his remaining cards can be chosen in $^{22}C_9$

ways. Hence the chances of A holding all four are $^{22}C_9$ in $^{26}C_{13}$.

$$\text{Chance} = \frac{22, 21, 20, 19, 18, 17, 16, 15, 14}{9!}$$

$$\times \frac{13!}{26 \times 25 \times 24 \times 23 \times 22 \dots 14}$$

$$= \frac{13 \times 12 \times 11 \times 10}{26 \times 25 \times 24 \times 23} = \frac{11}{230}$$

Similarly, the chances of A holding three cards and B holding one card, or of A holding two cards and B holding two cards, can be found to be $\frac{143}{575}$ and $\frac{239}{575}$ respectively. The results are set out in the following table.

A	B	Chances
4	0	$\frac{11}{230}$
0	4	$\frac{11}{230}$
3	1	$\frac{143}{575}$
1	3	$\frac{143}{575}$
2	2	$\frac{239}{575}$

On the face of it equal division of the cards appears most likely. We are not, however, concerned with how many cards each player holds but only with the way the cards are divided. For our purposes, A holding three and B holding one will produce the same result as A holding one and B holding three.

The table of chances can then be rewritten as:

Distribution	Chances
4 and 0	$\frac{11}{230}$
3 and 1	$\frac{286}{575}$
2 and 2	$\frac{239}{575}$

The most probable distribution is therefore three cards in one hand and one card in the other. If the Ace and King are led the Queen will fall either if the distribution is two and two or if the distribution is three and one, provided the single card is the Queen. Now the single card may be any one of four and the chances of its being so are 1 in 4, or $\frac{1}{4}$. In the three-and-one distribution, therefore, the Queen will occur alone in $\frac{1}{4}$ of the possible cases. The chances of this happening are $\frac{1}{4}$ of $\frac{286}{575}$, or $\frac{286}{2,300}$.

From our results we see that in 286 cases out of 2,300 the cards are divided three and one, with the Queen as the singleton, and that in 936 cases out of 2,300 (that is, 239 out of 575) the cards are divided two and two. In 1,222 cases the Queen will fall on the successive lead of the Ace and King and in 1,078 cases it will not. The odds on the Queen falling are thus 1·13 to 1, or better than an even chance. Hence it will pay to lead the Ace and King if the Queen and three other cards are in the opponents' hands.

You will see that the mathematics involved in these calculations is purely arithmetical provided the ideas underlying permutations and combinations and probability are understood.

FAITES VOS JEUX!

One of the most popular gambling games in the world is roulette, though it is illegal in this country. In essence it is closely akin to the simple game of "heads and tails," since most of the betting takes place on approximately equal chances.

Roulette is played, as everyone knows, with a wheel which spins rapidly and a small ball or marble which finally comes to rest in one of the numbered compartments round the edge of the rotating wheel. In official casinos such as those at Monte Carlo, every effort is made to ensure that the wheel is mechanically perfect so that the game can be played under the fairest possible conditions. On the Monte Carlo wheels (Fig. 11) there are thirty-seven compartments numbered from 0 to 36. Half these compartments are coloured red and the other half black. There are three forms of approximately even-chance betting on these wheels and these are independent of each other since the outcome of one does not affect that of the others. A gambler can bet that the ball will stop in either a red or black compartment (*rouge et noir*) or that it will fall into an even or odd compartment (*pair et impair*) or that it will finally come to rest in a compartment numbered 1 to 18 or 19 to 36 (*passe et manque*). In all such bets the number 0 is neither a win nor a loss. The amount won or lost is the amount staked. When the 0 turns up the stake is neither won nor lost but goes to "prison," as one part of the table is called, and remains there until some number other than 0 appears. If this number is favourable to the player his stake is returned, if it is unfavourable his stake is lost. On the "0" play, therefore, he has nearly a 1 in 2 chance of getting his money back but he has no further chance of winning.

Let us define "expectation" in gambling as the result of multiplying the chances that a player will win by the total amount of the stakes. If this is equal to the amount invested by the player, then the odds are fair to both sides. Consider what happens to a player who bets 100 francs on one of the even chances at roulette. Of the thirty-seven possible results, eighteen are favourable to him and his chances of winning 200 francs are $\frac{18}{37}$. He has 1 chance in 74 of regaining his

FIG. 11. *Roulette wheel of the type used in the Casino at Monte Carlo.*

stake of 100 francs by a 0 turning up followed by a favourable result. His total expectation, therefore, is $\frac{18}{37} \times 200 + \frac{1}{74} \times 100$, or 98·65 francs.

In the long run the player should lose 1·35 per cent of what he stakes and this small advantage to the bank is decisive. It is like playing a game of "heads and tails" in which the player gives the bank odds of 50·675 to 49·325. You may feel that the odds are heavily against the player but in actual fact the percentage of 1·35 at Monte Carlo is smaller than in many other countries. In America, for instance, some wheels have two zero compartments both of which represent outright losses to the player. You can easily calculate that in this case the advantage to the bank is 5·26 per cent.

Other forms of betting on a roulette wheel are on single numbers, in which case the player wins thirty-five times the amount staked, or on two adjacent numbers, when the gain is seventeen times the amount staked, and so on. It can be shown that in these cases his expectation for every 100 francs invested is 97·3 francs, so that there is ultimately a decisive advantage to the bank of 2·7 per cent. It appears that the casino is prepared to offer an inducement to the even-chance players by accepting a smaller profit. This may well be, because practically all systems are played on the even chances.

Most players who gamble on the even chances at roulette believe that by following some particular method or system they will win in the long run. A very large number of systems have been invented for players on the even chances. One of the best known of these is called the Martingale, which is really an application of "double or quits" to roulette. The player begins by investing the minimum stake on one of the even chances. If he wins he again places the minimum stake, but if he loses he doubles the stake, and so on. In short, the stake is doubled after every loss and reverts to the minimum stake after every win. Provided the player has sufficient capital to continue redoubling in the face of a long unfavourable run, then he will win the unit stake for every win in the series.

Try this experiment for yourself by tossing a penny a hundred times and using an imaginary £1 as your unit stake. If you bet always on heads and there are 57 heads including the last of all, in the hundred tosses you will find yourself an imaginary £57 in pocket! If a player were assured that he would never lose enough times to be forced to discontinue doubling, the Martingale would be a profitable investment. Apart, however, from the strain on his resources there is a further restriction placed on him by the bank, which limits the bets which can be placed to certain minimum and maximum amounts. These restrictions have important consequences for the gambler as well as the bank. Before the War, for instance, in the outer rooms at Monte Carlo the minimum stake was 10 francs and the maximum 12,000 francs. A player using the Martingale system makes an initial bet of 10 francs and doubles the amount after each loss. Successive bets will be 10, 20, 40, 80, 160, 320, 640, 1,280, 2,560, 5,120, 10,240, and the initial bet can be doubled ten times before the maximum is reached. The maximum total losses at this stage are 20,470 francs and he now has to revert to the minimum stake if the system is to be maintained. Had the minimum stake been 1 franc instead of 10 francs the player could double three additional times, making thirteen in all. Check this for yourself and confirm that his total losses would then be 16,383 francs.

Even assuming the bank places no limit on the maximum bet, the player's resources are necessarily limited and if he continues playing

How Many Fence Posts?

With his stock of fence posts Farmer Brown found he could make a simple square enclosure, or two adjoining squares of equal size, or three adjoining squares of equal size. The distance between the posts had to be the same in every case. What is the least number of fence posts he could have had?

Solution on page 444

400

long enough he is bound to encounter an adverse run long enough to bankrupt him. If, however, he ends his play only after a win, he is bound to be in pocket. Normally—that is, with the limitations imposed by maximum and minimum stakes—the bank must win in the long run; it places a limit on the size of bet only to restrict the inevitable fluctuations in its profits and losses and to guard against the strain on its resources which an unprecedented run of luck on the part of several players might produce.

There are many variations of the Martingale system, all essentially alike; they consist of a progression of stakes and rules as to how the progression shall take place. One system, called the Anti-Martingale, adopts the reverse process to the one we have been discussing. In this system the bet is doubled after each win and reverts to one unit after each loss.

These systems are mentioned here and some indication is given as to how they are played because they are all founded on a fallacy known as the maturity of chances. This can be illustrated by the toss in the Test matches during the 1953 series. The Australian captain called "heads" five times in succession and was successful each time. It might well be argued that having called heads successfully four times it would be wiser to call tails on the next occasion, since it is surely to be expected that a tail is due. Such is the argument of gamblers. They cannot be convinced that even if twenty heads appear in succession the chances that a head will appear on the next toss is still evens. In a long series of tosses we are just as likely to have as many runs of six heads followed by another head as of six heads followed by a tail.

Thus at roulette a gambler who watches a long succession of winning blacks is prepared to plunge on red appearing next despite the evidence of theory and experience which asserts that the chances still remain even. It is the proprietors of gambling establishments who put their full faith in experience and who never fail to establish the rules of play so that the odds of the game are in their favour! There are many other aspects of the mathematical theory of roulette which cannot be dealt with here. Like many interesting problems which arise in other games of chance and skill, such as poker and dice, the treatment belongs more appropriately to the realm of probability.

12

Mathematics for the Citizen

THE language of number, of quantity, measurement and comparison has become so much a part of our everyday life that we are hardly aware of it. When we speak of "fifty-fifty," for example, we do not realize that we assume a knowledge of percentages, 50 per cent being equal to $\frac{1}{2}$. The colloquial phrase "there's no percentage in it," meaning "it will do me no good," assumes that everybody knows that profit is measured in hundredth parts of turnover or costs, as the case may be.

A glance at a daily newspaper will show how important to the average citizen, irrespective of the requirements of his occupation, a knowledge of mathematics may be, if he wishes to understand what is going on around him. Here are some extracts, taken at random, from the day's news:

> Born the day before yesterday, the . . . triplets, weighing $4\frac{1}{2}$ lb., $4\frac{1}{4}$ lb. and 4 lb. respectively, landed here today with their 43-year-old mother.
>
> The 26,000-ton liner . . . has had her masts shortened by 40 ft. to get her safely under Quebec Bridge.
>
> About £400,000,000 was subscribed yesterday for the £10,000,000 of 5 per cent loan stock. . . . It is expected that nine-tenths will go to the 17,000 staff and 60,000 stockholders of the £94,000,000 company and £1,000,000 will be distributed by ballot to outside applicants.
>
> An invoice measuring 16 in. by 13 in. carrying only two lines of typing, and an account, 13 in. by 8 in., with one line, both for the same amount, were received from. . . .
>
> Britain has just lost £16,155,000 more in gold to Europe. This was paid to cover a deficit of £20,193,000 in the European Payments Union for April. The balance of just over £4,000,000 was met by increasing our overdraft, now more than £226,000,000.
>
> Sun rises 5.10, sets 9.01. Moon, 1.26 a.m., 8.53 a.m. Lights 10.01, 4.09. High water, 2.51, 3.23.

These are only a few items, taken from a single page of a typical daily paper. They show how much mathematical appreciation, or the understanding of mathematical ideas, is assumed by the writer, how much a few figures light up a dull statement, and how necessary it is for the intelligent reader to be aware of these ideas.

Consider some of these paragraphs. The weights of the triplets at once give you a picture of three very small babies and remind you of the progress of modern medicine and the checking of health by weight. Even the weight, the establishment of common standards which everybody can understand, involved a good deal of mathematical progress. The weighing of the liner, and the measurement of the invoice to point an argument about waste, are other consequences of this progress and its acceptance as part of the language.

The figures of income and expenditure, of distribution of stock, of gold payments, all show how much commerce and industry and economics are founded on mathematical considerations. Although we may not be able to do the calculations ourselves, we must at least be able to understand the significance of the results, if only to be able to read the newspaper intelligently.

Let us consider some of these problems, first as they affect the private individual, then as they affect the population as a whole.

LIVING WITHIN YOUR MEANS

One of the first mathematical problems that affects the individual is that of accounting for his own income. If we spend without planning and budgeting, we get frequent shocks. We should often be unable to buy anything costing more than a week's wages, unless we could persuade the shopkeeper to give us credit. Even so, we should soon get into difficulties, unless we made some estimate of how much we owed and allowed for it. The workman who was regularly spent out by Tuesday, and came for a "sub" on his next week's wages, is, fortunately, a thing of the past. Most people now have some idea of estimating expenditure in advance, and many people, especially in these days of rapid variations in the cost of living, keep household accounts.

A young man, having decided to marry, estimated how he would spend his annual income of £500. As a single man he had been comparatively well off; after paying his parents a modest weekly sum he had plenty left to spend as he felt inclined. Prudently, he made up his mind to be more systematic when it came to keeping a partner in a home of his own.

His first problem was to choose between forecasting his expenditure by the week, the month or the year. While many frequent and regular purchases must be made with cash, there would be bills for fuel, outlay on clothes, and so on, to be met intermittently. How would you have advised him?

It is simpler to forecast for the year than for the week or month because multiplication of the small weekly amounts is easier than

403

division of the larger annual sums. Division by 52 will produce awkward fractions.

This was his first estimate:

Receipts	£	Expenditure	£
Annual Income	500	Income Tax	40
		Rent	75
		Food	150
		Fuel, Light, etc.	30
		Clothes	100
		Balance	105
Total	£500	Total	£500

This was rather a shock, because the balance had to cover all the items he had not yet mentioned, such as personal expenses, both for his wife and himself, smoking, entertainment, and an annual holiday, which did not appear possible. He had hoped to buy furniture and even to save a little. It looked as though he must think again about marrying, or get a better job.

Let us examine these figures more closely. In terms of his weekly earnings of about £10, he spends $\frac{40}{500}$ or 16s. on tax, $\frac{75}{500}$ or £1 10s. on rent, £3 on food, £2 on clothes, 12s. on fuel and light, and has just over £2 each week left to spend on cigarettes, entertainment, furniture, holidays, and savings against a rainy day.

Of course these figures are only an estimate, for we should have had to divide by 52 in order to find the weekly figures. In fact, to be perfectly correct, we should have divided by $52\frac{1}{4}$, as this is the number of weeks in a year, and $52\frac{2}{7}$ for a leap year. The figure of £10 a week, which we have used in the estimate, would bring in £521 8s. 7d. in a normal year. Unless we watch very carefully, we may find ourselves overbudgeting.

We might have tried to avoid this by taking the weekly income more accurately as £9 12s. 4d., but the heavier calculation would not have been worth while, because most expenses cannot be foreseen and budgeted as closely as to the nearest penny, or even to the nearest shilling, over a whole year. That is one reason why it is better to estimate over a whole year.

The housewife who receives her housekeeping allowance monthly and pays her bills weekly is faced with a similar difficulty, because there are $4\frac{1}{3}$ weeks in a month. She has to allow for this by having one five-week month in three, or she would soon be in difficulties.

We may compare the estimate of income and expenditure given above with the figures of national expenditure issued as a summary

FIG. 1. *How the nation spends its money. The whole area of the drawing represents the total expenditure; the small rectangles represent the amounts spent on the items named.*

FOOD
24%

DRINK AND
TOBACCO
13%

RENT, RATES
AND FUEL
10%

CLOTHING
9%

OTHER GOODS
AND
SERVICES
28%

TAXES AND
NATIONAL
INSURANCE
15%

NATIONAL
SAVINGS
1%

just before the national Budget Day. The figures for a recent year show that, for the country as a whole, 24 per cent of personal income was spent on food, 13 per cent on drink and tobacco, 10 per cent on rent, rates and fuel, 9 per cent on clothing, 28 per cent on other goods and services, 15 per cent on taxes and national insurance contributions, and 1 per cent on savings (Fig. 1).

It would be interesting to compare the young man's budget with these figures. This we could do in two ways:

(1) Express the figures in this young man's estimate as percentages of his income and compare them with the national figures.

(2) Express the national figures as weekly payments out of an annual income of £500 and compare them with the figures in the estimate above. It will be sufficiently accurate to take fifty weeks in the year, as above, provided that we do not forget that we are doing so.

Here are the figures. Do you agree with them?

The estimate provided by the first method allows 8 per cent for tax, 15 per cent for rent, 30 per cent for food, 6 per

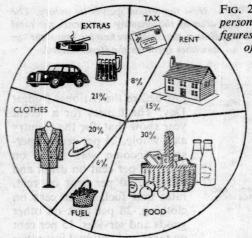

cent for fuel, 20 per cent for clothes, and a balance of 21 per cent for extras (Fig. 2). This shows that his estimate of 21 per cent for rent and fuel is rather high, being more than double the national figure. The same is true of the estimate for clothes. This is a very useful comparison, as it shows him where he must adjust his ideas. His tax estimate is lower than the national average, but this is only to be expected, as the larger-income groups pay at a much higher rate.

Turning now to the second method of comparison we arrive at the following weekly payments: Food £2 8s.; drink and tobacco, £1 6s.; rent, rates and fuel, £1; clothes, 18s.; other goods, £2 16s.; taxes, £1 10s.; savings, 2s.

Write down an estimate of your own expenditure, express it both as a percentage of total income and as a weekly payment under each heading, and compare it with the national figures to see how far they represent your own case.

This analysis of personal expenditure could be used to show how much the cost of living goes up from time to time. To do so we must analyse the figures further. The cost-of-living index is calculated by taking the estimated costs of an average family at one time as represented by 100 and expressing as a percentage of this the cost of the same budget at prices prevailing at another time.

There is a good deal of controversy about the index, because a budget which describes the needs of one family never quite does for another. We shall take our figures as referring to the young man and his wife alone, as he will obviously need to revise his estimates very severely when his family begins to arrive.

Let us suppose that the item of £2 8s. for food is made up as follows: Bread 3s., basic rations 5s., meat 2s. 4d., milk 7s., vegetables and fruit 15s., fish 10s., other items 5s. 8d. A year later we find that bread has gone up from 6d. to 7d. a loaf, milk from 1s. to 1s. 1d. a quart, and fish costs 10 per cent more, the other prices being unchanged. At the same time, suppose clothes are up by 5 per cent, drink and tobacco by 1s. in the £, other prices being much the same. Now calculate the new budget for the same family. (The answer is 4s. 3·4d. more.)

If we take the original budget of £9 18s. (leaving out the 2s. savings, which cannot really be counted as expenditure) and represent it by 100, the increase is 2·2 per cent; in other words, the new figure for the cost of living index is 102·2. This is a guide to how wages should go up to keep pace with costs.

Personal accounts are very useful, but most people rely on memory instead. This may be satisfactory for a small number of transactions, but as the number increases it becomes more and more difficult to keep check. In business, the problem is so involved that elaborate systems of entry and periodic check are essential. In fact, the problem of finding out the exact financial state of a company at any given moment is one that often takes weeks to solve.

In small businesses, and often in small societies, accounts have to be kept by persons untrained in this work. The accounts need not be elaborate, but must show as much accurate information as possible. The shopkeeper who wishes to separate his receipts for tobacco from those for sweets need not put the money into two separate boxes if he does a few simple calculations.

Some people have curious ideas about accounts. Here is what one man wrote in balancing income and expenditure:

Started with £10.

	Spent	Had left
	£6	£4
	£1	£3
	£1 10s.	£1 10s.
	15s.	15s.
	10s.	5s.
	5s.	0
Total	£10	£9 10s.

Where have I lost 10s.?

He had observed that for a while, after the first line, the totals of the two columns agreed, and assumed that they must always do so. Of course this was a mere coincidence. There is no reason whatever why a column of remainders should have the same total as the column of spendings.

Another attempt at amateur accounting read as follows:

Income	£	Expenditure	£
Salary	35	Rent	12
		Housekeeping	15
		Cashed cheque	5
		Paid grocer	4

No wonder this account did not balance! The grocer's bill was down three times in the expenditure column, first as part of the housekeeping, then as part of the cheque, then in its own right. If these simple accounts of income and expenditure are to balance, each item must occur once on either side. In more elaborate accounts, where more than one book is kept, each item is entered twice, on opposite sides, although in different books.

PROFITS AND LOSSES

Here are some figures relating to the transactions of a small, private film society, which showed films to its members and made a programme charge of 1s. They had obtained an exemption from entertainment tax. The treasurer entered up receipts and expenditure in two columns, as follows:

	Receipts		£	s.	d.	Expenditure	£	s.	d.
Sept. 21	Balance		9	5	6				
21	Film A,	show	6	0	0				
23		show	1	6	0				
24		show	10	0	0	Phone and post		7	10½
	subs		5	0	0				
25	subs		1	0	0	Post (Film A)		3	4
28	Film B,	show	3	18	0	Film A	5	4	2
30		show	3	9	0	Cash book		1	0
Oct. 2	subs		2	0	0	Stationery and post		5	0
4						Film (outstanding)	6	9	5
						Post		5	0
						Keys		2	0
5	subs		2	10	0				
5	Film C,	show	3	7	0				
7		show	3	9	0				
9						Post (Film B)		9	4½
11						Film B	5	10	9
13	Film D,	show	2	14	0	Film C	4	11	8
15	Film E,	show	4	15	0	Film D	2	9	6
						Post		5	4
21	Film F,	show	4	19	0	Post (Film F)		8	5
24						Projector lamp	2	7	6
28						Hall and lighting	5	0	0

By the end of two months the treasurer realized that this would not do. He totalled up the two columns, which gave £54 2s. 6d. and

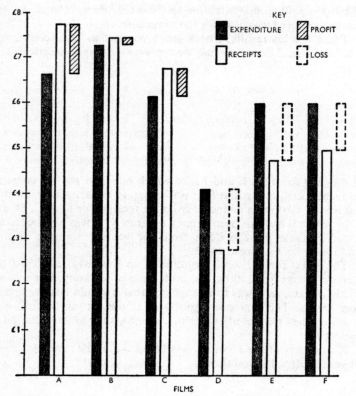

FIG. 3. *Profit and loss on each of six films. Which film showed the highest profit? Did the same film give the greatest percentage of profit on receipts?*

£34 0s. 4d., showing a balance of £20 2s. 2d., but this did not give very much useful information, beyond checking that he had not lost any money, or failed to make an entry. What he needed were accounts which showed as much useful information as possible at a glance, how much the society really had in hand, and which types of film his audience liked best. He had been shocked when the bill for £6 9s. 5d. for a film from last season came in, because there was nothing in the accounts to lead him to expect this.

So he decided to start afresh, at least to ensure that this did not happen again. He separated the accounts for each individual film, to find which was most profitable. In some cases the postage for returning the film was not stated; he estimated this as the average of the others. He paid special attention to the week when, by mistake, the secretary ordered two films for the same date.

These are his results. Check them yourself as an exercise, and note from Fig. 3 how they may be represented diagrammatically.

	£	s.	d.
Film A, profit,	1	3	11
Film B, profit,		2	3½
Film C, profit,		12	8½
Film D, loss,	1	7	1½
Film E, loss,	1	5	7½
Film F, loss,	1	3	0
General Account, balance,	3	15	6

In allowing for films E and F, for which bills had not yet come in, the average cost of the first four was taken. In the same way, average postage (7s. 0½d.) was deducted from the receipts for films C, D, and E, for which it had not been entered separately. It was also necessary to deduct these postage items from the general account, or they would have been charged twice.

The items for hall and projector lamp were also averaged out amongst the six films, although, in the case of the lamp, this was not strictly correct, as it was to be assumed that it would last for several more shows. This was not important, as the accounts could only estimate. They did not allow for other items, such as depreciation of apparatus.

A summary of the accounts now showed that the actual state was a loss of £1 16s. 10d. on shows.

	£	s.	d.
Balance in hand on taking over	9	5	6
Balance on general account	3	15	6
Bills unpaid (Films D and E) estimated at	8	18	0
Total	21	19	0
Deduct loss on shows	1	16	10
Balance to date	20	2	2

This was checked with the original column totals and found to agree. It will be seen that there is a great deal more than simple addition and subtraction, even in a small account of this type, but that most of it is common sense.

The tradesman who looks into his accounts wishes to be able to compare different items or different periods, in order to see which brings him in the best profit. To do so he expresses his profit as a percentage, usually of his turnover or takings. It is important to

410

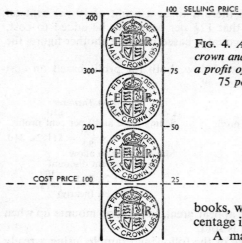

FIG. 4. *An article bought for half-a-crown and sold for ten shillings shows a profit of 300 per cent on cost price, 75 per cent on selling price.*

notice that this is contrary to the procedure in the theoretical examples which occur in arithmetic books, where the basis of the percentage is always the cost price.

A man who buys articles at half-a-crown each and sells them at ten shillings each would be described in the text-books as making a profit of 300 per cent, because, if his cost price is taken as 100 per cent, his profit of 7s. 6d. is three times this. He himself would most likely say he is making 75 per cent on his turnover, because he takes his selling price of 10s. as 100 per cent, his profit being three-quarters of this. It is easy to calculate one form from the other, as they are in the same ratio, but inversely, as are the cost and selling prices. Since the selling price is four times the cost price, the profit as a percentage of the selling price will be one-quarter of the same profit expressed as a percentage of the cost price (Fig. 4).

From the point of view of the tradesman, it is easier to work on the basis of turnover, because this is available at once, without further calculation. Some articles, such as cigarettes, or other proprietary brands of goods for which the selling price is fixed by the manufacturer, are sold to the retailer on terms which specify the percentage of profit on turnover. This is described as a trade discount.

For example, a book priced at 10s. 6d. may be sold by the publisher to the bookseller at a trade discount of 33⅓ per cent. This is based on the selling price, so that he actually pays 3s. 6d. less, or 7s. His gross profit is 3s. 6d. on 7s. spent, or 50 per cent on cost price. If cigarettes are sold at a trade discount of 15 per cent, this is a gross profit of 15 per cent on turnover, or 15/85 of the cost price, which is 17·6 per cent profit on cost.

Another complication in the calculation of profit is the allowance of cash discount. If the goods cost £10, and after 2½ per cent discount

411

has been allowed for cash there is to be a profit of 10 per cent on cost, this does not mean that $12\frac{1}{2}$ per cent is to be added to cost, because the $2\frac{1}{2}$ per cent discount is based on quite another figure, the unknown marked price.

The calculation is shown below, both for profit based on cost and for profit based on turnover.

Profit on Cost Price	Profit on Turnover
Cost of goods £10	Cost of goods £10
Selling price at 10 per cent profit	Selling price at 10 per cent profit
$= £10 \times \dfrac{110}{100} = £11$	$= £10 \times \dfrac{100}{90} = £11$ 2s. $2\frac{1}{4}$d.
Marked price to allow $2\frac{1}{2}$ per cent discount	Marked price to allow $2\frac{1}{2}$ per cent discount
$= £11 \times \dfrac{100}{97\frac{1}{2}}$	$= £11$ 2s. $2\frac{1}{4}$d. $\times \dfrac{100}{97\frac{1}{2}}$
$= £11$ 6s. (nearly)	$= £11$ 8s. (nearly)

The difference may not appear great, but it soon mounts up when a large number of articles is sold.

See what you can make of the following example, using a ready reckoner if you have one.

You have bought 1,000 yards of material at 6s. 11d. a yard and, having marked it at 9s. a yard, have succeeded in selling 715 yards. It is now sale time and you are prepared to mark down the remainder, but wish to make 15 per cent on turnover for the whole transaction. What percentage of discount on the previous selling price can you allow?

The problem of calculating net profit involves a good deal more than subtracting cost price from selling price, if the true cost is to be considered. There are a good many other factors to be taken into account. In the preceding example there are all the expenses of sale and the cost of upkeep: rent, wages, lighting and heating, advertisement. These have all to be paid and an appropriate portion of these costs should be set against every sale.

This is difficult for the small trader, but the manufacturer, most of whose costs are of this type, must assess them all against the cost

Books and Papers

(1) Copies of a book are stacked so that the spine of one is above the opening edge of the next. On one side seven spines are visible and on the other side seven opening edges. How many books must there be?

(2) When Father picked up the paper page 13 was missing. If the back page was numbered 20 what other pages were missing?

Solution on page 444

412

of each small article manufactured. Suppose, for example, a manufacturer produces an article at the rate of twenty an hour, for which raw material costs 5d. and labour 4d. Suppose also that the fixed costs, or "overheads," referred to above, work out at 1s. an hour. Then the total cost of each article is 5d. + 4d. + 0·6d. = 9·6d. If, through lack of orders or lack of materials, he can produce only ten articles in an hour, the cost per article at once goes up to 10·2d. He has to consider the question of closing the works for part of the time, in order to reduce the cost of the article by cutting down some of the overheads.

Another point to be considered in calculating profit is the distinction between capital expenditure and recurring charges. If a man buys a house for £2,000 and lets it for £250 per annum, he appears to be making a profit of 12½ per cent on cost. If he pays rates of £20 a year, these must be deducted from the rent when calculating profit. If, once every three years, he repaints and does minor repairs which cost £30, he must deduct one-third of this from each year's receipts, because this is a recurring charge. If he makes structural alterations which are not likely to be repeated, costing £100, they must be regarded as an addition to the capital cost. From these figures he receives £220 a year in return for his capital outlay of £2,100, or 10½ per cent.

Profits vary considerably from one field to another. This is because, in addition to the ordinary element of risk, there may be a long normal waiting period. A man who sells goods for which there is a ready and immediate market may be content with a small profit, because there is a quick turnover, so that he is using his money several times over. The man who sells, say, second-hand books, which may lie on his shelves for months or longer, is losing the use of his money, which could be earning interest, for a long period, and must expect larger profits to compensate for this.

THE CITIZEN'S RATES AND TAXES

There are many items of expenditure which are not left to the individual, because they are bound up too deeply with the interests of the whole community. In these cases it is the duty of the citizen to contribute. The problem of estimating in advance how much is needed, and of allocating the individual contributions fairly, involves large-scale calculation.

When we read, for example, that the total national income is £12,414,000,000, and that of this, 2s. 3d. in the £, or 11¼ per cent, equal to about £1,400,000,000, is collected in the form of direct taxes on income, it is difficult to realize how vast a problem it is.

413

How big is a million? How much space would be needed to store this total tax of fourteen hundred million pounds? How long would it take to count? Although we are accustomed to reading about these large sums of money, few people realize how large they really are. If this sum of money were all in pound notes, it would cram full every available space in an empty, normal-sized house. If 200 people counted the notes, each at the rate of 5,000 an hour, working steadily an eight-hour day and a five-day week, it would take them 35 weeks to count.

Fortunately, we do not have to depend on this sort of counting, because there are elaborate mechanical devices for the purpose. It is a good thing, none the less, to think about this, because once figures become too large for normal counting they are easily misinterpreted.

The needs of the community are large and involve detailed budgeting. There is a distinction between those which affect the community as a whole and those which are largely a local concern. The cost of the armed forces, for example, is a national affair and is met from taxes. Street lighting, on the other hand, is a matter which may vary with local needs and tastes; the cost is accordingly collected by local contributions, or rates. The division between local and national needs is not always as clear as this. Education, for example, or the police service, although administered locally, can hardly be regarded as a matter to be left entirely to local tastes. In such cases there is a compromise. Some of the cost is borne from the local rates, but the bulk of it is paid for from a government grant, which comes from taxation.

Let us consider the mathematics of the rate bill. To the householder this comes simply as an annual or half-yearly demand for a sum of money, which is paid with some show of reluctance but with an underlying sense of duty. In the Treasurer's department, however, this is the climax of a long series of calculations. Each year's working begins with a series of estimates, based on the previous year's figures. Each department must say how much it will need for next year.

These estimates are very carefully checked before they are agreed, due attention being paid to any balances or deficits from previous years. Let us suppose that this total estimate is £75,000. Next comes the problem of equitable distribution of the cost. Who is to pay for this and how much should each person pay?

It is obviously unjust to expect all to pay alike. Apart from the fact that many of the poorer residents would not be able to pay their share, it is assumed that the benefits of these communal services are proportional to the size of each property, so that the larger owner is expected to pay more.

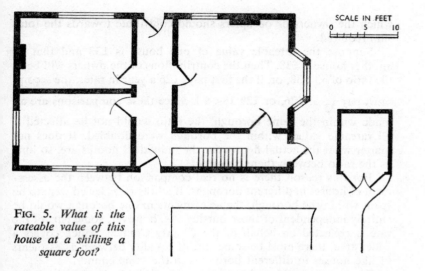

SCALE IN FEET
0   5   10

Fig. 5. *What is the rateable value of this house at a shilling a square foot?*

There are minor variations in the details of assessment, but the general principles are the same. The total floor area of the living accommodation is very carefully measured or estimated; a built-in chimney breast, for example, or an encroaching doorway, would be deducted, and a window bay charged at a flat rate.

A scale of assessment per square foot (known as a foot super) of floor area will already have been worked out. In a small uniform district there might be one flat scale of a shilling a square foot. In a larger district there might be three grades of street, one of very large houses, one of smaller houses and the third of poor houses. The value of the same floor area would be different for each, say 1s. 3d., 1s. and 9d. per square foot, respectively.

If a house is in the middle-grade section and has a floor area of 600 square feet, its assessment, subject to any extras, would, according to these figures, be £30. There might be an extra of £1 for a bay not included in the measurements, and £2 for a brick garage, making a total of £33. This is the gross assessment, or rateable value of the house (Fig. 5). In some areas there is a deduction of 20 per cent from this, giving a net assessment, which is used as the basis for rating.

There is a legal fiction that this figure of £33 is the annual value of the property, or a reasonable rent for letting the house. Possibly this may once have been the idea behind the calculation, but no one would suggest that present assessments bear any relation to rent. They are now little more than arbitrary figures to show the ratio in which the owners or occupiers should contribute towards the total sum required.

Suppose the rateable value of one house is £33 and that of another house is £38. Then the contributions of the owners will be in the ratio of 33 : 38, or, if the first pays £26 a year in rates, the second must pay $\frac{38}{33} \times$ £26, or £29 18s. 9d. Since these comparisons are all made within the same borough, the ratio would not be affected if all rateable values within the borough were doubled. It does not matter what the actual figures for the individual houses are, so long as the ratio between them is correct.

For this reason there is no real comparison between the assessment of houses in different boroughs. If all the rates levied were to be spent within the borough, the assessments in one borough would be entirely independent of those outside. As, however, some part of the rate is collected on behalf of the County Council, which covers a wider area, there must be some sort of equality between assessments of like houses in different boroughs in the same county.

The total rateable value of the borough is used as the basis for equitable distribution of costs. Let us suppose that in one particular borough this total value was £95,000. The estimate of total requirements has already been given as £75,000. Then the amount needed to be raised is $\frac{75,000}{95,000}$ or $\frac{15}{19}$ of the rateable value. Each house owner or occupier is called on to pay $\frac{15}{19}$ of the assessment of his own property. If his house is assessed at £33, he should pay $\frac{15}{19}$ of £33, or £26 1s. 1d.

Instead of calculating in this way, the practice is first to find this fraction of a pound, $£\frac{15}{19}$, and describe it as 15s. 10d. in the £. According to this method, a rate of 15s. 10d. in the £ would be levied, so that the householder assessed at £33 would pay 33 × 15s. 10d., or £26 2s. 6d.

The second method gives the higher result because $£\frac{15}{19}$ is somewhere between 15s. 9d. and 15s. 10d. and is rounded off to the next penny. It is not even to the nearest penny, as is usual in most calculations, because a rate of 15s. 9d. in the £ would fall a little short of the total requirements. By how much? As this fraction is hardly ever likely to work out to an exact number of pence, the total rate always provides a small surplus.

416

FIG. 6. *Of the total rateable value for all England and Wales, London accounts for more than one-sixth.*

LONDON

THE REST OF ENGLAND AND WALES

The total rateable value for England and Wales in 1950–51 was £330,978,000, of which £55,989,365, over one-sixth, came from London (Fig. 6). The total receipts from rates for the same year were £293,000,000, or an average rate of 17s. 8d. in the £. The figures for 1940–41 were £324,271,000 and £203,892,000 respectively, or an average rate of 12s. 7d. in the £. This shows (Fig. 7) that rateable value has increased only a little (about 2 per cent), whilst the demands of the local services have increased by almost a half (about 44 per cent).

It is convenient, for comparison, to express the rateable value of a district in terms of the product of a penny rate, which is $\frac{1}{240}$ of the total. In the case of Birmingham, Liverpool and Manchester

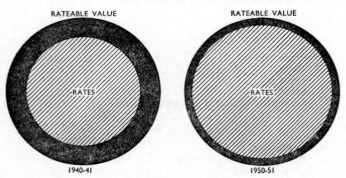

RATEABLE VALUE   RATEABLE VALUE

RATES   RATES

1940-41   1950-51

FIG. 7. *The changing times. Whilst the gross rateable value has only slightly increased during the period shown, gross rates have risen appreciably.*

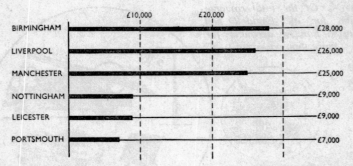

FIG. 8. *Amount produced by a penny rate in six cities of different sizes.*

every penny of the rates produces £28,200, £26,282 and £25,400 respectively, while in Nottingham, Leicester and Portsmouth it produces £8,900, £8,750 and £7,400 respectively (Fig. 8). The amount of rates raised per head of population (Fig. 9) does not differ very widely from one district to another and is usually about £10. The figures for these towns per head of population for 1950–51 were: Birmingham £9 1s. 2d., Liverpool £9 14s. 4d., Manchester £10 10s. 0d., Nottingham £9 3s. 3d., Leicester £9 13s. 6d., Portsmouth £8 10s. 11d.

Every demand note for rates carries an analysis which shows how the money has been spent. Here is a typical example from a county borough with a rateable value of about £1,000,000.

Services administered by the Council:

Public Health		
Sewage disposal		8·15d.
Removal and disposal of house refuse	1s.	1·29d.
Street cleaning		6·42d.
Health services	1s.	2·41d.
Housing		5·63d.
Education	6s.	4·28d.
Street lighting	1s.	1·21d.
Parks	1s.	5·22d.
Police	1s.	7·32d.
Other services	6s.	4·21d.
Services administered by County Council		5·23d.
		21s. 3·37d.

Deduct		
Exchequer Equalization grant	2s. 8·42d.	
Other receipts	9·95d.	3s. 6·37d.
Rate in the £ payable by Ratepayer		17s. 9d.

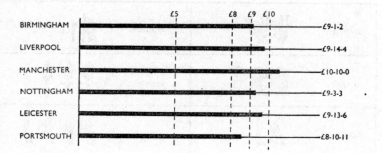

FIG. 9. *Amount of rates paid per head of population in the same cities.*

Let us examine these figures to see what they mean. They have been rounded off to the nearest hundredth of a penny; in fact, somewhere, probably in the other receipts, they have been further rounded off so that the final figure shall come to an exact number of pence. It will therefore be quite sufficient if we take our estimate to the nearest pound.

A penny rate on £1,000,000 produces $\frac{1}{240}$ of this sum, or £4,166 13s. 4d. We shall call this £4,167, a tenth of a penny £417 and a hundredth of a penny £42. According to this, the amount required for sewage disposal was £33,958. It is more likely that the actual estimate was £34,000.

We find that, approximated in the same way and rounded off to the nearest hundred pounds, the departmental net estimates must have been as follows:

Sewage disposal	£34,000
House refuse	£55,400
Street cleaning	£26,800
Health services	£60,000
Housing	£23,500
Education	£317,800
Street lighting	£55,000
Parks	£71,700
Police	£80,500
Other services	£317,500
County Council	£21,800
Total	£1,064,000
Deductions	£176,500
Final Estimate	£887,500

419

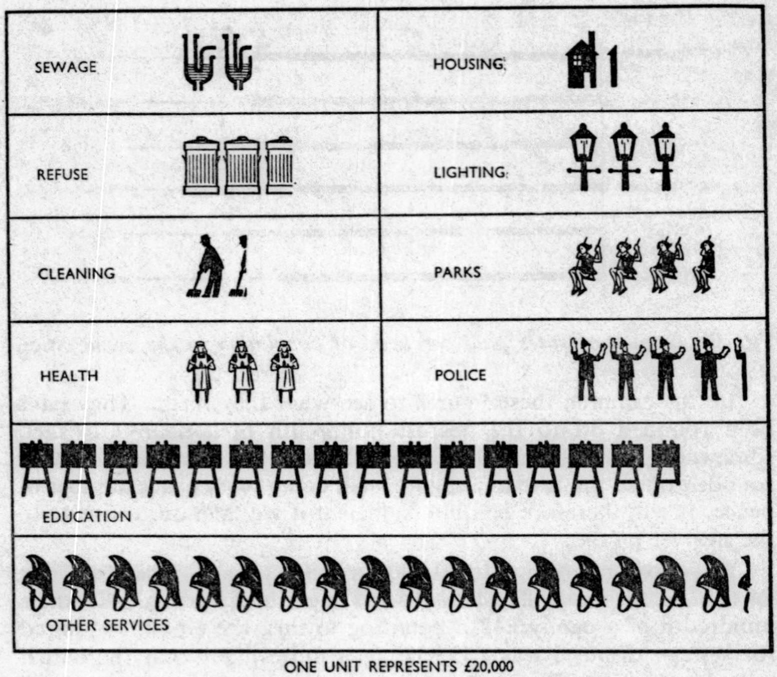

FIG. 10. *Pictorial method of showing how the ratepayer's money is spent.*

This estimate may not quite agree with the figures given before, as the rate of 17s. 9d. in the £ will bring in £887,500 only if we assume that there will be no defaulters, for whom allowance must always be made. There may also be a difference due to our approximation. Although the figures are sufficiently accurate for the purpose of comparison (and for pictorial representation as in Fig. 10), it is important to realize that, although we may neglect what seems a small quantity in each item, the total will be out by the sum of all these small items, which may be large enough to matter. That is why the analysis is worked out to the nearest hundredth of a penny, even though the actual rate is rounded off to the nearest penny.

We may use this analysis to calculate how the rates paid by any particular householder are distributed. If we consider the case referred to above, of a man whose house was assessed at £33, we find that the amount he pays, at 17s. 9d. in the £, is £29 5s. 9d. We may calculate his contribution towards sewage disposal, for example, by taking thirty-three times 8·15d., or £1 2s. 5d. This would not, however, be quite accurate, as it would make no allowance for the deductions due to Council receipts.

A glance at the figures will show that the total deduction of 3s. 6·37d. is very nearly one-sixth of the total expenditure of 21s. 3·37d. Taking one-sixth of itself from the figure of £1 2s. 5d. we find that this particular householder contributed 18s. 8d. (rounded off to the nearest penny) towards the cost of sewage disposal. A full analysis of his rates may be made as follows:

Sewage	18s. 8d.	Refuse	£1 10s. 6d.
Street cleaning		Health	
Housing	12s. 11d.	Education	
Lighting		Parks	£1 19s. 5d.
Police		Other services	£8 14s. 8d.
	County council	12s. 0d.	

The reader is invited to work out the missing figures.

The total of these items, you will find, does not quite agree with the actual rate, being 4d. short. This is due to the rounding off.

NATIONAL FINANCE

The accounts of a nation involve much larger sums of money than those dealt with above and must be planned with much greater care. Here are some figures of British revenue and expenditure:

	Ordinary Revenue	*Ordinary Expenditure*	*Difference*
1930–31	£775,895,000	£799,171,000	− £23,276,000
1940–41	£1,408,867,000	£3,884,288,000	− £2,475,421,000
1950–51	£3,897,800,000	£3,455,069,000	+ £442,731,000

There are remarkable differences between the three years, as Fig. 11 demonstrates, but they are easily accountable for by conditions.

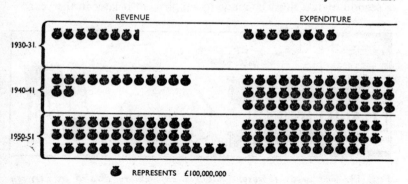

🜚 REPRESENTS £100,000,000

FIG. 11. *Differences in national revenue and expenditure for selected years.*

421

FIG. 12. *Income tax is only part of the national revenue. Its relationship to other revenue is indicated here by comparative areas.*

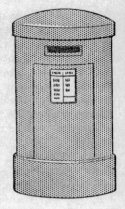

The figures for 1930–31 were normal for that period. 1940–41 was an early war year, when Britain was spending heavily on her mounting war effort and drawing on all her available resources. 1950–51 was a year in which, although expenditure was heavy, both as a result of wartime loans and post-war conditions, revenue had increased because of greater taxation until it was greater than expenditure.

The large differences, although in 1950–51 amounting to about £10 per head of the population, are not surprising. The Chancellor of the Exchequer may, as he did in that year, plan his budget to produce a large surplus of revenue in pursuance of a particular economic policy. Also, there are so many different items which enter into the estimates, and so many changes in conditions during the course of the year, that it is very difficult to plan with any kind of precision. There is always a certain amount of guesswork about the effects of a new or increased tax. It is no use working on last year's figures, because the effect of the increase in cost of the taxed article may be to reduce the demand. Sometimes conditions change so much during the year that the first budget, made in March, is quite inadequate and a second budget must be made to supplement it later in the year.

FIG. 13. *The areas represent national expenditure divided as between Consolidated Fund (mostly interest on National Debt) and Supply Services.*

422

The figures for ordinary revenue for a typical year, 1949–50, show that income tax brought in £1,450,279,000, other taxes £2,247,474,000, and other receipts, including such items as Post Office, Crown lands, loans and trading, £400,271,000, out of a total of £4,098,024,000 (Fig. 12). Against this, the ordinary expenditure for the same year was £550,392,000 on Consolidated Fund services, chiefly interest on the national debt, and almost £3,000,000,000 on supply services (Fig. 13).

INCOME-TAX CALCULATIONS

Such large sums of money as are needed for the national purse require great skill and variety in their collection. Some are collected indirectly. For example, the tax on beer of a certain standard strength is £7 15s. 4½d. for every thirty-six gallons, or about sixpence a pint. This is included in the price, so that the man who buys a pint of this beer contributes his sixpence of tax usually without being aware of it. The tax on unmanufactured tobacco is £2 16s. 5½d. per pound, or more than 3s. 6d. an ounce (Fig. 14).

FIG. 14. *About half of what you pay for a pint of beer is tax —and an even higher proportion of what your pipe of tobacco costs.*

These indirect taxes are gradually accepted by the purchaser as part of the price of the commodity. He pays his 4s. and receives in exchange an ounce of tobacco. He is not compelled to buy the tobacco if he can do without it. After a time he comes to look on the whole price as value for money and forgets that part of it is tax.

Direct taxes are different. They come direct from the pocket; in fact, since the introduction of "pay as you earn," income tax is deducted before the money even reaches the pocket. The man who earns £10 for his week's work, but draws only about £8 10s. in his pay packet, knows well that thirty shillings has been taken from him and will want to know what has been done with it. Some of it has gone to pay for the national insurance services, but what about the rest?

The answer is best seen from a diagram. Fig. 15 shows how each pound of the national revenue is spent. As only about one-third of

423

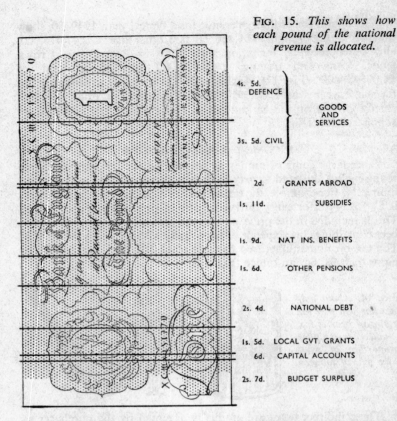

4s. 5d. DEFENCE	GOODS AND SERVICES
3s. 5d. CIVIL	
2d.	GRANTS ABROAD
1s. 11d.	SUBSIDIES
1s. 9d.	NAT INS. BENEFITS
1s. 6d.	OTHER PENSIONS
2s. 4d.	NATIONAL DEBT
1s. 5d.	LOCAL GVT. GRANTS
6d.	CAPITAL ACCOUNTS
2s. 7d.	BUDGET SURPLUS

this revenue comes from income tax, a little thought will show the taxpayer what a great deal he is getting for his payment. If we think of an item of expenditure of a million pounds, how much does the man referred to above, who pays about £1 4s. tax each week, contribute towards this item?

The taxpayer will wish to know how his tax is calculated, if only to make sure he is not paying too much. He can check the answer from the tables which are available in every income-tax office and public library. But he should also know how these tables are worked out. As tax rates change from time to time, we shall take the 1954 scales for our example. The standard rate of tax is 9s. in the pound.

At first glance this seems much worse than it really is: 9s. in the £ is nearly a half. If this rate applied to his whole income, the man who earned £10 a week would find only £5 10s. in his pay packet! In fact

424

he will find at least £8 15s. there, the precise amount being dependent on his circumstances. The average rate of tax is less than 15 per cent, or 3s. in the £, although the standard rate is 45 per cent. The apparent discrepancy is due to the "allowances," which make the calculation more difficult but the payment less onerous.

In the first place, there is an allowance for earned income. The full tax rate is payable only on unearned income, such as dividend on shares or interest on investments. Many companies describe their dividends as "free of income tax." This does not mean that the tax is not paid, but merely that the company pays the tax first. A building society, for example, which offers $2\frac{1}{2}$ per cent free of income tax is really paying $4\frac{6}{11}$ per cent, but, as it must first pay 9s. in the £ to the tax authorities, this leaves $2\frac{1}{2}$ per cent to be paid to the shareholder.

The earned-income allowance for 1954 is two-ninths. This means that the tax on income which is earned is really seven-ninths of 9s., or 7s. in the £. Most people forget this allowance in estimating their tax. The workman who is considering overtime to see whether it is worth while, and takes off half for tax, because 9s. is nearly half of £1, gets a very poor estimate, because the actual tax is $\frac{7}{9} \times \frac{9}{20}$; that is, just over $\frac{1}{3}$.

Next there is the "personal allowance" for living expenses, which is left tax-free. This ensures that no tax is paid at all by persons whose income is below a certain level. This allowance depends on the size of the family. It is least for a single person, who is allowed £120. A married man is allowed £210. If his wife is earning she is allowed the single person's tax-free allowance of £120, in addition to her husband's £210. Then there is an allowance of £85 for each child under sixteen; this allowance is extended to children over sixteen if they are still in full time attendance at school or college. There are also allowances for dependant relatives, and other items such as age relief, small-income relief and a reduced rate on life insurance, of which details are to be found in the notes issued by the authorities. As they are small and do not affect general principles, we will not deal with them here.

After the earned-income and personal allowances have been deducted, the remainder is called the Taxable Income. If this is nil, that is, if the allowances together are equal to or greater than the income, no tax is due. If the taxable income is £100 or less, tax is levied on this amount at the lowest rate of 2s. 6d. in the £.

If the taxable income is between £100 and £250, tax on the first £100 is still at 2s. 6d., but the rest is taxed at 5s. in the £. In the same

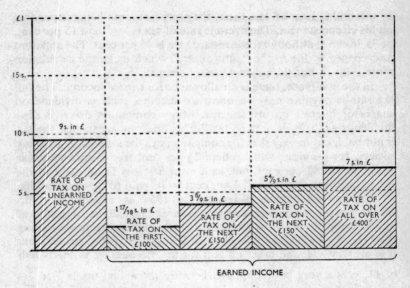

FIG. 16. *Rates of taxation on taxable income, earned and unearned.*

way, anything between £250 and £400 is taxed at 7s. in the £. It is only when the taxable income exceeds £400 that the full rate of 9s. in the £ begins to operate, and then only on the excess (Fig. 16).

Let us take some examples. In each case it is assumed that all allowable deductions for expenses have already been made. In making these deductions, it is important to know the distinction between expenses incurred in doing your work, which are allowed, and those which put you in the position to do your work, which are not allowed. The commercial traveller, for example, may claim his travelling expenses; but not the man who merely travels to work, because he lives away from his work by choice.

Here are some sample cases, illustrated in Fig. 17:

> (1) Mr. A, a single man, earns £9 a week, or £468 a year.

Income		£468
Earned Income Allowance (⅔ of £468)	£104	
Personal Allowance	£120	
Deduct		*£224*
Taxable Income		£244
Tax on the first £100 at 2s. 6d.	=	£12 10s.
Tax on the rest (£144) at 5s.	=	£36
Tax payable	=	£48 10s.

This works out at just under 19s. a week. He should find £8 1s., less other deductions, such as insurance contributions, in his pay packet each week. In practice he may find the deduction a shilling more or less some weeks, because of the way the tables are worked out, as explained later. But this does not matter, as the totals are checked at the end of each year. If he has paid too much it is refunded, while anything he still owes is carried on to the next year. The amount involved is usually quite small.

(2) Mr. B, a married man with no children, earns £630 a year. See what tax you think he should pay per annum.

According to our calculation there should be a deduction of £5 0s. 10d. each month; but as the tables are worked out in whole numbers of shillings, he may find, owing to the method of coding, that the actual deduction in one month is £5 and in another month £5 1s.

(3) Mr. C, a married man with two children, earns £900 a year. He also has a little nest-egg of £600 put away in the Post Office Savings Bank. This brings in 2½ per cent per annum (£15) in interest.

Earned Income		£900
Unearned Income		£15
Total Income		£915
Earned Income Allowance	£200	
Personal Allowance	£380	
Deduct		*£580*
Taxable Income		£335
Tax on the first £100 at 2s. 6d.	=	£12 10s.
on the next £150 at 5s.	=	£37 10s.
on the rest (£85) at 7s.	=	£29 15s.
Tax payable	=	£79 15s.

It will be seen that, although the standard rate of tax is 9s. in the £, he is, in fact, because of the allowances and lower rates of tax, paying only about 1s. 9d. in the £.

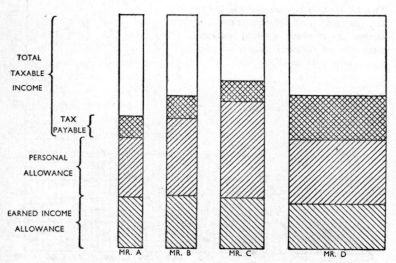

FIG. 17. *The cases of four taxpayers. Amounts are represented by areas.*

(4) Mr. D, a married man with four children, earns £1,800 per annum. He also has investments which bring him in £200 per annum.

Total Income		£2,000
Earned Income Allowance	£400	
Personal Allowance	£550	
Deduct		*£950*
Taxable Income		£1,050

How much does he pay? The answer is £395, and although this is a large sum the *effective* rate is still below 4s. in the £.

A good way of comparing rates of tax is by graph. In Fig. 18 examples have been drawn for several cases. These graphs may be used as ready reckoners for each particular case. If you wish to find the tax payable by a single man, on, say, £600, find the point on the graph which is vertically above £600; then read along horizontally on the other scale to find the amount of tax. Notice that the graphs consist of straight lines, where the tax rate is constant, with sharp joins at the points where the rate changes; note also that the graph becomes steeper as the tax rate increases. This will help you to draw a graph to suit your own case, if it is not amongst those given.

In practice the calculation of tax is done from tables. The net allowance is given a code number, from a code table supplied. The clerk simply looks up the particular code number under the particu-

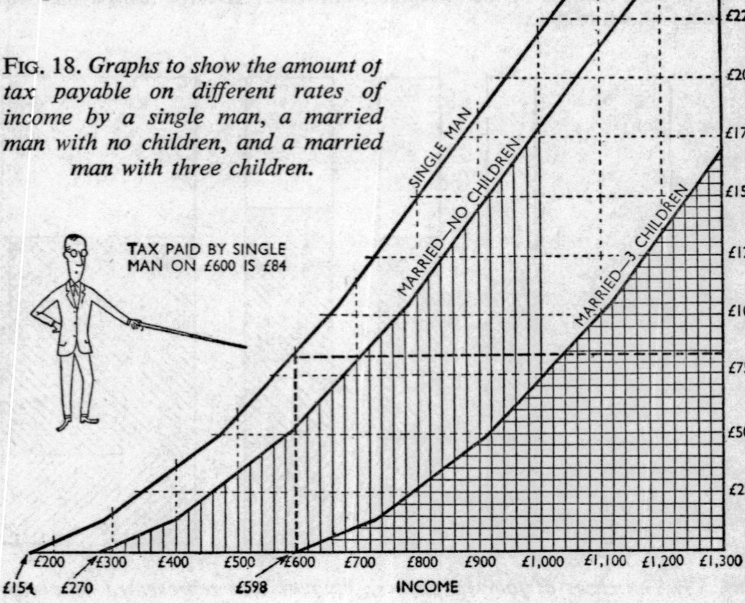

FIG. 18. *Graphs to show the amount of tax payable on different rates of income by a single man, a married man with no children, and a married man with three children.*

TAX PAID BY SINGLE MAN ON £600 IS £84

lar week, and reads off the amount of tax to be deducted. The net allowance is the personal allowance, corrected to allow for other sources of income, but does not include the earned income allowance, as that is provided for in working out the tables.

In order to condense the tables, the same code number covers several pounds; for example, code number 24 includes all cases of net allowance between £83 and £88. This sometimes results in a small overpayment or underpayment, which is corrected at the end of the year.

Much larger discrepancies, however, arise when the income varies from week to week. If a man earns £8 in the first week and £16 in the second week, he is taxed on the average, or £12 a week, on the assumption that this will happen regularly. It may be that it is a long time before another week as good as this comes along. In this case, although the tax deduction is large at the moment, the extra tax comes back to him in the form of smaller payments later on. Sometimes, where the extra payment is large, there will be no tax to pay at all for a week or two later on.

In one office the clerk turned over two pages of tables by mistake and thought, using next week's figures, that everybody on the staff was entitled to a refund, to their surprise and joy; but there were long faces next week, when the right page was found, and there was double tax for everybody.

THE IDEA OF INTEREST

We have become so accustomed to the idea of interest on money that we tend to regard it almost as a natural growth. We have some money which we do not wish to spend at the moment; we take it to the bank for safety; and the bank, instead of making a charge for looking after the money, actually pays us for the privilege. This is astonishing and almost a paradox.

Nor has this always been the case. One has only to go back three or four hundred years to find that the practice of charging interest on loans was looked on with considerable disfavour. Nowadays the term "usury" is limited to exorbitant rates of interest and one expects a fair rate of interest, except in private loans to friends.

This change of attitude has been brought about by the elaborate system of banking which has grown up. There are established rates of interest for deposits, for short loans and for longer loans. The whole system is so strong that we may feel that the money is safe.

Interest is usually expressed as a rate per cent per annum. If the rate is, for example, 4 per cent per annum, this means that if you lent £100 for a year, you would receive £104 back, the additional

£4 being the interest. If you had left the money on loan for two years, on this basis, you would have been entitled to £8 interest.

This assumes that the interest is not asked for until the end of the two years. If, in the case of the £100 loan for two years at 4 per cent per annum, the interest had been paid by the year, there would have been £104 owing at any time during the second year. As 4 per cent of £104 is £4 3s. 2d., this means that at the end of two years you would have been entitled to £108 3s. 2d., not £108. This is called compound interest; the additional 3s. 2d. is interest on the first year's interest, which is put in and regarded as part of the loan. In practice all interest for longer than a year is compound interest, because interest is always worked out and added to the account. Fig. 19 illustrates graphically the difference between simple and compound interest.

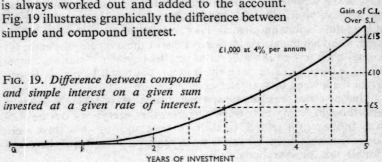

FIG. 19. *Difference between compound and simple interest on a given sum invested at a given rate of interest.*

The best known form of loan for interest is in the Post Office Savings Bank. Money is lent to the Government, whose security, together with the easy methods of deposit and withdrawal, make this form of banking very popular. Furthermore, whilst the larger banks pay only a small rate of interest, sometimes as low as ½ per cent per annum, on deposits, and no interest at all on current accounts, the Post Office pays 2½ per cent per annum on all deposits.

Let us see how this interest is worked out. We must remember that interest is paid on whole pounds only, extra shillings being disregarded, and for whole months only; any sum in the bank for

×÷×÷×÷×÷×÷×÷×÷×÷×÷×÷×÷×÷×÷×÷×÷×÷
÷   ×
×   **The Golf Enthusiast**   ÷
÷   Whenever I can get away from business for a morning or afternoon   ×
×   of golf I do so. My week-ends are invariably given up to golf. Since ÷
÷   the beginning of June I have gone to the office on eleven days but   ×
×   never for the whole day. Up to last evening I have had nine mornings ÷
÷   and ten afternoons of golf. What date is it?   *Solution on page 444* ×
×   ÷
×÷×÷×÷×÷×÷×÷×÷×÷×÷×÷×÷×÷×÷×÷×÷×÷

430

less than a month does not earn interest. As $2\frac{1}{2}$ per cent $= \dfrac{2\frac{1}{2}}{100}$, or $\dfrac{1}{40}$, and $\dfrac{1}{40}$ of £1 is 6d., it is easiest to reckon the interest as 6d. on every £1 for a year, or $\frac{1}{2}$d. on every £1 for a month.

Here is a copy of the entries in a typical savings book:

		Deposits			Withdrawals
	Balance from previous year	£220	2s.	11d.	
Jan. 24	Crossed warrant				£20
Feb. 13	Demand				£3
Mar. 19	Demand				£3
22	Demand				£3
25	Demand				£3
29	Demand				£3
Apr. 2	Crossed Warrant				£25
16	Demand				£3
22	Cheque	£18	2s.	8d.	
May 20	Cheque	£24	17s.	6d.	
June 15	Four pounds four shillings	£4	4s.	0d.	
19	Cheque	£2	9s.	10d.	
July 20	Two pounds five shillings	£2	5s.	0d.	
Aug. 24	Two pounds two shillings	£2	2s.	0d.	
Sept. 29	Twelve pounds eight pence	£12	0s.	8d.	
Oct. 1	Cheque	£53	16s.	6d.	
8	Demand				£3
15	Demand				£3
19	Demand				£3
22	Demand				£3
26	Crossed Warrant				£50
Nov. 6	Demand				£3
16	Cheque	£8	1s.	7d.	
Dec. 21	Cheque	£43	7s.	2d.	
	Total	£391	9s.	10d.	£128

Withdrawals of £10 or less may be made on demand, and are entered in this way. A few days' notice is required for larger amounts, for which a warrant must be obtained. A crossed warrant is like drawing a cheque, as it can only be paid into another bank.

In order to work out the interest, we need to know, for each month, the smallest number of whole pounds which remained in the bank for the whole month. These figures are as follows:

Jan.	£200	Apr.	£157	July	£206	Oct.	£215
Feb.	£197	May	£175	Aug.	£209	Nov.	£212
Mar.	£185	June	£200	Sept.	£211	Dec.	£220

Notice that it is the smallest balance for the month which is used. At the beginning of April, for example, the balance was £185 2s. 11d.

and at the end of the month it was £175 5s. 7d. But because the balance fell to £157 2s. 11d. on April 16, only £157 is reckoned for interest.

Interest for the month is now reckoned at $\frac{1}{2}$d. on each £1. Adding up these monthly figures, the total is £2,395. We are therefore entitled to 2,395 halfpennies, or £4 19s. 9d. interest for the year. You will notice that the odd halfpenny has been disregarded.

BUILDING SOCIETY RECEIPTS AND LOANS

Another familiar organization, both to borrowers and lenders, is the building society. First set up to help the man of moderate means to have his own house built, this type of society has become a popular medium for the small investor.

The man who has, say, £1,000 to invest and wishes to have a steady income from it, will often lend it to a building society. He will receive interest at the current rate; let us suppose that this is $2\frac{1}{2}$ per cent free of tax; as explained earlier, this means that tax is paid for him, so that the society is paying out, in all, $4\frac{6}{11}$ per cent.

On his £1,000 he will receive £25 a year; on 1 January, and again on 1 July, he will receive a dividend warrant for £12 10s. He might, if he watched the stock markets, or asked a stockbroker to advise him, have been able to get more than this. If, for example, he found that there was a certain stock which, although it paid only $3\frac{1}{2}$ per cent, could be bought at 60 (that is, £60 buys enough stock to bring in £3 10s. interest each year), then his £1,000 will, in this stock, bring in $\frac{£1,000}{60} \times 3\frac{1}{2}$, or £58 6s. 8d. interest each year. Tax at 9s. in the £ on this sum is £26 5s., leaving him £32 1s. 8d. This amount would, of course, be further reduced by expenditure on stamp duty, contract stamp, commission, and so on.

If, however, he wished to be more secure, he might prefer the lesser interest in the building society, because increased interest often means increased risk. Or, he may wish to be sure of getting exactly his £1,000 back again when he needs it; this he can do in the case of the building society, which will repay it to him on being given reasonable notice; whereas, if he has bought the stock, he must sell it at the current market price, which may have fallen just when he wishes to sell.

What happens to the money deposited with the building society? On the other side of the picture is a man who wishes to buy a house. The society will lend him the money, possibly at $4\frac{1}{2}$ or $4\frac{3}{4}$ per cent interest. This does not seem to offer a large margin of profit, but the sums involved in the large number of similar transactions make it well worth while.

432

It is rarely that he will be able to borrow the whole cost of the house in this way, because the lender must protect himself against possible depreciation in value of the house. The amount owing must be no greater than the market price of the house, even in a slump. The borrower will therefore be expected to pay some part of the cost himself.

Let us suppose that the house costs £2,500, of which the building society is prepared to lend 80 per cent, or £2,000, at 4½ per cent interest. If the borrower agrees to pay £200 a year, how long does it take him to repay the debt?

We must remember that part of this £200 pays interest so far due, and the rest repays capital. Each year the amount of capital owing will be less, so that the interest will be less, and the repayment larger. If we assume that the payments are made at the end of each year, there will be 4½ per cent of £2,000, or £90, interest owing when he pays the first £200, so that there is £110 over for repayment. He then owes £2,000 − £110, or £1,890.

Next year's interest will be only 4½ per cent of £1,890, or £85 1s., so that he will be able to repay £114 19s. Here are the figures for the full transaction; they are represented by a graph in Fig. 20. You will see that, after the first few years, the amount owing decreases rapidly. Interest has been calculated correct to the nearest shilling.

No. of years	Amount still owing	Interest for the year at 4½ per cent	Balance for capital repayment
1	£2,000	£90	£110
2	£1,890	£85 1s.	£114 19s.
3	£1,775 1s.	£79 18s.	£120 2s.
4	£1,654 19s.	£74 9s.	£125 11s.
5	£1,529 8s.	£68 16s.	£131 4s.
6	£1,398 4s.	£62 18s.	£137 2s.
7	£1,261 2s.	£56 15s.	£143 5s.
8	£1,117 17s.	£50 6s.	£149 14s.
9	£968 3s.	£43 11s.	£156 9s.
10	£811 14s.	£36 10s.	£163 10s.
11	£648 4s.	£29 3s.	£170 17s.
12	£477 7s.	£21 10s.	£178 10s.
13	£298 17s.	£13 9s.	£186 11s.
14	£112 6s.	£5 1s.	

It will, therefore, take fourteen years to repay the loan under these terms, the final payment being only £117 7s., as that will clear both interest and capital.

The total amount paid in interest over the whole period of fourteen years is £717 7s., or an average of just over £51 a year. Although this is just over 2½ per cent of the total loan of £2,000, it would be wrong to describe this as a rate of interest of 2½ per cent

433

per annum, because the amount owing, which must be the basis of the percentage, is only £2,000 for a very short while. In fact, when we come to the last year, we find that only £113 6s. is owing.

This may seem too obvious to be worth mentioning; but this is not so, because unduly high rates of interest on loans are often hidden under this type of incorrect description. This sometimes happens in *hire-purchase* transactions.

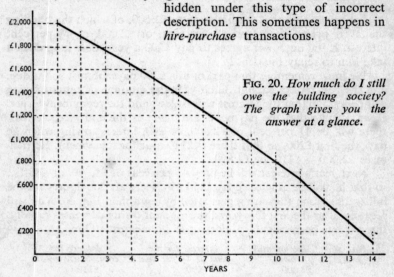

FIG. 20. *How much do I still owe the building society? The graph gives you the answer at a glance.*

HIRE-PURCHASE CALCULATIONS

Suppose, for example, that you wish to buy some furniture for £140, but are prepared to pay only £40 down, the rest to be spread over two years; and the seller adds 10 per cent to this price for interest. Then, if this interest is calculated as 10 per cent on the £100 owing per annum, or £20 for the two years, and added to the £100, making £120, the monthly instalments will be £5 each. This calculation will be incorrect, because it assumes that the £100 is owing right down to the end of the two years.

As we saw in the case of the building society payments, each instalment includes part interest and part repayment. The amount owing steadily decreases, and the interest decreases with it. The last payment is nearly all repayment.

To calculate the exact rate of interest in this so-called 10 per cent is complicated; but we may arrive at a very good estimate if we say that, since the debt is being steadily reduced over the two years, this is roughly equivalent to an average debt of half the amount for the whole period. Instead of paying £20 interest on £100 for two years,

434

we are paying this interest on £50, so that the real interest is round about 20 per cent per annum, not 10 per cent.

Nowadays the borrower is protected by law from exorbitant rates of interest, but it was not so long ago that those who were so unfortunate as to need to borrow, especially small loans, could be charged very high rates by unscrupulous persons. These rates were sometimes cleverly concealed. Here are some examples:

(1) You borrow £1 and pay 1s. a week interest. This is described as "a shilling in the £," but in fact a year's interest is £2 12s. On £100 for a year this would be £260, so the rate of interest is 260 per cent per annum!

(2) In the same way, a penny in the shilling every week, at one time a common rate on small loans, is $433\frac{1}{3}$ per cent per annum.

(3) You borrow £1 and pay back 1s. 1d. a week for twenty weeks, the extra penny being interest. The interest you are paying is 1s. 8d. for twenty weeks; but, because of the steady repayment, the average debt is approximately 10s. On this basis the rate of interest is $43\frac{1}{3}$ per cent per annum.

(4) You borrow £10 and are charged 1s. in the £ interest. The repayment is in twenty-one weekly instalments of 10s., the first instalment to be paid at once, by deduction from the loan. The actual loan is therefore only £9 10s., and the average loan about half of this, over twenty weeks. On this basis the rate of interest is $27\frac{7}{19}$ per cent per annum.

TABLES AND GRAPHS

The person who makes only occasional calculations does not often bother to keep them, because he is unlikely to need them again. In advanced work, where the calculation is heavy, it is important to store the results in case they may be needed again. In business, where the same sort of calculation is often repeated, it is a great saving of time to have a set of answers worked out, carefully checked and neatly tabulated for future use. Banks, for example, do not calculate interest as we have done, but keep a book of tables as a ready reckoner.

÷×÷×÷×÷×÷×÷×÷×÷×÷×÷×÷×÷×÷×÷×÷×÷×

Hiring a Bus

The cost of hiring the bus was shared equally among all those who went on the outing. It was a 34-seater and the bill came to £8 11s. 7d. How many empty seats were there?   *Solution on page 444*

÷×÷×÷×÷×÷×÷×÷×÷×÷×÷×÷×÷×÷×÷×÷×÷×

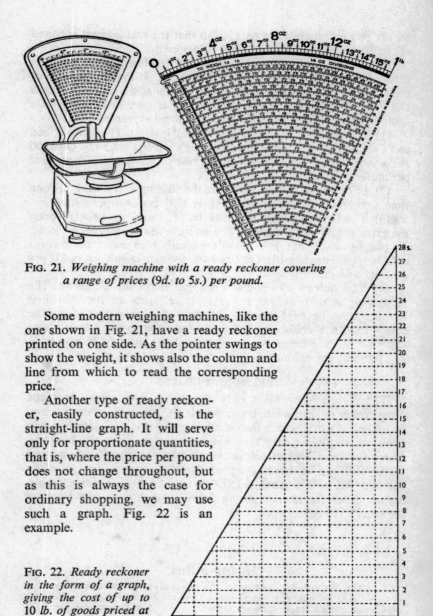

FIG. 21. *Weighing machine with a ready reckoner covering a range of prices (9d. to 5s.) per pound.*

Some modern weighing machines, like the one shown in Fig. 21, have a ready reckoner printed on one side. As the pointer swings to show the weight, it shows also the column and line from which to read the corresponding price.

Another type of ready reckoner, easily constructed, is the straight-line graph. It will serve only for proportionate quantities, that is, where the price per pound does not change throughout, but as this is always the case for ordinary shopping, we may use such a graph. Fig. 22 is an example.

FIG. 22. *Ready reckoner in the form of a graph, giving the cost of up to 10 lb. of goods priced at 2s. 10d. a lb.*

Along the horizontal scale, or axis, is marked the number of pounds, and on the vertical scale the number of shillings and pence. The scales are chosen to cover the range of values we need; so that if we wish to cover prices up to ten pounds, the pence scale must go up to 340. The larger the scale, the more accurate the answer. As we wish, from this graph, to read weights to the nearest ounce and prices to the nearest halfpenny, we shall need a second diagram, as shown in Fig. 23, to do this.

Two points will be needed to fix the straight line. In the first graph we have taken 1 lb. and 34 pence, the price of one pound, for one point; this point is found by reading 1 lb. along the horizontal scale and 34 pence vertically above this reading. A second point is found by reading the price of another quantity, say 10 lb., vertically above it. These two points are joined and the straight line produced as far as possible, to give the graph.

To check that we have made no mistake, we read another price from this graph, say 4 lb. We find the point on the graph vertically above 4 lb., as shown by dotted lines; from this point we strike out horizontally until we meet the axis; the price reads 11s. 4d., which is correct. In the same way we may find the price of any number of pounds, or, by starting from the vertical scale, working to the graph and down, we may find the weight for any price.

To be accurate for small weights, we had better use this first graph for whole numbers of pounds, and the smaller graph for ounces. This was drawn in the same way, by joining the points corres-

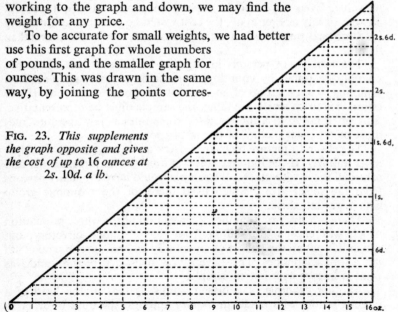

FIG. 23. *This supplements the graph opposite and gives the cost of up to 16 ounces at 2s. 10d. a lb.*

ponding to 0 oz. (price 0d.) and 16 oz. (price 34 pence). Notice that we have chosen our units for these scales so as to fill the graph; the larger the scale, the more accurate the reading.

An important statistical problem, in which another type of graph is used, is that of measuring a group. The business man may wish to know whether his advertising campaign is reaching the public; or the politician may feel the need for some measure of public opinion. How is he to obtain the information?

MEASUREMENT OF A GROUP

We read in the Press that according to the BBC Listener Research Department more than seventeen million people listen regularly to a certain programme. There is a great deal of mathematical thought behind this simple statement, which most people are ready to accept without question. How has this figure been arrived at? Not by straightforward counting. Try counting the number of times each letter of the alphabet occurs in this page of print, to see how long it takes before you can be quite sure no mistake has been made.

If you could employ a thousand persons to go round to ask, say, fifty people a day, which programme they liked, it would take about a year to get round, by which time the information would have lost its value. Even if you could depend on people to give a truthful answer, or any answer at all, the cost would be prohibitive. Counting for statistical purposes is a tremendous task, not to be undertaken lightly.

The number of persons in a group as large as this could not possibly be found by counting. It must be an estimate, based on sampling, from a group of, at the most, a thousand persons. If our estimate is to be worth anything, the sample must be representative. This small group of a thousand (or sometimes as few as a hundred) must be an exact picture of the whole population.

To get such a picture by chance, from a random group, would be most unlikely. If the inquirer stood at a particular street corner and asked all those who passed, the sample would have too many persons from the social group which lived there, or the economic group which worked there.

There is a story of a sample cross-section of the whole population which was chosen at random from the telephone directory, but which left out all the people of an entirely different group who could not afford telephones. This gave a very one-sided picture, and was what is known as a biased sample.

Another example of a biased sample is that of the head of a famous school who made an inquiry amongst the boys in order to estimate the average size of family in the social class represented at his school; but he made two mistakes. He forgot that every family which had more than one boy at the school was counted at least twice; and that families with no children were unrepresented in the survey.

A random sample which gives an accurate picture of the whole population is very difficult to achieve. If the picture is to be reliable, it must be carefully planned, or matched. First we must decide what are the relevant considerations; that is, those which are likely to affect choice of listening programme.

Let us suppose that we have decided that the important factors are sex, age, social-economic group and home area. It will be sufficiently accurate for our purpose if we regard the population to be half men and half women, so that we must include five hundred of each in our sample thousand.

We shall limit our inquiry to adults. We need about four easily recognizable age-groups. As there is a limit to the number of questions which a reasonable person may be expected to answer, the interviewer will usually have the difficult task of estimating age from appearance. A little training and experience will soon make his results sufficiently reliable for the purpose.

Practice has shown that the best division lines are at 30, 50 and 65. We shall take our four age-groups to be 21–29, 30–49, 50–64 and over 65. A picture of the whole population is given in Fig. 24, with about 20 per cent in the first group, 40 per cent in the second, 25 per cent in the third and 15 per cent in the fourth. This type of group graph is called a histogram.

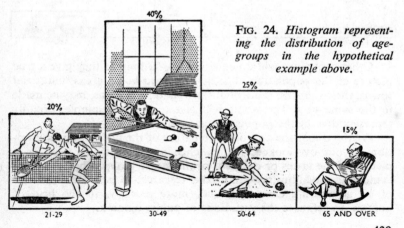

Fig. 24. *Histogram representing the distribution of age-groups in the hypothetical example above.*

These figures are based on census calculations. To follow this pattern, our sample thousand must include 200, 400, 250 and 150 in the respective groups.

In the same way, it will be necessary to divide the population into a small number of groups according to social-economic level. The groups must be clearly defined, if the task of the interviewer is not to be too difficult. Fig. 25 shows the histogram of such a grouping. According to this distribution, we shall need 200 people of a good average type, including office and professional and skilled workers, 600 artisans, 50 noticeably above average and 150 below. Exactly what the divisions mean and how they are to be recognized is a matter for the interviewer.

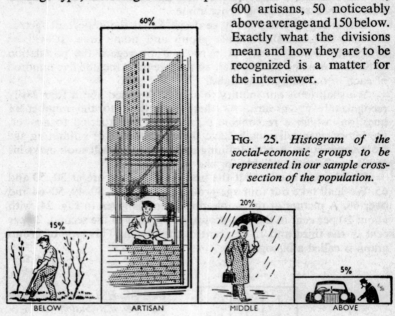

FIG. 25. *Histogram of the social-economic groups to be represented in our sample cross-section of the population.*

Other groupings will do equally well, so long as they give a true picture of the population. The division into home areas, industrial towns, their suburbs, residential towns and rural areas, may be made in the same way. The whole will give a matched sample, broadly representative of the population as a whole.

Provided that the approximate nature of the underlying assumptions is not overlooked, the matched sample may be used as a picture of the tastes or opinions of the larger group. This technique is much in use in business, in market research, to estimate the effects of an advertising campaign, and, more recently, in the field of politics, to estimate the variations of public opinion.

It has been said that statistics can prove anything. This obviously foolish idea has arisen because of the readiness with which people will accept unsound arguments when there are a few figures or diagrams inserted into them. As a warning against too hasty acceptance of this sort of argument, we end the chapter with some examples of unsound reasoning from numerical and graphical data.

(1) During the last war, the earned-income allowance for income-tax purposes was lowered from one-sixth to one-tenth. Later on, when it was suggested that it should be raised again, the Chancellor of the Exchequer said that he was prepared to go halfway, by raising it to one-eighth. Most people accepted this statement.

If you find one-sixth, one-tenth and one-eighth of any sum of money, say £600, you will see that it is wrong to say that one-eighth is halfway. $\frac{1}{6} - \frac{1}{8} = \frac{1}{24}$, whilst $\frac{1}{8} - \frac{1}{10} = \frac{1}{40}$ only.

(2) Some time ago, the then Minister of Labour said in the House of Commons that an increase in production of 10 per cent was needed every week. This, he said, was the same as 2 per cent every day in a five-day week.

This is wrong, if the basis of the percentage, as was clearly understood, is the day's work. To get a 10 per cent increase on the week's production, you need a 10 per cent increase every day.

(3) A car goes at 20 m.p.h. over a certain distance, then back again over the same distance at 30 m.p.h. Most people, if asked what the average speed for both journeys was, will at once say 25 m.p.h. This is wrong; if you work it out for a convenient distance, say 60 miles, you will find that the average speed is only 24 m.p.h., as the total journey of 120 miles takes five hours.

This is a warning against drawing hasty conclusions from "averages," which occur frequently. They are really fractions (in this case $\frac{miles}{hours}$) which may only be added in this way if the denominators are equal. Had the times of the two journeys been equal, instead of the distances, 25 would have been the correct answer.

(4) Another example of unsound reasoning from averages is the case of the two bowlers, A and B, who have the same average, having so far each taken 28 wickets for 84 runs. In the next match, A takes 1 wicket for 30 runs, while B takes 8 wickets for 60 runs. Which has now the better average?

Unless you are very suspicious, you will at once say B, as he has done so much better in this match. Yet you will be wrong, for his average is now $\frac{144}{36} = 4$, while that of A is $\frac{114}{29}$, or just less than 4. The reason for this anomaly is similar to that of the previous example;

441

we are dealing with fractions, and the effect of adding 30 to the numerator is too great to compensate for.

(5) Fig. 26 is a graph of temperature readings, taken at noon each day, but one day was missed. It would be wrong to assume that the missing temperature may be read from the graph, even though all the readings seem to lie on a straight line. There is no information whatever about the temperature between readings. It is well known that temperature is subject to quick, irregular variations.

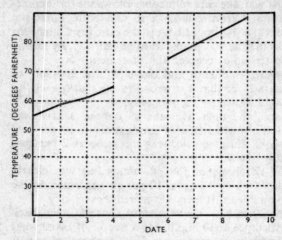

FIG. 26. *On the fifth day no reading was taken. Can the missing reading be deduced from the graph?*

(6) Fig. 27 shows the annual sales in a business. Can we predict next year's sales? The first answer is no, because the graph is so irregular. On further examination, however, we can see a definite trend, as shown by the dotted line. Provided we know of nothing which is likely to produce a sudden change, we may say that if everything continues as before, the sales should be somewhere near the point shown on the dotted line.

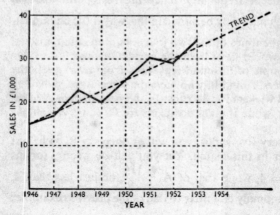

FIG. 27. *From the sales chart on the left can the probable figures for 1954 be estimated?*

(7) Fig. 28 shows the number of road accidents occurring to people in age-groups. It is wrong to assume that the peak of the graph shows which age-group is most susceptible to accident, because here again the information is incomplete. The number of persons in each group, and the proportion of the group likely to be crossing roads at particular times of the day, would be needed before any deductions could be made from the graph.

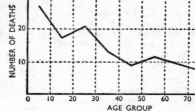

Fig. 28. *Road deaths according to age-groups during a given period of time.*

(8) A recent report on the conditions under which road accidents occurred in a northern town gave the following figures: dry roads 87 per cent, wet roads 10 per cent, icy roads 3 per cent. These figures appeared in a local paper under the heading, "The Menace of Dry Roads."

Of course this was not intended to be taken seriously, but less obvious arguments of the same sort are often made and accepted. This is the case of incomplete information. Before these figures can be compared, each must be divided by the relative frequency of occurrence. It is the number of accidents per day that should be compared under each heading. Even this is incomplete, because there may be many other factors which will affect the figures.

(9) There is a story that a man, on reaching his eightieth birthday, looked up tables of vital statistics, which include death rates. He was very happy to find that the number of deaths per annum at the age of eighty or over was very small indeed.

This is another example of incomplete information. As the number of persons in each age-group is so different, it must be taken into consideration in any comparison. The percentage or per thousand figure would have been a better though less reassuring figure to use.

Solutions of Teasers and Puzzles

444

Index

445

446

447

© Odhams Press, Ltd., 1960

S.760.5R.RA

MADE AND PRINTED IN
GREAT BRITAIN BY ODHAMS (WATFORD) LTD.
WATFORD, HERTS.